Four Rabbis at Lunch

FOUR RABBIS AT LUNCH

CANDID CONVERSATIONS AMONG
AMERICAN CLERGY

DOV PERETZ ELKINS

KTAV Publishing

I would like to take this opportunity to express my profound appreciation to Tzvi Mauer and his staff, Michal Alatin and Pearl Friedman, at Urim, and Ktav Publishers for their cooperation and high level of professionalism in producing this book.

Four Rabbis at Lunch
Candid Conversations among American Clergy
By Dov Peretz Elkins

This is a work of fiction. Names, characters, places and incidents either are the product of the author's imagination or are used fictitiously, and any resemblance to any actual persons, living or dead, events or locales, is entirely coincidental.

Printed in USA
First Edition

ISBN 978-160-280-348-0

Library of Congress Cataloging-in-Publication Data
Names: Elkins, Dov Peretz, author.
Title: Four rabbis at lunch : candid conversations among American clergy / Dov Peretz Elkins.
Description: Brooklyn, NY : KTAV Publishing, [2019] | Includes bibliographical references.
Identifiers: LCCN 2019012540 | ISBN 9781602803480 (pbk. : alk. paper)
Classification: LCC PS3605.L412 F67 2019 | DDC 813/.6—dc23
LC record available at https://lccn.loc.gov/2019012540

KTAV Publishing House
527 Empire Boulevard
Brooklyn, NY 11225
www.ktav.com

Rabbi Elkins has written an engaging book, involving discussions among four rabbis of different religious movements. Through these conversations, readers gain insight into major – and minor – issues in Judaism. It's an opportunity for readers to "eavesdrop" on rabbis who are on the front lines of Jewish life . . . to agree or disagree with them, to engage in their discussions.

> – Rabbi Marc D. Angel, Founder and Director of the Institute for
> Jewish Ideas and Ideals (jewishideas.org), and author of many books
> including a commentary on *Pirkei Avot*

At a tumultuous moment in our society, Jews are searching for ways to understand and address the many controversies in our faith and society that threaten to overwhelm us. Many feel unequipped to answer these questions because they do not have formal religious training. Dov Peretz Elkins, by allowing us to be the proverbial "fly on the wall" during conversations between four rabbis, enriches, educates and entertains us. At the same time, he shows the very human side of our faith's leaders.

> – Professor Jeffrey Herbst, President, American Jewish University

What do rabbis discuss when they get together in private? Dov Peretz Elkins, a rabbi of many years and a writer, makes that question the intriguing basis for his new novel, *Four Rabbis at Lunch*.

> – Professor Susannah Heschel, Dartmouth College

Since the 60s, I have cherished the books by Rabbi Elkins. He is generous and brave, traditional and cutting edge. He is a great teacher because he is a great student. Rabbi Elkins is a gifted Rabbi and teacher and writer. I always purchase his new books sight unseen, and I am always grateful for what he has written.

> – Arthur Kurzweil, Author of *On the Road with Rabbi Steinsaltz*

Four Rabbis at Lunch is a marvelous discussion sprinkled with seriousness, humor and a great amount of important information about what rabbis have to deal with whatever their denomination and struggles. Much to learn from, to have a good laugh, and think what Judaism is all about and why it is of crucial importance. The most important message of this book is that rabbis with very different ideas about Judaism can sit together, listen to each other and have an actual discussion. A hopeful sign!

> – Rabbi Dr. Nathan Lopes Cardozo, Jerusalem,
> author of *Jewish Law as Rebellion*

If your curiosity ever tempted you to eavesdrop on your Rabbi's conversation with his colleagues in order to overhear their thoughts on some of the most significant and relevant topics of Judaism for today, this is the book you must acquire and read.

> – Professor Shalom Paul, former Chair, Dept. of Bible, Hebrew
> University

Based on his lifetime of experience in the Conservative rabbinate, Dov Peretz Elkins invites readers to eavesdrop as four fictional rabbis – Conservative, Orthodox and Reform – gather weekly to converse and schmooze. Major issues that rabbis face in their work – everything from intermarriage and Israel to circumcision and sex – fill out these conversations, which are punctuated by learning, humor and practical wisdom. More eye-opening than any sermon, this is a guide to what rabbis really talk about among themselves.

> – Jonathan D. Sarna, University Professor and Joseph H. & Belle R. Braun Professor of American Jewish History, Brandeis University, and Author of *American Judaism: A History*

Through the lunch-table conversation of four imaginary rabbis, *Four Rabbis at Lunch* offers the reader an original perspective on the Jewish community and Jewish religious leadership in our time by a master rabbi drawing on his decades of experience in the Jewish community. The book's unprecedented fictional format provides the layman with a witty, anecdotal, and memorable entree into the complex, sometimes contradictory intellectual, moral, and social currents that lie behind the polished words of the preacher and the wise counsel of the pastor.

> – Raymond Scheindlin, Professor Emeritus, Jewish Theological Seminary

Rabbi Elkins has written a book that richly reflects his many years on the pulpit. His liberal Conservative perspective is balanced by other rabbinic voices he has created. The result is a book that teaches his valuable Torah in an engaging and charming way.

> – Rabbi David A. Teutsch, Wiener Professor Emeritus, Reconstructionist Rabbinical College

"So, four rabbis walk into . . . a deli. . . ." Sounds like the beginning of a joke, but fortunately for us, it is actually the set up for a compelling peek behind the closed door of the rabbi's study. These thoughtful colleagues bring all sorts of fascinating questions to discuss with each other as they grapple with the key Jewish questions of our time: Jewish practice, intermarriage, fostering welcoming and inclusive communities.

The rabbis may be fictional, but the brilliant Rabbi Dov Peretz Elkins is sharing truths stranger and more meaningful than fiction. If you've ever wondered how rabbis make decisions, grab this book. You'll find it hard to put down!

> –Dr. Ron Wolfson, Fingerhut Professor of Education, American Jewish University, Author of *Relational Judaism*

In memory of BART J. AXELROD

There never was a man more deserving
of the term *"mensch"* than Bart

Beloved husband, father, grandfather,
brother, and friend

The ZOHAR is framed as the narrative
of what scholar Nathan Wolski describes
as a group of "wandering mystics headed by the
grand master, Rabbi Shimon bar Yohai," who converse with each other and interpret the Torah while
traveling through the Holy Land. The act of traveling
allows for freedom of imagination, and hence anywhere along the journey is considered the ideal
place for expounding the deepest
mysteries of Torah.

Contents

Introduction

Many friends have asked me the question: "What do rabbis talk about when they know that no laypersons are listening? Oh, that we could be the proverbial fly on the wall and hear what kinds of discussions they have!" Well, friends, what I have done in this volume is to provide an attempt at replicating some of these candid – no lay persons present – conversations. I have attempted, to the best of my ability to avoid any discussions that would be embarrassing or upsetting to any colleague.

Is this book fiction or non-fiction? It's fiction, but like a historical novel, it is based on fact.

None of the names, places, dates and other identifying information is factual, and have no relation to anyone living or dead with the exception of the talk by Deborah Harburger and the articles by Rabbi Reuven Hammer, Rabbi Richard Rubenstein, Rabbi Menachem Creditor and Rabbi Philip Scheim, which are used with permission. However the discussions on Jewish law, Jewish theology and synagogue business, found here, reflect the kind of discussions in which rabbis engage on a daily basis – the ones in this book are my attempt to replicate the conversations I have actually heard, or heard of, over many years.

I have spent over a half-century laboring in the vineyard of Jewish values, tradition and heritage, and hope that the presentation of these discussions will add to the understanding of what rabbis do, and talk about, and struggle with, during their devoted ministries. Serving the Jewish community is a great honor and privilege, and a deeply satisfying joy. I am hopeful that what I have written in this book enables non-clergy to better understand the commitments of Jewish clergy, and to hold up a mirror for colleagues to be reminded of a small fraction of the issues that we deal with on a regular basis.

May this small contribution to the understanding of American clergy and their dedicated work find favor in the eyes of God and humankind.

Dov Peretz Elkins
Jerusalem, Israel

Four Rabbis at Lunch

꿏

THREE NEIGHBORING RABBIS have lunch together once a week. Sitting at the table is Rabbi Don Levin (Orthodox), Rabbi Bob Goldberg (Conservative), and Rabbi Sam Cohen (Reform). Some weeks after the inception of the meetings, the group decides to invite a fourth colleague, Rabbi Susan Berkowitz (Conservative).

Mainly they enjoy being able to discuss issues that they do not feel free discussing with their parishioners. In the quiet booth in the corner of Jeff's Kosher Deli Market, no one can hear them, and they can "let it all hang out."

Sometimes their conversations are serious, sometimes just normal clergy bantering. Sometimes they share religious jokes. What we record below are more of the serious discussions that these astute and distinguished clergy have on their minds, and some of the questions posed to them by their members.

The conversations, while fictionalized, are based on actual discussions that rabbis might have in private meetings. None of the people mentioned in this book are real people, and any resemblance to people living or deceased is purely unintentional.

It's the beginning of the New Year, and they resume their meetings, after a month-long December break.

Week 1

DON: So what's goin' on?

BOB: I was reading some of the passages in Leviticus recently. Wow!

Why so much detail? What bothers me about the sacrifices in the Torah, aside from the concept itself, is this question: Why are so many details about the slaughter, the sprinkling of the blood, the slicing of the animal, the number of animals, and so many other ritualistic details, specified in the text of the Torah? So many other topics are mentioned briefly and the details are found in the commentaries. But in the case of the sacrifices every last detail is given in the Pentateuch. Would it not have been nice if the details of "Love your neighbor as yourself" would have been spelled out? Is the life of your fellow, equal to yours, or does your neighbor take precedence over you? Is the commandment fulfilled by giving your fellow charity, helping him in trouble, visiting him when he is sick, consoling him when he is in grief?

For that matter, why not specify the details of loving and fearing God, instead of relying on a general statement: Love the Lord your God, Fear the Lord your God? How do we love Him? How do we fear Him? For the details of the moral and ethical and spiritual commands we have to rely on commentaries. It is puzzling.

SAM: Great questions, Bob. Let me see if I can give you some of my thoughts.

In the case of the moral and ethical matters, so much depends on the details of each case and on the context of time, place and situation, that each era and case requires painful analysis. Ergo, the commentaries still struggle with these issues today, and will continue to do so.

With regard to sacrifices, I would point out that these verses in Leviticus were specifically intended for the priests, not for us; and that what is so important about these details is, not what's in our text, but what's been left out. Maimonides tried to tell us in the *Guide for the Perplexed* (Part III, Chapter XXXII) that one major purpose of the Torah was the elimination of paganism. Take a look at the famous section about the question, "Why did the One God demand, in His worship, the pagan custom of animal sacrifice? Why not offer prayers or words? In fact why not simply thoughts?" Maimonides' answer is "The One God understood that man's nature is such that he can't change overnight, so God allowed the continuation of pagan animal sacrifice, but without the paganism, and the sacrifices are to be directed to the One God." At the end of this section is a little noticed sentence: "And the same thing also applies to fringes, *mezuzah* and *tefillin*, and similar kinds of divine service."

In other words, many of our practices may have had their origin in paganism, such as fringes, *mezuzah*, *tefillin*. These were originally pagan amulets, but the Torah permits their practice without the paganism: "Look at them and remember the commandments . . ." [Numbers 15]. Passover, *Sukkot*, *Shavu'ot*, were originally pagan agricultural festivals. And on and on.

So it is, I conclude, with the sacrifices. What's most important is what has been left out of the text. If we had the pagan book of sacrifices, it would tell us to which pagan god the sacrifice was directed AND the purpose and desired effect that it was expected the sacrifice would produce. "Baal's Book of Sacrifices" is the antithesis of our "Book of Leviticus." The Torah has to tell us each and every type of sacrifice in great detail, but even more importantly, how to do it without any mention of the then familiar pagan deities. This is how the sacrifice is now to be performed, dedicated to the One God.

BOB: Aahh! I still think they could have reduced all those bloody details. It would make it much more interesting for my folks to read Scripture without all that.

DON: I have another topic I want to raise today. I've been listening to NPR (National Public Radio), and I'm getting sick of it. We need to contact our representatives in Congress, who fund it.

Without making a total judgment on the matter, I would note that the folks behind Project Veritas [Truth] are committed to anything but. Their previous videos about ACORN and Planned Parenthood have both been shown to be edited and not a true picture of what happened.

SAM: Should there be any doubt anymore that NPR is an anti-Zionist medium? I hope to be calling my representatives in Washington and asking them to defund NPR and the Corporation for Public Broadcasting. I hope others will follow suit.

I love it when the former CEO of NPR, Schiller, states that he doesn't find "Zionist or pro-Israel" people among NPR's funders. It may not be accurate and descriptive, but it surely is prescriptive.

It's time for the USA to stop funding NPR, which I call National Palestinian Radio!

Ron Schiller resigned this past Tuesday night. He was the National Public Radio executive who was caught in a sting video bemoaning "Zionist" control of U.S. newspapers and listening passively while a supposed potential Arab funder talked about "Jew influence" in the media. In a statement, Schiller said: "While the meeting I participated in turned out to be a ruse, I made statements during the course of the meeting that are counter to NPR's values and also not reflective of my own beliefs. I offer my sincere apology to those I offended. I resigned from NPR, previously effective May sixth, to accept another job. In an effort to put this unfortunate matter behind us, NPR and I have agreed that my resignation is effective today."

The video was produced by Project Veritas.

In the video, two men present themselves as representatives of the Muslim Education Action Center, a fictional organization. They go out to lunch with Ron Schiller, president of the NPR

Foundation and a vice president for development, and Betsy Liley, senior director for institutional giving. The meeting took place recently at Cafe Milano, a Georgetown restaurant.

The "Muslim" representatives explained their desire to give up to $5 million to NPR because, the Zionist coverage is quite substantial elsewhere. Indeed, the two men clearly represent their organization as founded by the Muslim Brotherhood, a fact that evinces no reaction from the NPR executives. At about the seven-minute mark of the video, one of the "representatives" of the Muslim front group begins to discuss Israel and "Jewish control" of the media. He praises NPR as one of the few places that has the "courage" to present the Palestinian point of view and says he is not troubled that Jewish funding for the radio station is drying up. "I'm not too upset about a little less Jewish influence of money into NPR. The Zionist coverage is quite substantial elsewhere." Schiller, eating his lunch calmly, then says that he doesn't find "Zionist or pro-Israel" people among NPR's funders.

BOB: I agree. Let's all write our Congress folks about NPR, and try to get them to defund them.

SAM: So what else is on your minds today?

DON: I received a phone call the other day, inviting me to take a tour of the local Cathedral, with a group of my men's club. It reminds me of something that happened many years ago, when the local Cardinal invited a group of rabbis for a "Cook's Tour" of the Cathedral where I lived at that time.

In the course of the visit, he told us about how much he envied us for two reasons – for our wives, and for having *Seders* on Passover. He urged us to invite our non-Jewish neighbors and friends to our "meaningful" *sedarim*. The Cardinal may have had an ulterior motive behind his enthusiasm for the *Seder*. Nevertheless, my wife and I took him up on it and invited the pastor of the neighboring church and a couple of nuns to our *Seder* table. They seemed not only to enjoy it but contributed a great deal to the discussion.

SAM: I got an email the other day, on my rabbinic listserv, from a colleague in the mid-West, who apologized for his "brevity." He wrote: "Please excuse the brevity of this message." This certainly must be a crazy discussion group if someone has to apologize for brevity. I can understand why he wrote that. The number and volume of some colleagues' messages often tend to be, well, voluminous. I often ask myself where these fellows – it's usually fellows – get the time to write all that they write and the digital strength to type it. And the tone is often a tad shrill, as exchanges of the last few days indicate. Instead of burning their unleavened bread on Passover, some simply send it to the Listserv.

BOB: Changing topics a bit, I have an interesting quandary that most probably is not unique. For an upcoming bar mitzvah, I have been asked what is the status of some of the youngster's cousins, whose father is Jewish but the mother is not, yet were raised in a Reform congregation, were called to the Torah at their thirteenth birthday, etc. Needless to say, the question pertains to the list of honors for the forthcoming bar mitzvah, and whether or not the cousins can be called for an *aliyah*.

Mind you, I am very aware of the current position of my rabbinical organization, which doesn't permit patrilineal descent etc., but given that these cousins were raised as Jews, I have a difficult time dismissing them as non-Jews.

According to Jewish Law, how do we accommodate our position with the reality so prevalent in our communities?

SAM: Simple, Bob! Just become Reform and accept patrilineal descent. Presto – problem solved.

BOB: No so easy. Not sure my folks would go for that. Anyway, something to think about. I'm sure we'll have lots of opportunities to discuss it again.

DON: Here's another question for us to chew on. I have a congregant who is matter-of-factly looking at her and her husband's funeral plans. She has decided that her children's difficult financial situation has made it a priority to take the money that she had set aside for cemetery plots and funeral services and make as much of it available to her family as possible. She has asked me about the permissibility of cremation for no other reason than to make this possible. In talking with her it is clear that she has great respect for Jewish tradition and had every intention of a proper burial. I would appreciate any practical suggestions you may have to help reduce and defray the costs of burial. As an aside, it is ironic to me that our colleague Harold Listonfeld waged a fight against a funeral industry whose lavish funeral trends were threatening to Jewish traditions of a simple wooden casket. Now, in difficult economic times, the simple wooden casket, plus plots, liners and mandatory cemetery fees, is being compared to the minimal expense of cremation.

BOB: Talking about cremation, when I entered the rabbinate many years ago, there was no question in my mind that I couldn't, and wouldn't, play much of a role in funerals or services that involved cremation. It seemed so "un-Jewish." It seemed so "unnatural." It seemed so obvious to be an example of *nivul ha-met* [desecration of the deceased], to be a case where *y'kara d'shakhvei* [the dignity of a corpse] was being violated, to be a case where, even if requested by a dying person, one should refuse to comply. To hasten decomposition in this way seemed so violent, so offensive. I was abhorred by the thought of cremation. I couldn't understand how, in the wake of the Holocaust, a Jew could consider it.

But then, after some years in the rabbinate, something odd happened. One after another, I was approached by people – nice people, decent people, people with positive Jewish identities – who were electing to be cremated. One was a Holocaust survivor: a very sweet man, whose extended family was and is very involved in my *shul*. How could that be? How could he, of all people, want to be cremated? I said no, I couldn't officiate. His son understood. Fortunately, his niece, a rabbinic colleague, officiated at that one, and fortunately, the family and I have remained close. Then there was another request: again, a Holocaust survivor. I agreed to officiate at the funeral, with the body present, with the understanding that the cremation wouldn't take place until afterwards. That was odd, but it felt right. Then, my third request: again, a Holocaust survivor. Do you see a pattern here? This time, I again officiated at the service, in the presence of the body, and then, several weeks later, at the burial of the cremains. My feeling was that however those cremains had been cremated, they deserved to be buried in the earth.

Coincidentally, shortly thereafter, I was approached by someone else who asked me to officiate at the burial of his mother. The mother had died a year earlier, but had willed her body to science. The son had been informed that the body was now available to be buried and so we set a time and a place, and arranged it all. A day before the funeral, the son told me that his brothers had, unbeknownst to him, authorized the cremation of his mother, and that all we would be receiving the next day was a little box of ashes to be buried. Fine, I said. Those ashes should be buried. And so I came to develop my practice.

But still new twists developed. A long-standing, beloved congregant died, a former Israeli, who had, in later life, learned to read Torah and who had become as Jewish as you could ever imagine a secular-from-birth-Israeli could be. His friends and I, all well-connected at the *shul*, arranged for his funeral to take place at our *shul*, never imagining for a moment that she would be cremated. But indeed that's what her husband decided to do. And so, after the funeral, attended by hundreds and hundreds of people, the hearse drove off into the proverbial sunset, and there was no place for us to go. It was awful. Her friends and I stood around, feeling bereft and frustrated. His wife later took his cremains with her to Israel and buried them on the kibbutz where he had been born and where they had met.

Looking back, I have no regrets. I feel bad that I wasn't able to be there for that first family that approached me. But at the time I couldn't have done anything. It wouldn't have been authentic for me; I would have been too conflicted. As far as the other families whom I have helped are concerned, I am disappointed, of course, that they made the decisions that they did, but I don't regret that I helped them in each of these instances, in a pastoral capacity. I don't for a moment believe that any of them, or anyone else for that matter, made their decisions or would make their decisions, in this regard, because of my willingness to participate.

And so the saga, the re-thinking, continues. I officiated at the grave-side funeral of a family member recently. As we lowered his suitably-wooden coffin into the large, sarcophagus-like concrete vault, required by the Jewish cemetery in which he was being buried, and as we prepared to lower the massive, imposing concrete cover onto the vault, I asked myself, "Is this more traditional than cremation?" It certainly didn't feel any more "natural," any more "authentic" than burying cremains, or, for that matter, scattering them into the wind. I felt instead as though I were in ancient Egypt, entombing bodies meant to be preserved and removed at the end of days.

And now another question has arisen. I've been asked to officiate at the funeral of the parent of a congregant. The mother is suffering from a terminal condition, and isn't expected to live longer than a few weeks. The mother has decided that she wants to be cremated. Yes, I told the daughter, I'll officiate at a funeral so long as the body is present. But this afternoon I learned something rather disturbing. The funeral home will charge much, much more money if the body is present. Odd, but true. If all they need to do is to provide a room for a memorial service, the cost will be X. But if the body will be present, the cost will be X plus $4,000. Hard to believe, but true.

And so, my insistence that the body is present comes at a price. Roughly four thousand dollars. Now, one could say that this is irrelevant. After all, we insist on kosher food, whatever the cost, right? And we insist on refraining from working on the Sabbath, whatever the cost. So it shouldn't matter. But, at the very least, it raises the question why it *does* matter that the body is present at the funeral. Maybe it doesn't need to be there. Maybe that's a distinction that no longer makes sense.

What do you guys think?

SAM: Thank you for being honest, Bob, concerning officiating at a funeral of a cremated body! Indeed, we are all still in the era of Post-Holocaust-trauma, and not only in this respect. It will take another generation, I think, to see the rationale behind a person's wish to be cremated: The corpse has no significance once the soul departed from it.

As for the last part of your message: An extra cost of $4,000 if "the body is present." I wish to remind you of Rabban Gamliel's struggle against costly funerals and burials in Tractate *Mo'ed Katan*, which succeeded when he left instructions to bury him in the cheapest shroud.

BOB: OK, now I want to raise a similar issue, with a slightly different wrinkle. A congregant's adult son died a few months ago. His wife made the decision to have him cremated; there was a funeral service prior to cremation at his synagogue. There is a complicated family situation, and the daughter-in-law does not talk to the mother-in-law, who is my congregant. My congregant called me to tell me that she had suddenly been given her son's ashes. This is seven months later. She is going to have his ashes buried. The question for me is what would be the ritual for burial in this case? There's already been a funeral, there was no burial, and now all we have is cremated remains.

Here's my plan – see what you think. I've done it a number of times and the circumstances are similar to what this woman wants. I do it very much like a burial service, ending with *El Malay* and *Kaddish*. I don't do *Tzidduk Hadin*. I recite some psalms, and deliver a kind of abbreviated eulogy, but more like I would do at an unveiling. I might quote a few *midrashim* that are appropriate, and then the *El Malay* and *Kaddish*. These people almost never chose to do it this way and don't need to be "punished" or "reminded" that this is not how we prefer to do it – cremation, etc. They already know that. I prefer this to having them spread the ashes somewhere or keep them in the house.

SAM: Sounds reasonable to me.

DON: Of course, for me, the question of cremation is not a question. We would never permit it. But I know you guys have different views on that, as well as on many other things.

BOB: OK, now I've got another question for you – a first for me. Here goes:

Here's a weird request. Friends in the congregation called to see if I would attend the Jewish wedding of their daughter to a Jewish man, BUT performed by a Jewish judge. The bride and groom are close to their clergy yet want no clergy to officiate. It gets better. The bride's parents, who are upset with her decision, have promised a kosher meal following the ceremony.

Obviously the bride has some issues. She is struggling with her belief in God and ritual.

Would you attend?

DON: Not me, would you, Sam?

SAM: Why not, in strict Jewish law you don't need a rabbi to perform a wedding. As long as bride and groom are Jewish, and the officiating person is Jewish and knows Jewish law, I have no problem with it.

DON: Bob, you have identified these people as friends, so they want you to be at the wedding and it's nice to give them the honor. Once I had a family who wanted the cantor to officiate, and not me, but invited me to attend the wedding. I did not go. A few other times people have asked the cantor to officiate without me. I have said it would not be proper to invite him without him officiating, so in the end they asked him to officiate with me.

But this sounds quite different. They don't have a problem with *you* per se, but with clergy, or perhaps religion in general. If the bride is "close to her clergy" as you say, perhaps you could suggest to the parents that she meet with you to see what her issues are. As we all know, we are much more capable of making a life cycle moment such as this more meaningful than a

Judge might, even if we were to take religion out of the picture. I often say, we are "masters of ceremonies."

So, Bob, what did you reply?

BOB: Thanks for your interesting insights. I spoke at length with the bride who very much wants me to attend, I offered to work with the couple, and for them to decide in September what route they want to take. Regardless of their decision, I affirmed my love and support for whatever they decide.

For me this is an issue of compassion and outreach. I have known the bride from birth. Her parents are dear friends. I have taught the bride when she was in Day School and she is a product of Ramah. The lesson in all of this is the importance of not judging people. What could possibly lead a bride to want a wedding without her rabbi officiating?

I believe the bride is going through a rough theological patch, which has her justifiably confused. The groom, who is a sweetheart, suffers from a disease which will dramatically shorten his lifespan. And yet, love has brought these two Jewish kids together. My attitude is to stress their love, and to be there if they need me, which Lord knows, she will some day. I told the bride that I love her and will respect whatever she decides to do.

Sam and Don, your responses were helpful and sensitive and reaffirmed the approach I want to take.

SAM: Here's one for you. A member of my *shul* asked to put up a *yahrtzeit* plaque for his deceased non-Jewish wife. It was discussed at a committee meeting, and it was decided to recommend that the board approve the request. I am personally in favor of the request. However, a member of the original committee has reconsidered his position, thinking now that we are acting like Mormons and posthumously virtually converting someone who chose not to convert in life. This means another round of discussion.

It would be helpful to know if either of you have addressed this issue and how you resolved it. I see it as a very simple thing: a Jew wants to mourn his late wife.

DON: I wouldn't do it, but I know you have your own views about such things. I guess you'll have to figure it out for yourself.

SAM: I think you're right, Don. I'll mull it over some more before making a decision.

BOB: Here's another issue for your brilliant minds. I have a congregant who has been very active in the Masonic world, and whose passing is imminent. Given that most funeral services in our community are performed in the Synagogue, the question has been raised as to the possibility of holding a Masonic Service in the *shul* prior to the Jewish ceremony.

Not being very familiar with the particulars of the Masonic ritual, I would like to get your views as to how appropriate it would be to allow such a ceremony to be conducted in the synagogue; or whether the whole thing falls under the rubric of *Avodah Zarah* [idolatry], and therefore it would definitely not belong in our building.

DON: Disclosure: I am not a Mason nor am I a member of any such group. Given the history of Masonic rites in congregations I served, I arrived at a compromise which "spoke" a great deal to the congregational community.

I would permit the Masonic rites before the funeral in the chapel which permitted their Masonic representatives who were often members of the congregation and/or the Jewish community. However, neither the Cantor nor I would be present. We would enter the chapel and lead a Jewish ritual after the Masons completed their rites and removed their ritual attire.

Of course in the synagogue the Masonic ritual was not permitted and when confronted – yes, confronted – I urged them to do so at the funeral chapel but not in our building.

As I think about it, I never consulted with my Christian colleagues to see how they handled it. The suggestion for my compromise came from a non-Jewish funeral director and perhaps it was also the way that some Christian clergy handled it.

This approach worked for me as far as I know, and for the Masonic community.

SAM: I'm a freemason. Have been for thirty years. We are a midrash on the building of the *Bet Hamikdash* and use the operative tools of masonry – bricks, mortar, stones – to create an environment where people improve themselves through faith, hope and charity – admittedly not a Jewish formulation. However, we believe in One God and *tehiyat hamaytim* [resurrection of the dead] also, which we include in our ritual. Despite the popular perception, we are not funny men in funny hats who do and say funny things. We teach and do charitable work in the community. You can find explanations of Freemasonry on the websites of the various Grand Lodges. At one time I was in touch with over a dozen other rabbis who were also Freemasons.

BOB: Well, sounds like it can be done. Thanks, guys. So now, here's another issue.

I can think of no social transformation in my lifetime as rapid and sweeping as the acceptance now accorded gay people. I understand if some gay people view their public embrace as less than quick or irrevocable. But from the lynching of Matthew Shepherd to Brokeback Mountain to gay marriage, it spins your head how fast it has all come.

Not too long ago, New York State authorized same-sex marriage, making New York one of only a small number of states, along with DC, to take this bold stance. Such a revolution deserves a little faithful and honest Judaic reflection.

I celebrate New York's decision.

This whole social, ethical transformation poses undeniably hard questions for how we relate to Torah norms about sexuality, family and authority. We are only beginning to articulate a religious vision for this new world. Gay marriage will help us approach that new vision.

Those of us who are Conservative Jews worked our way toward accepting homosexuality partly through a legal argument passed in 2006 by our Committee on Jewish Law and Standards, written by my colleague Rabbi Daniel Nevins, and two of my esteemed senior colleagues, Rabbis Elliot Dorff and Avram Reisner. They argued, in brief, that it was unfair, socially unproductive, and ultimately un-Jewish, to condemn constitutionally gay people to lives without love partners. So, while affirming that heterosexual marriage remains the ideal, and affirming that the Torah itself forbids male-to-male anal penetration, they argued that all other sexual restrictions on gay men, and all sexual restrictions on lesbians may be considered to have lapsed.

The key ethical leverage of their paper comes from the Talmudic dictum that "protecting human dignity supersedes a Torah prohibition." It wounds people's dignity, to say the least, to tell them that God forbids them from loving or being loved.

There are many virtues to this work, and if I had been on the CJLS [Committee on Jewish Law and Standards] at that time, I would have voted in favor of this paper. But while both its head and its heart are in the right place, I think it is only a first step in transformed religious thinking. By restricting themselves to arguments that could be plausibly based in authoritative sources, Nevins, Dorff and Reisner felt they hewed to a legal method with integrity. Their work still looked like *halakhah*, even if its conclusion was unprecedented.

But their method was not suited to asking and answering a more fundamental question, which should be central to our approach: What confers *kedushah*, sanctity, on a romantic and sexual relationship? The classical answer was inextricable from rules governing specific sexual acts. Undeniably, that is a *halakhic* question, which cannot be evaded. The Dorff-Nevins-Reisner position helped us respond to it and helped us progress. But now it is time to respond with additional religious depth to the more pressing question: What makes a relationship holy? To answer that question in a Jewish way demands that we identify interpersonal norms for all relationships, no matter the shape of the partners' bodies, or who they might be.

As a Jew, I find it ludicrous to affirm gay relationships for the sake of a sexual liberation ethic, as if everyone has a natural right to maximize pleasurable experiences. I was mortified, for instance, by the San Francisco gay synagogue's prayer book which included a blessing for having anonymous sex, when a partner's identity is not even known. What value can this possibly be expressing? A libertarian line is also inadequate. Does Judaism have nothing more profound to say than "everyone should do what is right for themselves?"

If Jewish communities are to affirm what has, until now, been an outlawed sexuality, it must be because we have come to see that gay relationships can conform to our deepest vision of human relationships, as expressed in norms of love, commitment, mutuality and family.

And that is why I celebrate same-sex marriage: because it allows more people to build stable families with loving partners. As Jews we should affirm the Torah's proclamation: it is not good for people to be alone. We should celebrate when they bind their lives together, aspiring to remain a couple until death parts them. We should believe Isaiah's prophecy: God did not create the world as a wasteland; rather for people to settle, build homes and raise families in it.

By coincidence, the morning after Governor Cuomo signed the same-sex marriage bill, we celebrated a bat mitzvah of a fine young woman in our *shul*, who was brought to the Torah by her two mothers. Those women have built a home and family. They are raising their two children to be ethical, kind and creative people. They are giving the children a Jewish education and identity. What more can you ask of them or anyone?

This local celebration deserves a blessing. So does the new possibility for more couples to follow their paths: Blessed are You, Master of the cosmos, who kept us alive and sustained us and brought us to experience this moment.

DON: Though I may not agree with everything you say, Bob, I cannot but admire your conviction, and the depth of your moral feeling on this matter.

SAM: Amen!

BOB: By the way, I have another question which was presented to me very recently, and I would love your collective wisdom on this question.

One of the actions which is forbidden to members of the Conservative association of rabbis, the Rabbinical Assembly, as listed in the "standards of conduct," is the very presence of a member at an intermarriage. While it is clear that this is a *seyag* [fence] to the rule that we may not officiate at the weddings of Jewish individuals who marry non-Jews, the reality of the world we live in is that in the overwhelmingly irreligious and secular society, some members of the R.A. may be faced with the fact that siblings, children and grandchildren may be indifferent to Judaism and elect to marry non-religious, non-Jewish partners, in a non-religious ceremony.

To deny a member of the R.A. the opportunity to be present at the wedding of a close relative who may be beloved even if he or she elects not to live as a Jew is unnecessarily cruel. I believe that the standard should be modified to allow the presence, though not the participation of the rabbi, in such a situation. The heartbreak and sadness at witnessing a sibling, child or grandchild marrying a non-Jew in a non-religious ceremony is great enough. Let us not create a situation where the rabbi member is forced to violate rabbinical standards in order to be loyal to a loved relative. It is my observation, from speaking with Conservative colleagues, that when push comes to shove, the rabbi will attend such a wedding anyway. Are we then to adopt the "don't ask, don't tell" attitude in this matter? Better not to have the rule, in my opinion.

SAM: As long as we are speaking of the role of non-Jews, let me raise this interesting issue:

One of my congregants has a son who is in his mid-thirties, and the son identifies with Jews for Jesus. He has never told me directly of his affiliation, but apparently "everyone" knows. The son wants to lead a shofar blowing clinic at my *shul*. My initial thought is "no." What would you do in this situation? What language would you use to gently explain why this might not be the best match?

DON: I agree. I would urge him to worship in, and blow the shofar for, the congregations that relate to God as he does.

BOB: This thread brings to mind one of my favorite stories of Prof. Schwartz, one of my Seminary professors. A friend of mine at the Seminary asked the professor what he thought about Jews for Jesus. The professor was unfamiliar with the group and asked "what are they?" My friend responded, "They are Jews who observe some of the *mitzvot*, but believe in Jesus as their savior." Prof. Schwartz's response was, "Ya know what I think, ya know what I think . . . I think they should all go to hell! That's what I think."

One of the few instances where Prof. Schwartz's theological stance was not abstruse.

SAM: A colleague of mine who is chaplain at the local nursing home had a problem with a similar group, and I asked her what she did about it. She told me something like this:

"I think the reason that we are less than outraged about Jews for Jesus is that they have proven to be less than the frightening evangelical group that we all feared at first. Our local group, "Seed of Abraham," has attracted a lot of Christians who "want to pray like Jesus prayed" and observe the holidays he celebrated. They haven't been aggressively seeking Jewish converts, and the Jewish community has not really had to deal with them very much. Yes, some Jews may have joined, but, around here at least, they have not gone after the Jewish community; a few people may have found them. I've kicked them out of our Jewish nursing home twice in the fifteen years I've worked here, and their presence infuriates me, but we've kicked out other groups too. Nobody is permitted to just show up and walk around talking to residents. I think most of us now have the attitude that we just need to keep redirecting them back to their group. If the man blows shofar, let him blow shofar for his group, whatever they believe."

BOB: I wonder if it is too bold to claim that modern Jews are essentially non-messianic to the extent that the majority of us – I'm guessing here, but it's my intuition speaking – do not believe in a personal messiah? At most, we seem to believe in a messianic era, ushered in by the efforts of many, but certainly not via the agency of one "Messiah." Rather than enter into discussion with Jews for Jesus about whether Jesus was the right or the wrong messiah, why not explain and bill ourselves as Jews who no longer embrace the belief in that personal messiah. When I tell people that I see the personal messiah as an idealized version of a monarchy that most moderns see as a relic of the past, they concur. There's never been a good monarchy and there never will be. The messiah was that good king that all hoped for, but never came, and do I dare claim, never will come. Salvation is certainly an idea that is central to our belief system, but messiah . . .? What other concept in our history has given us more troubles? Isn't it time to take a discredited idea and say of it, "good riddance?"

DON: I have a question about teaching the Bible. A recent chapter I was teaching during Shabbat morning services includes chapter thirty one of Numbers. I frequently give a brief *d'var Torah* on the weekly *parashah,* and then lead a discussion in lieu of a formal sermon. Chapter thirty-one is a text that is especially difficult to teach, as it relates the utter vengeance commanded by God against the Midianite women, and the reprimand of the officers for sparing the married women, their slaughter, the taking of booty, etc. My standard way to teach this is as an example of a problematic text which we try to understand in a historical context. I may also cite the thesis of a lecture I heard recently, that much of the history of religion – including parts of our *Humash* – is the elevation and sanctification of new violence to supersede the previous immoral violence, and unfortunately chapter thirty one is an example of that in our Torah. My question is how any of you would handle that chapter differently? Any thoughts?

SAM: Did you squirm as I did when we read that God tells Moses to tell Israel to commit genocide against Midian, killing men, women and children? Guilty as Midian was, would we advocate killing all Germans after World War II – men, women and children? Divide Germany, yes, as Secretary Morganthau advised FDR, kill Nazis who killed Jews and other people. But wipe them out completely? Even God promises not to bring another flood after He brings the first one.

In his column in the Jerusalem Post, Rabbi Shlomo Riskin struggles and squirms with this problem. He goes back 3,000 years to explain that this mitzvah was necessary at that time, but that today there are no more Midianites, Amalekites, or Canaanites to be wiped out because Sennacherib mixed up the nations and they no longer exist.

Is this explanation satisfactory? Not to me. Does this mean that if we find Midianites, Amalekites, or Canaanites today, we have to wipe them out? Can Orthodox rabbis legitimately claim that a mitzvah in the Torah was given because of local and current circumstances, but that the mitzvah does not apply today under different circumstances? If the Torah is perfect – Divine, for all time and all places – how can we apply historical considerations to these atrocities? If it was right for them to commit genocide, it should be right now, and if it is wrong today it was wrong three thousand years ago. Maimonides rationalizes sacrifices as necessary because at the time of Moses it was impossible to tell Israel to worship with words alone, because all the nations worshipped by sacrificing animals. This is a surprising historical code for one who formulated in his *"Ani Ma'amin"* credo, that the Torah will never be changed. And indeed, he does include the laws of sacrifices in his Mishneh Torah, assuming that when Messiah comes they will be reinstituted.

What does that do to the rationale of the necessity of sacrifice in the days of Moses? Rabbi Riskin also tries to analogize between the Midian story and the terrorists in Gaza who hide behind children and Israeli soldiers are forced to shoot the children to get at the terrorists. Would Rabbi Riskin advocate the killing of all the children in Gaza as well as those used as human shields?

DON: Let's get off the topic of Israel for the moment. I had a call last night from a colleague who complained that during major holidays he's always on the pulpit, and can't share the festival with his family. This is a common issue among clergy. Our Hasidic predecessors often shared the same problem.

It was an old country custom in many Hasidic communities, for Hasidim to pack their bags for Yom Tov and travel to see their masters for the holiday season, leaving their families behind. This seems to conform to the Talmudic dictum, *chayav adam l'hakbil p'nei rabbo b'regel*, "a person should visit his master during the festival" (Rosh HaShanah 16b, Sukkah 27b).

On the other hand, this practice runs counter to another rabbinic principle, *hayav adam l'same'ah banav u'vnei beito b're-gel*, "a person should rejoice in the festivals together with all the members of his household" (Pesachim 109b). And so at least one Hasidic master — but I can't remember who — forbade his followers leaving home to spend festivals in his court. He urged them instead to stay at home and spend "quality time" with their families!

I recalled all this while rereading a portion of Cicero's "Orations" with a helpful interlinear translation, and happening upon this passage:

> *Quoniam supplicatio decreta est ad omnia pulvinaria, cele-bratote illos dies cum vestris coniugibus ac liberis.*
>
> "Since a thanksgiving has been decreed at all the temples, celebrate those days with your wives and children." (Cicero's Orations, "Cataline," Book I, par. 23)

This may be something to think about when planning our congregational programs for the coming year. They should be family-oriented.

I guess we clergy have to wait until we retire until we can spend the holidays together with our families in *shul*.

BOB: Good point. Yet there are some colleagues who, during Shabbat services, go down from the pulpit and sit with their families. Maybe more of us should do that.

SAM: I'm all for that.

BOB: A colleague of ours in the Midwest emailed me the other day about troubles he was having with his board about use of the rabbi's Discretionary Fund. They were objecting to his contributions to non-Jewish organizations, like the NAACP. I told him that I think it's up to the rabbi where contributions go. The Board was arguing that when people contributed, they believed that their money was going to Jewish organizations. That seems so narrow-minded to me.

SAM: I believe that the Discretionary Fund is like the canary in the coal mine. When our congregants start asking questions about it, it indicates a far deeper issue than simply control of money or transparency. The bigger issue is trust. Do they trust their rabbi to use money properly, do they trust their rabbi to use his/her time properly.

DON: You are so right! Scrutiny of the Discretionary Fund indicates a lack of trust that goes beyond the handling of the fund. On the other hand, sometimes when a new rabbi is engaged and there were problems with his predecessor with the Discretionary Fund, the congregation might wish to have greater safeguards over the account, and I can understand that.

Some years back I occupied a pulpit where it was FORBIDDEN for the rabbi to have a couch in his office. When I inquired about this, I found out that one of my predecessors had been using the couch in his office for "extra-curricular" activities. I have heard of rabbis who have had similar restrictions placed on their Discretionary Funds.

We often pay for the sins, real or perceived, of our predecessors. *Avot akhlu boser, v'shinei banim tikhena.* ["The fathers eat sour grapes and the children's teeth are set on edge] (Ezekiel 18:2).

BOB: Earlier we were talking about trying to explain difficult biblical passages in which the Israelite nation is told to wipe out all the Canaanite peoples who were in the Promised Land. I'd like to get back to that.

How do we, with our modern morality glasses, understand this part of the Torah? How do we even continue to read this part of the Torah, and how does modern Biblical scholarship help us see this issue and the reality it reflects? A counselor at Ramah asked me about this last summer when I was visiting the kids in my congregation who were there, and I'd like to steer him to something a little more convincing than my inarticulate recall.

SAM: Just to underscore Bob's question: I have recently been following a website that specializes in atheism and anti-religionism. Their very favorite chapter of Torah is Numbers 31. They love it. Can't get enough of it. My way of dealing with it over the years has been to ignore it. I have never mined that chapter of Tanakh in order to find *musar* or inspiration or *halakhic* values or anything else. I know that the Talmud sweeps away questions of genocide by talking of "the mingling of the nations" and other such devices. But, really, there are deep ethical questions of just what our God stands for, and just what our Torah, both written and oral, stands for.

Until I happened upon this anti-religious website it simply didn't occur to me that this chapter is seen by people as a major piece of Torah. Just because I ignore it doesn't mean that everyone else does, and should, ignore it. Note that the website I am following is NOT the work of anti-Semitic nut jobs. It is hosted by one of the world's most distinguished biologist/zoologist. A Jew. Some of the respondents are arrogant and ignorant. But this website seems generally to be written by and for reasonable people. It makes me realize how insular my own Jewish ethical thinking has been, repeating the same phrases and telling the same stories within the framework of self-contained teaching and preaching. It's imperative, I submit, that we be challenged. I freely confess that I have no *answer* to Bob's question. Just saying how salutary it is that this counselor at camp confronted him with the question.

BOB: I believe that the teaching of the Torah on genocide, is that it is wrong.

"Sennacherib confused the nations" is not a later comment, but an intrinsic part of the Torah's teaching. The Book of Numbers prescribes genocide. So what? God didn't give the Book of Numbers; he gave us the Torah. The only way, in my view, of upholding the Divine origin of the Torah is to understand Torah as being essentially open-ended. The word "Torah" has several meanings. It can refer to a scroll of the Pentateuch, or to the totality of God's teaching to the Jewish people. The Book of Numbers is an ancient Near Eastern text. The Babylonian Talmud is a Middle Eastern text from late antiquity. Each of them represents a slice of Torah but nothing more. Is that heretical? I thought that most of us believed something like that.

DON: I'm afraid I can't help you much on this one. Being Orthodox, I believe that the Torah was given all at once, totally, by God. Sometimes there are things we don't completely understand. When Elijah comes, he'll give us an adequate explanation.

I'd like to shift the focus a bit away from these deep theological issues, on which you know damn well that the three of us aren't going to agree on. Especially me versus the two of you "*goyim*." Don't take that literally, but I'm sure many of my colleagues do feel that way about your so-called "Documentary Theory," which says that men wrote the Torah, and not God.

Anyway, I've been teaching a class in my *shul* on wedding customs. Let me run some of my ideas by you before I present them to my students. OK?

BOB: Sure!

SAM: Sure, go ahead.

DON: OK, here goes. Let me take out some notes. Alright, here's what I've written so far:

1. Glass breaking – The custom would seem to be ancient, and I conjecture that the origin is actually unknown. However, the traditional view sees the source as Berakhot 30b–31a; "Mar, the son of Ravina, made a wedding feast for his son. When he saw that the rabbis were becoming overly merry, he brought a precious cup, worth four hundred *zuz*, and broke it in front of them, and they were sobered. Rav Ashi made a wedding feast for his son. When he saw that the rabbis were becoming overly merry, he brought a cup of white glass and broke it in front of them, and they were sobered." Commenting on this, the Tosafot writes: "This is the source of the custom of breaking a glass at a wedding."

2. Rings – The use of a ring of precious metal was first given legal significance in the Roman betrothal ceremony. The earliest

Christian references to the use of a ring in regard to marriage seems to be its popular use by Roman Christians in betrothal ceremonies. It would seem that this use of the ring by early Christians did not have any religious significance in the eyes of the Church, but reflected popular adoption of "secular" Roman culture. The wearing of rings by nuns to signify their betrothal to God, also appears to derive from popular custom. It would seem that the use of a ring in a ritually significant way by the Church began with the use of rings as symbols of ecclesiastical office, and that their formal ritual significance in marriage ceremonies was a relatively late development adopted from the symbolic meaning they had attached to ecclesiastical rings.

The use of a ring in the Jewish marriage ceremony is post-Talmudic, and the earliest Jewish references to the use of a ring for *Kiddushin* are Geonic. The earliest source for the formula *"harei at mekudeshet li betaba'at zo kedat moshe ve-Yisrael"* ["**Behold you** are consecrated to me with this ring, according to the laws of Moshe and the people of Israel"] of which I am aware, is from Rashi. The formula, in the form *"tehei at mekudeshet li betaba'at zo kedat moshe ve'Yisrael"* ["**You** are consecrated to me with this ring, according to the laws of Moshe and the people of Israel"] appears in *Sefer HaOra* and in *Mahzor Vitry*. The formula and practice would appear already to have become commonly accepted by that time.

How's that sound so far?

SAM: Frankly, Don, I'm pleasantly surprised that an Orthodox rav like you would use non-Jewish historical sources. I think it's great. And it really doesn't do any harm to the Jewishness of the ceremonies. I remember Harvard philosopher William James writing about the "genetic fallacy," which says that one cannot fault a present-day custom because of its origins, since the custom has probably evolved so much that its meaning no longer may, or may not, relate to its original intent.

BOB: I agree, Don. I think that material will give you plenty of discussion, and a great start for your course on marriage rituals. While we're on the subject of weddings, let me ask this:

I was at a wedding yesterday, attended by several Orthodox rabbis, including some very prominent ones. The *Mesader Kiddushin* was the brother of the bride, and a teacher, not a pulpit rabbi. After the *Kiddushin*, they did not read the *ketubah*, but rather simply mentioned who had signed the various documents such as the *ketubah*, the *tena'im*, a pre-nuptial agreement, etc. I have never been to a wedding where none of the *ketubah* was read. Like most of you, I read maybe a third, and at most Orthodox ones the entire *ketubah* is read. So, did the *Mesader Kiddushin* forget, or is this a custom I am not aware of?

I know we always read it, but I never understood why, as I could not find any requirement that it be read. I came to see it as the break between the two parts of the ceremony, *Erusin* and *Kiddushin*. I've asked Orthodox rabbis and they said it was *minhag*. I did a wedding with a highly educated rabbi. He didn't feel good and asked me if instead of just speaking to the bride and groom, would I do everything except not be the official *M'saderet Kiddushin*. I told him of course I would do whatever he needed. But I wouldn't read the whole *ketubah*, only about a third, as I usually do. He said "That's fine. It's not necessary."

I also went to a wedding at Shearith Israel, the Spanish Portuguese Synagogue in New York, and the rabbi did not read the *ketubah*. He said that it was not their custom to do so. Another example: I attended a wedding in Israel and the rabbi in charge simply reminded the couple that they had reviewed the *ketubah* with him in advance of the ceremony. Many elements of the ceremony that we include regularly, and we think they are *halakhah*, are simply *minhagim*, and they can vary from place to place and from time to time.

So I guess that's the answer to your question, Bob.

What else is on your minds to discuss today?

SAM: Well, this might seem very mundane, compared to what we've been talking about. But here goes: Can the *Sheva Brakhot* [Seven Wedding Blessings] be chanted from the congregation, or does the chanter need to be under the *huppah*?

DON: Easy one. They can be chanted from anywhere in the

room where the wedding takes place. The only ones who really have to stand under the *huppah* are the bride and groom.

BOB: I have another wedding question for you. I'm wondering what you've done when working with a bride who does not want, or plan to have, a veil with her wedding dress? How is the *bedeken* [veiling ceremony] done?

DON: A very interesting question. My personal answer is that I go ahead and recite the blessing for the bride, with or without a veil. Can blessing a bride and groom before their *huppah* ever be wrong? What I find so interesting about the question is that it reflects a growing trend. Whereas twenty or thirty years ago, there was virtually no question about wearing a veil, though brides generally refused to complete the seven circuits around the groom. Today the seven circuits are growing in popularity, whereas there is clearly a growing resistance to veils. I hope someone one- hundred-year-old researcher is recording these trends. Ritual observance may follow cycles.

SAM: Here is an odd question. We have *sifrei kodesh*, sacred books, like the Bible and Talmud, in need of burial. One option in our building is that we have an excavated, but unfinished room with a dirt floor under our sanctuary. Do you think it would it be at all appropriate to bury sacred books there, with the idea that sometime in the future we may need to use that space for use in our school, with *sifrei kodesh* buried underneath.

DON: I am not sure why this wouldn't be similar to the synagogue *genizah*, especially the one in Cairo we've all been reading about recently. You would thus be marrying, in effect, the tradition of burying books with the tradition of not destroying them, but saving them in some space within the synagogue dedicated to that purpose.

The question that is unasked is, if your *shul* needed that space, would the *genizah* be disrupted or would it be deep enough that the concrete would just be layered over the buried books? If there was a "good chance" it would be disrupted, I would feel it might be an inappropriate space. Otherwise, I would think it was a perfect space for the burial of *sifrei kodesh*.

BOB: That seems reasonable to me. I have a somewhat related question, though it may relate only to Conservative rabbis, but maybe you know someone interested.

Like so many other congregations, we are replacing our old *mahzorim* [High Holiday prayer books] with the new one that was just published. We may have as many as 2000 of the old ones, ranging in condition from excellent to moldy. Do you know anyone out there looking for *mahzorim*? We would be happy to give them away for the cost of shipping. When you talk to colleagues in your movements, perhaps there are some who are facing similar challenges. Can you please ask if they have been able to give them away? If not, what have they done?

DON: I'll be glad to ask my colleagues, and get back to you when I hear what they have to advise you.

SAM: Me too, no problem.

BOB: Well, I think we've covered the waterfront today. Let's meet again next week, and see what comes up. Have a great week!

DON: You too!

SAM: You too!

Week 2

ﬡ

SAM: I'd like to get the ball rolling today. I got a notice from some Israeli colleagues who are upset about the social inequality, especially the problems of the middle class not being able to afford housing. Let me read you this email I got this week:

"Israel is in the midst of an awakening, perhaps even a social revolution, but its official State Rabbinate and, indeed, virtually all religious officials, are silent. How can this be? Isn't it the role of religious leaders to provide guidance?

"Three weeks ago a few people set up tents on Rothschild Boulevard in Tel Aviv to protest the inability of people to find reasonably priced housing. There are now thousands of tent and camp sites in over forty cities, and 300,000 people marched in protest Saturday night.

"Although Israel has the twentieth largest economy in the world, we are forty-second in the average earned income per citizen. While the economy may be strong, many educated, hard-working, tax-paying citizens find that they are unable to finish the month on the salary earned. At the same time, significant segments of our society do not work by choice. Tens of thousands are excused from military service. Those who play by the rules, who work hard, who do military duty and pay taxes, are getting a raw deal. But the tipping point has surfaced and, in a wave of intensity that caught almost all by surprise, tens of thousands of working and middle class Israelis are demanding that Israel change social priorities.

"An ad hoc group of non-Orthodox rabbis in Israel has designated Tishah B'Av as a day of solidarity with the tent protest movement. On the evening of the fast, and for the duration of the day, we will hold events connecting the destruction of the ancient Temple with this struggle for the future of our homeland. These actions will link the senseless hatred in their time with the gaping economic disparity in Israel today. We call upon the government of Israel to concern itself with the welfare of all in the society. Not from the perspective of charity, but from that of justice; not *tzedeka* [charity], but *tzedek* [justice]. The government must repair the errors which have brought the working and middle classes to the brink. The continuing erosion of the middle class strikes at the heart of democracy. The government must alter national priorities in a profound and comprehensive manner, to be attentive to the cry of the people and to preserve our uniquely valuable homeland. Israel was established as a fulfillment of a Zionist dream that yearned for social justice and equity. 'Zionism,' Theodor Herzl wrote, 'as I understand it, is not solely about the desire to acquire a legally secure piece of real estate for our downtrodden people, after all, but also about the desire to grow towards moral and spiritual perfection.'

This Tishah B'Av, let us commit ourselves again to that vision." End of statement.

DON: I think we should try to get more of our colleagues here in the States to sign that document. Even though we're not Israelis, we should have a say.

BOB: Agreed!

SAM: Here's a question regarding cremation. I know we've discussed it already, and probably will again, but here goes. A congregant came to see me about her father, whose wishes are cremation after his death. No question on trying to change his mind.

His death is probably occurring shortly. He is currently in Florida, where the law says the state waits for two days after death to send the body to the crematorium. The crematorium says the cremation itself occurs eight to ten business days after they receive the body from the state, and then the ashes will be shipped here in one day. Here the ashes will be buried. Her question is: When does she begin *shivah*? If she really waits for the burial we have two full weeks of *aninut* [the time between death and burial]. There is no telling when exactly the body is cremated. My sense is that one could consider "final burial" from the moment the body is in the crematorium.

Any sources regarding this? I'd like to hear your thoughts and experiences in this area, too.

DON: The question said "No question on trying to change his mind." What about trying to change *her* mind – your congregant, the soon-to-be mourner?

I wholeheartedly agree with the strategy of trying to convince the soon-to-be mourner to choose traditional burial over cremation, when it is no longer possible – or perhaps never was possible – to convince the soon-to-be deceased to change his/her mind.

I think I have a valid *halakhic* argument in favor of arranging for a traditional burial despite the deceased's previously stated wishes: Neither *mitzvah l'kayyeim divrei ha-meit* ["It's a mitzvah to uphold the words of a deceased person"] nor *kabbed et-avikha v'et-immekha* ["Honor your father and mother"] requires us to violate *halakhah*. Further, the numerous philosophical or experiential arguments in favor of traditional burial, and in opposition to cremation, lead us, I think, to comfortably disregarding a loved one's request for cremation.

Beyond this specific *halakhah*, we should assert the following essential points: First, not every request that a loved one makes of us must categorically be obeyed. People make all sorts of requests and demands of us, and sometimes we legitimately disagree and legitimately disobey them. Second, not every request that a loved one makes of us, related to his or her impending death, must categorically be obeyed. Even though the emotional stakes may be higher, we have the right, when we disagree even with a death-related request, to disobey such an illegitimate request.

I have two stories which I'll share here:

The first is the story of convincing a man, whose mother was still alive and had requested cremation before her descent into dementia, to make his peace with the idea of disregarding her request when the time came, on the grounds that, or at least the hope that, if there had been time, that is, if she had remained lucid for a longer time, perhaps he could have convinced her to reconsider her request.

The other is a story of a dying woman whom I tried to convince to choose traditional burial, but whose final illness progressed too quickly for me to make much progress in that regard. When she died, convincing her husband, and then-teenage sons, to choose traditional burial was an easy task. It was, I believe, a decision that they were comfortable with in the days and years following. For myself, it's one of the best things I did in my rabbinical career.

BOB: My experiences are that emotional *shivah* begins when there is some physical, active closure for the mourners, and I try to officiate at a funeral before the cremation occurs.

My first advice is that I would urge your congregant to have some religious service, with the body present, in Florida after her father's death but before the body is sent to be cremated. Perhaps there is a rabbi her father knows in Florida, perhaps not, but to have some sort of service offers her, and perhaps other mourners, some ceremonial closure. *Shivah* begins at that time.

Then, step two, I agree with colleagues who would advise a service of burial in a Jewish cemetery and some memorial service, perhaps a study of texts, that offers a second level of "closure" that is more physically final than the first, which was unaccompanied by burial.

In the case in which there can be no funeral ceremony in Florida, or your congregant decides not to press the funeral issue with her father, I have found that a quiet ceremony, attached to *Minhah* or *Ma'ariv*, on the day following the death, where the mourner invites friends to a service on the day the funeral *would have* taken place, and at the end of the "traditional" *Minhah* or *Ma'ariv*, I deliver a brief remembrance of the deceased and chant *El maleh* [memorial prayer] and the mourner recites

Kaddish. This has filled the void left by not having a funeral ceremony with the deceased. Followed by step two, when the remains reach the mourner in your town.

Our Law Committee has few but weighty insights into this
issue. Practical Rabbinics dictates I follow the lead of my congregants in these cases where, as others point out, *halakhah* says
"don't go there" but compassion directs us towards a more gen-
tle approach, with kindness and mercy towards the mourner and
the deceased, a more *halakhic* approach. Godliness demands we
be compassionate and respectful.

So now I have a different question for your brilliant, creative,
experienced and well-informed rabbinic minds.

I have a congregant who is not observant, and who is a Jew
by birth, married to a Jewish woman. He himself never had a
Bris Milah. I suggested that he should undergo the process of a
bris back when we named his daughter, but he said he was not
interested. He's just interested in giving his daughter more of
a Jewish education than he had. Now they have a son, who is
around a year old. No *bris* was ever done. The congregant now
wants a naming ceremony. As far as I know, there is no medical
issue with the boy that would prevent a *bris*. Do you advise me to
do a naming ceremony, even though there was no circumcision?

SAM: I tell the couple that a naming takes place at a *bris*. However, we would be pleased to offer an *aliyah* to the entire family
and after the *aliyah* we will say a *Mi Sheberakh* for each member of the family, using the Hebrew name of the new born. We
will not, however, announce it as a naming nor say the liturgical
formula: *vayeekaray shemo b'Yisrael* ["May his name be called
among the Jewish People"]. The child is Jewish, and the child
has a Jewish name and is to be welcomed into the community
of Israel. Many families come for an *aliyah* to offer thanksgiving
after a *bris*. By just saying a regular *Mi Sheberakh* we are doing
what we would do for any family. I tell the family that they can
invite family and friends, but if they announce it as a baby naming, we can't do that. It's a "baby welcoming." Some accept it and
say thank you. Others leave and go to the less traditional *shul* one
town over, which is ok with me. By the way, this happens mainly

with families that have a *milah* (circumcision), but no *bris milah*. I have had only one case over the years where there was no *milah* at all, and it was the result of a trauma with the first child who had a botched *milah*. Not my fault, of course. They went to a *mohel* I told them not to go to, and I was very sympathetic to the family as their motivation was not rebellion nor were they even making a statement. They were simply scared, because of their previous experience.

DON: I realize that rabbis who say "no" too often, run the risk of being asked to find another pulpit. As a colleague once said to me: "There are just so many times that you can threaten to fall on your sword before the *shul* says 'go ahead.'" That having been said, I think this is one of those occasions. Whatever can be said about naming being separate from the actual *bris milah*, according to the *halakhah*, in this case it is beyond clear that the parents desire an alternative to *bris milah* and wish to have this alternative endorsed by the congregation and the rabbi. To me this is a gross affront to Jewish tradition. Short answer: NO!

BOB: I believe this is an important matter and I believe you can expect requests like this to become increasingly common in the future. I have probably had four in the past six months alone. To be sure, most were not affiliated with a synagogue, so did not have a rabbi to speak to, but were also not concerned about future ramifications. Typically they were interfaith families who wanted some type of naming ceremony to satisfy the Jewish grandparents. I would first find out what their objection was either to a *bris* ceremony, or to circumcision altogether, and if it was based on erroneous information, I would correct that.

A few months ago I asked some colleagues informally if they were not Jewish, would they have their sons circumcised. Most colleagues were quite unaware of the social and medical issues being argued in the ongoing debate in parts of America. Frankly, I think it behooves rabbis to become more aware of what the issues are because congregants will certainly be. If the parents continue to refuse to have their son circumcised, I explain that they do not need a rabbi, or a *mohel*, to name their son. I refer them to *The New Jewish Baby Book* and suggest they create a ceremony for themselves and their family. I feel that in this way I have not closed any door, should they ever choose to become more Jewishly involved, but have also not taken part in a ritual that I believe has no place in our tradition. The parents typically thank me for the suggestion and I have no idea what they actually do. I realize it is different when there is an ongoing relationship with a rabbi or a synagogue, but that is how I have handled these requests.

By the way, in terms of future sanctions for people who have been circumcised but without *bris milah*, by the time they grow up, no one seems to know or care much. I can tell you that it probably will have no effect on getting accepted into rabbinical school.

DON: I have another issue to pick your brains about. Here goes: A year ago I was invited by a member family to co-officiate with a Reform rabbi from a different city at a wedding here at a local hotel. The Reform rabbi is the *Mesader Kiddushin*. I am participating in only a very limited way. Even so, the Reform rabbi has been very gracious in seeing that all the liturgical elements of the ceremony are according to *halakhah*. I have just been informed, however, that the *ketubah* is not kosher. It is an egalitarian, non-traditional document prepared by the couple and endorsed and approved by the Reform rabbi. The rabbi explained to me that the traditional document is "offensive," and that both he and the couple refuse to use a traditional *ketubah*. When I suggested using both, that is, signing the traditional *ketubah* at the *bedeken* along with the non-traditional one, I was turned down.

I do not see how I can co-officiate at a wedding with a *non-halakhic ketubah*, but before I bow out – which the family will understand – I want to see if anyone has any ideas to help me here.

BOB: I was in a similar predicament a dozen or more years ago. It involved not a Reform colleague, but a Conservative colleague.

I don't remember what my role as "co-officiant" had been. Chanting the *Sheva Berakhot*? Doing a wedding talk? I do remember that my role didn't include reading the *ketubah*, and

I noticed during the wedding preliminaries that the *ketubah* was not *halakhically* valid. Nevertheless, I reminded myself that I was not the *mara d'atra* of that congregation, nor the *Mesader Kiddushin* at that wedding, and I happily co-officiated at the wedding. Did I personally disapprove of at least one of the choices that the rabbi had made? Yup. Did that deter me from participating at my friends' son's wedding? Nope. Did I retain a little bit of ambivalence afterwards? Of course.

A few weeks after I returned home, I happened to be chatting with a colleague who was expert in Jewish Law. I shared with him my "lingering dilemma." His after-the-fact advice, as I recall, was simple and clear: "Bob, you weren't the *mara d'atra* in that congregation. It would have been inappropriate for you to make an issue about the *ketubah*."

SAM: I have always insisted that they sign two *ketubot*, at least one of them being strictly kosher. But I will tell you that I have officiated with Orthodox rabbis who have let me be *Mesader Kiddushin*, and did nothing but speak under the *huppah*. The *ketubah* was kosher, so that wasn't a problem, but the reason he only spoke was so he could say "I didn't co-officiate with anyone. I was asked to say a few words and I did." Neither did the Orthodox rabbi participate in the *ketubah* signing.

So if you feel you can't or don't want to bow out, you could make it clear that you cannot co-officiate, but you would be pleased to be called to the *huppah* to address the couple. And I would not walk down the aisle but rather ask to be called to the *huppah* at some point to say a few words. And I would leave the *huppah* after speaking. But if you "co-officiate" I think it's a real problem.

BOB: I have a very contemporary issue to ask about. I was asked this morning about the proper *berakhah* to say following a recent East-coast earthquake. I can think of a number of possibilities. But I have limited direct experience with earthquakes. Therefore, I'm curious about what my learned colleagues would suggest.

DON: I know that our colleague Harry Schwartz posted on Facebook the *berakhah* ". . . *shekoho u'gevurato malei olam* [". . . Whose power and mighty fill the world"], which I think appropriate, but in light of the regenerative effects earthquakes have on the crust of the earth, one might opt for the somewhat less dramatic *berakhah* – but no less appropriate, in my view – *oseh ma'asei bereishit* [. . . Author of Creation].

Additionally, there were few injuries, but knowing how dangerous earthquakes can be, perhaps "*gomel*" [recited after escaping danger, "Who bestows upon me much good"] is also appropriate.

This may be a good *d'var Torah* for Shabbat, maybe giving the congregation the options and letting them decide which might be best.

SAM: This conversation eludes me. If there is an earthquake then the only possible *berakhah*, in my humble opinion, is to "bench *gomel*," since you didn't get killed. To say any *berakhah* that suggests that God is responsible for this kind of disaster is to me a 'disaster'. And I don't take "*gomel*" literally. I don't think God for one moment did anything to save me, but I need a way to say I am appreciative of being saved and that is what our tradition gives us. A gift to *tzedakah* is even more appropriate, and the best *berakhah* after an earthquake is to give *tzedakah* to help rebuild.

BOB: Hey, guys. I have an important issue that I've been struggling with, and I'd love your input. For the last year and a half I have been struggling with a guilty conscience about what I eat. And I don't like the feeling.

It's not that I run off somewhere for an occasional secret bacon fix, God forbid. I still follow all the rules, at least the letter of the rules, found in the Torah portion of *Re'eh*, which spells out the basics of keeping kosher. But I'm worried about whether everything I'm eating follows the spirit of the laws.

What happened a year and a half ago? A colleague, who is both an observant Jew and a vegetarian, recommended I read the book *Eating Animals*, by Jonathan Safran Foer. It should be required reading for anyone who is NOT a vegetarian. If you are going to eat meat, including chicken and fish, you should at least do it consciously, and you should be aware of the consequences of your actions.

The consequences are severe. The vast majority of meat we eat, including kosher chicken and beef, is raised on factory farms, in horrible, inhumane conditions. When we eat fish we are contributing to a process that may lead to a complete collapse of the oceans' eco-systems. Already populations of many fish have dropped by 90% from past levels. An illustrative excerpt from the book, which you might not want to read before eating, follows below.

> *The typical cage for egg-laying hens allows each sixty-seven square inches of floor space – somewhere between the size of this page and a sheet of printer paper. Such cages are stacked between three and nine tiers high – Japan has the world's highest battery cage unit, with cages stacked eighteen tiers high – in windowless sheds.*
>
> *Step your mind into a crowded elevator, an elevator so crowded you cannot turn around without bumping into (and aggravating) your neighbor. The elevator is so crowded you are often held aloft.*
>
> *This is a kind of blessing, as the slanted floor is made of wire, which cuts into your feet. After some time, those in the elevator will lose their ability to work in the interest of the group. Some will become violent; others will go mad. A few, deprived of food and hope, will become cannibalistic.*
>
> *There is no respite, no relief. No elevator repairman is coming. The doors will open once, at the end of your life, for your journey to the only place worse.*

Safran Foer makes a compelling case that eating animals causes tremendous damage. It is:

• Bad for animals
• Bad for the environment. The UN says "raising animals for food is one of the top two or three most significant contrib-

utors to the most serious environmental problems, at every scale from local to global . . . [animal agriculture] should be a major policy focus when dealing with problems of land degradation, climate change and air pollution, water shortage and water pollution and less biodiversity. Livestocks's contributions to environmental problems is on a massive scale." Safran Foer has some very colorful descriptions of the methane ponds found on factory farms . . . thousands of cows generate a lot of "waste."

- Bad for workers. Working conditions are often very poor; the Jewish community, of course, is very familiar with the scandal at Postville.
- Bad for consumers. Most factory-raised animals are pumped full of all sorts of hormones and prescription drugs and are not healthy to eat.
- Bad for society (which must bear huge hidden costs).

But what would Judaism have to say about all that? The Torah certainly does not mention these issues in any kind of explicit way, does it?

The Torah reading, "Re'eh," contains one verse which is the basis for the rules the later rabbis developed regarding kosher slaughter of animals, including beef, lamb, chicken, etc. Deuteronomy 14:21 tells us "lo tokhlu kol neveilah [do not eat any neveila]. The simple meaning of neveila is an animal that died of natural causes.

The verse is understood as prohibiting more than animals that died of natural causes. It is understood as prohibiting animals that are treifah, literally "torn," which includes both animals that were killed by other animals and animals that were killed by people not using the particular procedure of kosher slaughter. So while deer may be kosher, we can't eat deer killed through hunting. We can only eat deer that were raised on a farm and subjected to kosher slaughter. No eating road kill.

The rules of kosher slaughter for animals are very stringent. Eating meat is seen as a kind of compromise – we are taking an animal's life to benefit ourselves. The rabbis have traditionally understood that the ideal is to be vegetarian, but since we have a strong appetite for meat, God allows us to eat it, though there are restrictions. A blessing is said before the slaughter. The animal must be killed with a very sharp knife, without even a single nick. A very clean cut must be made across the majority of the trachea and/or esophagus. If the knife drags a little in the cut, the meat is not kosher. All the blood must be removed. And the animal must be inspected to make sure it was not diseased.

Most of these rules – the requirements for a sharp knife and a clean cut in particular – clearly are based on preventing unnecessary suffering for the animal. *Sefer HaHinukh*, a thirteenth century commentary on the commandments says: "The reason that slaughter must be done at the throat with a knife that is thoroughly inspected is in order that there will not be unnecessary suffering to animals, for the Torah permits people to sustain and nourish themselves and take care of their needs, but NOT to cause gratuitous pain. The sages spoke at great length in the Talmud about the prohibition against *tza'ar ba'alei hayim*, causing pain to animals, and these things are prohibited by the Torah."

For most of Jewish history, the practice of kosher slaughter was clearly in line with both the details of the law and the intent of the law. But when we come to twentieth century America, a problem arose. In 1906 the passage of the U.S. Pure Food and Drug Act required that animals not fall on the floor or come into contact with the blood of other animals. For a long time the way this rule was typically implemented – at both kosher and non-kosher slaughterhouses – was with what is called the "hoist and shackle" method, where chains are placed around the rear legs of the animal and it is hoisted up in the air by its rear legs. This technique is patently cruel – not infrequently breaking the leg of the animal, and clearly causing a great deal of pain, fear, and discomfort. After hoisting the animal in the air, sometimes nose tongs would be used to pull the head back to expose the throat, which could then be slit with the carefully prepared knife without a nick in it. In 1958, the US government banned hoisting conscious animals because of the cruelty involved – yet, ironically, kosher slaughter was exempted, because there was no other way to meet both the *halakhic* requirement that the animal be conscious when slaughtered, and the sanitary requirements of the Federal government.

Talk about a great irony! Kosher slaughter – whose rules were designed to minimize suffering to animals – was exempted from a rule of the US government, and was conducted in a way that was crueler than secular slaughter. By 1963 alternative methods of kosher slaughter were developed which could keep the animal upright and calm during slaughter, but many kosher slaughterhouses failed to implement them because they were more expensive than using hoist and shackle.

To use a very sharp knife to kill an animal that is hanging upside down and thrashing in distress is clearly a case of following the letter of the law, but not the spirit!

A few years ago I got into an email discussion with someone who presented the following case: if someone who keeps a kosher home lives in a rural area and only has access to kosher meat that was processed at a plant using inhumane techniques for slaughter, would it be better for them to eat local meat and poultry that is slaughtered on farms by local farmers who demonstrate compassion and consideration for their animals?

The question is basically asking "what's more important? – to follow the letter of the law, or the spirit of the law?"

Clearly there are Orthodox rabbis who say that the letter of the law is what's important. They continue to certify as kosher, meat that is slaughtered in cruel ways.

Just as clearly, many Reform and Reconstructionist Jews would go with eating the meat of the local farmers.

The Conservative movement has addressed the issue in a te-shuvah [responsum], a legal opinion, written by two of the leading lights of the Conservative movement, Rabbis Elliot Dorff and Joel Roth, who ruled "Now that kosher, humane slaughter using upright pens is both possible and widespread, we find shackling and hoisting to be a violation of Jewish laws forbidding cruelty to animals and requiring that we avoid unnecessary dangers to human life. As the CJLS [Committee on Jewish Law and Standards], then, we rule that shackling and hoisting should be stopped."

Personally, I don't believe that the CJLS went quite far

enough. They said shackling and hoisting violates the laws forbidding cruelty to animals, but they did NOT say it renders the meat not kosher.

My own view is that the meat is literally rendered not kosher. You might as well eat a hamburger from McDonald's as meat that has been slaughtered using the hoist and shackle method. So here is an instance where I'm more stringent than many Orthodox rabbis. Meat they would consider *glatt* kosher, I would consider *treif.*

At the same time, I would not say that it is OK to eat "compassionately raised and killed" meat from a local farmer that was not done in accordance with the rules of kashrut. It is not enough to follow only the spirit of the law, no more than it is enough to follow only the letter of the law. The intent behind the law is part of the law.

Look at speed limits for example. Why do we have speed limits? We have speed limits to keep people safe. Excessive speed is dangerous. Now if you are driving a new Porsche on a long straight stretch of the interstate where there are no other cars in sight, and it's a nice clear day, you could drive ninety miles an hour and certainly still be safe – well within the spirit of the law. But I don't recommend you try it – the Highway Patrol will still give you a ticket. The letter of the law says the speed limit is sixty-five miles an hour, not ninety.

Similarly, you could be driving sixty miles an hour in that sixty-five mile an hour zone, and get a speeding ticket. How? If it's a very foggy day and visibility is seriously reduced, sixty miles an hour is a very dangerous speed. And the spirit of the law is the law as well. The law states the speed limit is a maximum "if conditions permit."

I maintain the same principle applies in Jewish law. It is not enough to follow only the spirit, or only the letter of the law. What God wants of us is both. One of the reasons we have the laws is to refine our characters. Nahmanides [Ramban] has an interesting comment on the other part of the verse that we've been considering, the part that deals with separating meat and dairy: "You shall not boil a kid in its mother's milk." Ramban says that we are given this rule in order that we will be holy, that we will not be cruel, so lacking in compassion that we could milk the mother and cook the child in the same milk.

If the laws were given to us in order that we should be kind and considerate to animals, that we should not be cruel, it is totally ludicrous to think it is OK to follow the technicalities while violating the essence.

So what should the people trying to keep kosher in a rural area do? I offered three options:

1. Go vegetarian, or just stock up on meat on those occasions then they visit the big city.
2. Order kosher meat over the internet. You can get kosher meat delivered anywhere these days.
3. Learn how to supervise the *shehitah* [slaughter] of the local farmers to make it kosher, or import a rabbi to supervise.

But I realize now that my response did not go far enough. Just "kosher" meat is not really kosher enough, because the kosher food industry generally only cares about the letter of the law, not the spirit of the law. And as demonstrated above, following the letter of the law is not enough.

Besides the concerns for the well-being of the animal, Jewish law calls on us to be concerned about the environment. When God gives Adam "dominion" over the earth, he is appointing Adam a steward to take care of the earth, not a despot to despoil the earth.

What the Torah expects of us, and what Jonathan Safran Foer calls for in his book, is for us to be "ethical omnivores." If you are going to eat meat, you should only eat animals that have not been tortured during their lives, that died a death with minimal pain, and that causes minimum harm to the environment.

It is theoretically possible. There are free-range kosher chickens that live what would seem to be happy lives for a chicken. But since there isn't much in the way of regulation for the use of terms like "free range" you can't necessarily tell from what it says on the package: there are also some "free range" chickens that are really factory raised chickens where they leave a door open so a few chickens can wander outside but most can't get to the door.

There is a whole "eco-kosher" movement, which seeks sources of grass-fed, free range cattle and does kosher slaughter. Unfortunately, the movement is still pretty small, and the vast majority of kosher meat you find will not be "eco-kosher." It takes effort to find it.

Being an ethical omnivore when eating fish is also challenging. For some species of fish, to eat one fish results in the deaths of another five or ten that are not desired that are simply thrown away. There are 145 different species of fish commonly killed in the hunt for tuna. The damage of "factory fishing" to the world's oceans is horrific. And "farm-raised" fish create a different kind of environmental damage. Eating only line-caught fish certainly helps to reduce the environmental consequences of eating fish.

So why do I have a guilty conscience? After reading Safran Foer's book, I resolved to be an "ethical omnivore." I have more or less given up eating beef, and at home we make an effort to only purchase free range eggs and chickens. But I still occasionally eat chicken when I'm eating out, and I still occasionally enjoy a piece of tuna sushi. I recognize I am being inconsistent. If I believe the hoist and shackle method of slaughter renders meat not kosher, I have no choice but to also believe that animals raised in the inhumane conditions of factory farms are also not kosher.

Thus, I am resolving to redouble my efforts, and not eat any meat whose provenance I am not sure of, whether at home or out.

And if you are an omnivore, I very strongly recommend you read Safran Foer's book for yourself, and give serious thought to what you are eating. If enough of us insist on only eating meat that is raised with a concern for the welfare of the animal, the environment, and for society as a whole, we can become a movement that can change laws and change industries.

DON: Bob, that is an amazing story. I can understand why you've been struggling with your conscience. I need to get that book and read it as soon as I can.

Meanwhile, I read something totally amazing about President Lyndon Baines Johnson that I'd like to share with you. It was in an article that appeared in The Jerusalem Post on September 9, 2008 by Lenny Ben-David [then deputy chief of mission of the Israeli Embassy in Washington]. Please let me know if you've heard anything confirming what I'm about to read to you about Johnson. I can't vouch for the authenticity of the facts reported in this piece. Nevertheless, it makes for very interesting reading and perhaps you will be able to verify some, if not all, of the facts. Perhaps it will be useful sermonic material associated with the Holocaust and/or Israel.

A Friend in Deed

. . . the Associated Press reported that newly released tapes from US president Lyndon Johnson's White House office showed LBJ's "personal and often emotional connection to Israel." The news agency pointed out that during the Johnson presidency (1963–1969), "the United States became Israel's chief diplomatic ally and primary arms supplier." But the news report does little to reveal the full historical extent of Johnson's actions on behalf of the Jewish people and the State of Israel. Most students of the Arab-Israeli conflict can identify Johnson as the president during the 1967 war. But few know about LBJ's actions to rescue hundreds of endangered Jews during the Holocaust – actions that could have thrown him out of Congress and into jail. Indeed, the title of "Righteous Gentile" is certainly appropriate in the case of the Texan, whose centennial year is being commemorated this year [2011]. Appropriately enough, the annual Jerusalem Conference announced . . . that it will honor Johnson. . . . Historians have revealed that Johnson, while serving as a young congressman in 1938 and 1939, arranged for visas to be supplied to Jews in Warsaw, and oversaw the apparently illegal immigration of hundreds of Jews through the port of Galveston, Texas. A key resource for uncovering LBJ's pro-Jewish activity is the unpublished 1989 doctoral thesis by University of Texas student Louis Gomolak, "Prologue: LBJ's Foreign

Affairs Background, 1908–1948." Johnson's activities were confirmed by other historians in interviews with his wife, family members and political associates. Research into Johnson's personal history indicates that he inherited his concern for the Jewish people from his family. His aunt Jessie Johnson Hatcher, a major influence on LBJ, was a member of the Zionist Organization of America. According to Gomolak, Aunt Jessie had nurtured LBJ's commitment to befriending Jews for 50 years. As a young boy, Lyndon watched his politically active grandfather "Big Sam" and father "Little Sam" seek clemency for Leo Frank, the Jewish victim of a blood libel in Atlanta.

Frank was lynched by a mob in 1915, and the Ku Klux Klan in Texas threatened to kill the Johnsons. The Johnsons later told friends that Lyndon's family hid in their cellar while his father and uncles stood guard with shotguns on their porch in case of KKK attacks. Johnson's speech writer later stated, "Johnson often cited Leo Frank's lynching as the source of his opposition to both anti-Semitism and isolationism."

Already in 1934 – four years before Chamberlain's Munich sellout to Hitler, Johnson was keenly alert to the dangers of Nazism and presented a book of essays, "Nazism: An Assault on Civilization," to the 21-year-old woman he was courting, Claudia Taylor – later known as "Lady Bird" Johnson. It was an incredible engagement present.

Five days after taking office as a Congressman, in 1937, LBJ broke with the "Dixiecrats" and supported an immigration bill that would naturalize illegal aliens, mostly Jews from Lithuania and Poland. In 1938, Johnson was told of a young Austrian Jewish musician who was about to be deported from the United States. With an element of subterfuge, LBJ sent him to the U.S. Consulate in Havana to obtain a residency permit. Erich Leinsdorf, the world famous musician and conductor, credited LBJ for saving his live.

That same year LBJ warned Jewish friend, Jim Novy, that European Jews faced annihilation. "Get as many Jewish people as possible out of Germany and Poland," were Johnson's instructions. Somehow, Johnson provided him with a pile of signed immigration papers that were used to get 42 Jews out of Warsaw. But that wasn't enough. According to historian James M. Smallwood, Congressman Johnson used legal and sometimes illegal methods to smuggle "hundreds of Jews into Texas, using Galveston as the entry port. Enough money could buy false passports and fake visas in Cuba, Mexico and other Latin American countries. . . . Johnson smuggled boatloads and planeloads of Jews into Texas. He hid them in the Texas National Youth Administration. . . . Johnson saved at least four or five hundred Jews, possibly more."

During World War II Johnson joined Novy at a small Austin gathering to sell $65,000 in war bonds. According to Gomolak, Novy and Johnson then raised a very "substantial sum for arms for Jewish underground fighters in Palestine." One source cited by the historian, reports that, "Novy and Johnson had been secretly shipping heavy crates labeled 'Texas Grapefruit' – but containing arms – to Jewish underground 'freedom fighters' in Palestine."

On June 4, 1945, Johnson visited Dachau. According to Smallwood, Lady Bird later recalled that when her husband returned home, "he was still shaken, stunned, terrorized, and bursting with an overpowering revulsion and incredulous horror at what he had seen."

A decade later while serving in the Senate, Johnson blocked the Eisenhower administration's attempts to apply sanctions against Israel following the 1956 Sinai Campaign. "The indefatigable Johnson had never ceased pressure on the administration," wrote I.L. "Si" Kenen, the head of AIPAC at the time.

As Senate majority leader, Johnson consistently blocked the anti-Israel initiatives of his fellow Democrat, William Fulbright, the chairman of the Senate Foreign Relations Committee. Among Johnson's closest advisers during this period were several strong pro-Israel advocates, including Benjamin Cohen (who 30 years earlier was the liaison between Supreme Court justice Louis Brandeis and Chaim Weizmann) and Abe Fortas, the legendary Washington "insider."

Johnson's concern for the Jewish people continued through his presidency.

Soon after taking office in the aftermath of John F. Kennedy's assassination in 1963, Johnson told an Israeli diplomat, "You have lost a very great friend, but you have found a better one."

Just one month after succeeding Kennedy, LBJ attended the December 1963 dedication of the Agudas Achim Synagogue in Austin. Novy opened the ceremony by saying to Johnson, "We can't thank him enough for all those Jews he got out of Germany during the days of Hitler."

Lady Bird would later describe the day, according to Gomolak: "Person after person plucked at my sleeve and said, 'I wouldn't be here today if it weren't for him. He helped me get out.'" Lady Bird elaborated, "Jews had been woven into the warp and woof of all [Lyndon's] years."

The Prelude to the 1967 war was a terrifying period for Israel, with the US State Department led by the historically unfriendly Dean Rusk urging an evenhanded policy despite Arab threats and acts of aggression. Johnson held no such illusions. After the war he placed the blame firmly on Egypt: "If a single act of folly was more responsible for this explosion than any other, it was the arbitrary and dangerous announced decision [by Egypt, that the Strait of Tiran would be closed to Israeli ships and Israeli-bound cargo]."

Kennedy was the first president to approve the sale of defensive US weapon to Israel, specifically Hawk anti-aircraft missiles. But Johnson approved tanks and fighter jets, all vital after the 1967 war when France imposed a freeze on sales to Israel. Yehuda Avner described Prime Minister Levi Eshkol's successful appeal for these weapons on a visit to the LBJ ranch.

Israel won the 1967 war, and Johnson worked to make sure it also won the peace. "I sure as hell want to be careful and not run out on little Israel," Johnson said in a March 1968 conversation with his ambassador to the United Nations, Arthur Goldberg, according to White House tapes recently released.

Soon after the 1967 war, Soviet Premier Aleksei Kosygin asked Johnson at the Glassboro Summit why the U.S. supported Israel when there were 80 million Arabs and only three million Israelis. "Because it is the right thing to do," responded the straight-shooting Texan.

The crafting of UN Resolution 242 in November 1967 was done under Johnson's scrutiny. The call for "secure and recognized boundaries" was critical. The American and British drafters of the resolution opposed Israel returning all the territories captured in the war. In September 1968, Johnson explained, "We are not the ones to say where other nations should draw lines between them that will assure each the greatest security. It is clear, however, that a return to the situation of 4 June 1967 will not bring peace. There must be secure, and there must be recognized, borders. Some such lines must be agreed to by the neighbors involved."

Goldberg later noted, "Resolution 242 in no way refers to Jerusalem, and this omission was deliberate." This historic diplomacy was conducted under Johnson's stewardship, as Goldberg related in oral history to the Johnson Library. "I must say for Johnson," Goldberg stated. "He gave me great personal support."

Robert David Johnson, a professor of history at Brooklyn College, recently wrote in *The New York Sun*, Johnson's policies stemmed more from personal concerns – his friendship with leading Zionists, his belief that America had a moral obligation to bolster Israeli security and his conception of Israel as a frontier land much like his home state of Texas. His personal concerns led him to intervene when he felt that the State or Defense departments had insufficiently appreciated Israel's diplomatic or military needs."

President Johnson firmly pointed American policy in a pro-Israel direction. In a historical context, the American emergency airlift to Israel in 1973, the constant diplomatic support, the economic and military assistance and the strategic bonds between the two countries can all be credited to the seeds planted by LBJ.

ADDITONAL NOTE:
Lyndon Johnson's maternal ancestors, the Huffmans, apparently migrated to Frederick, Maryland from Germany sometime

in the mid-eighteenth century. Later they moved to Bourbon, Kentucky and eventually settled in Texas in the mid-to-late nineteenth century. According to Jewish law, if a person's mother is Jewish, then that person is automatically Jewish, regardless of the father's ethnicity or religion. The facts indicate that both of Lyndon Johnson's great-grandparents, on the maternal side, were Jewish. These were the grandparents of Lyndon's mother, Rebecca Baines. Their names were John S. Huffman and Mary Elizabeth

Perrin. John Huffman's mother was Suzanne Ament, a common Jewish name. Perrin is also a common Jewish name. Huffman and Perrin had a daughter, Ruth Ament Huffman, who married Joseph Baines, and together they had a daughter, Rebekah Baines, Lyndon Johnson's mother. The line of Jewish mothers can be traced back three generations in Lyndon Johnson's family tree. There is little doubt that he was Jewish.

[End of published article].

I hasten to add this footnote, sent to me by email from a colleague who helped convert LBJ's granddaughter:

I was on the Bet Din for the conversion of LBJ's granddaughter. Her mother was there as well – LBJ's daughter. She brought with her books her mother (Lady Bird) used to read to her. They were books I read to my kids about Jewish holidays and Bible stories. She told me how her parents wanted them to understand that Christianity came from Judaism and that the Jews taught the world so many good things. She spoke about her Dad's concern for Israel, and his frustration that Viet Nam problems limited his ability to help Israel directly. She confirmed many of the things that are mentioned in the news release you sent me. She also mentioned that when his handlers were taking him and Lady Bird around Washington looking for a house they took them to only one neighborhood. They asked about the other neighborhood – "Oh you don't want to live there – that's where the Kikes live." They said to their handlers – "that's exactly where we want to live."

LBJ and Lady Bird were out almost every night. On Friday night the girls went next door to the Orthodox neighbors and did

Shabbat every Friday night. That's where their parents wanted them to be.

DON: Wow – we've sure had an interesting meeting today. I'm off to an appointment. See you guys next week – same time, same place.

SAM: See you then!

Week 3

❧

BOB: Hi fellas. I have an interesting question that occurred during the weekend.

I know a Jew by choice whose mother insists on bringing *treif* food into his kitchen. He's enlisted my help in finding a strategy for dealing with her. She's what my college sociology of religion professor would have called a "religious none." She grew up Protestant, and tried to raise her son with secular ethical values. He became an observant Conservative Jew.

Fortunately for our friend, she's in Seattle and he's in Dallas, so she's not around very much. But she might be coming this fall, and he's already worrying. She brings in *treif* food, and when he asks her not to, she tells him that he "owes" her this, and is ungrateful for all that she's given him.

It's clearly a control issue, but *kashrut*, and Shabbat and Yom Tov observance, are caught in the middle. Anyone have any experience with anything like this?

SAM: I say let him put up with the mother while she is there. Let her bring in *treif*, if she insists, but only on paper. It sounds like the mother has many issues, which he will not be able to solve while she visits. Better to hold his nose and let the time pass.

DON: I had a similar situation in my own family. For a long time, for years in fact, my mother attempted to bring *treif* into my house, and thought it was just fine to feed my kids *treif* when they were very young, and didn't know any better. And, by the way, she is very, very Jewish.

The answer, though, in my humble opinion, is fairly simple. I have made it clear to my mother that this is my house and that she has to abide by our rules in our house. Similarly, if she wants to have my children with her in her house, she needs to follow our rules. In reality, on both issues, my house or her house, it only required laying down the law once, and since then she has been accommodating. To her great credit, she realized the values of keeping kosher and increasing her personal observance, and even *kashered* her house for *Pesach* for the last two years so we could stay there with her.

BOB: To turn the discussion to something theological, I have a question for you learned gentlemen. It's the old question of "Why is there evil in the world?" The Talmud deals with it, but I have a congregant who wants a modern theological response in some depth. Can either of you direct me to any sources to help him?

DON: I can help. Since Bob alerted me a few days ago that he would raise this issue, I decided to bring a few books with me that can help us with this very difficult question – one that all of our congregants deal with, wonder about, and will sooner or later ask us about.

I want to base my reply on the thoughts of one of my professors at Yeshiva University. I'm personally familiar with Rabbi Dr. Joseph B. Soloveitchik, who served as guide, mentor and advisor, as well as role-model for generations of Jews. He is regarded as a major influential figure by Modern Orthodox Judaism. Over the course of almost half a century he ordained almost two thousand rabbis. He stressed a synthesis between Torah scholarship and Western secular scholarship. He was a descendant of the Lithuanian Jewish Soloveitchik rabbinic dynasty.

Rabbi Soloveitchik was born into a family recognized for its Torah learning. His grandfather and father emphasized a thorough analysis of Talmud, and it is using this method that Rav Soloveitchik studied and taught his own students at Yeshiva University where he served as Rosh Yeshivah. He was awarded a Ph.D. from the University of Berlin.

In all faiths, cultures, and communities, the question of evil plays a prominent role in that specific group's philosophies. What is evil, and how does one comprehend it in our lives? In Judaism, the question of evil and suffering is expressed in the following rabbinic statement "*Tzadik ve'ra lo*, "a righteous person to whom bad things happen," *rasha ve'tov lo*, "a wicked person to whom good things happen." The question is why do righteous people suffer and experience hardship, while others who are wicked do not experience pain and suffering?

After the *Shoah*, the Holocaust, one would have expected the Rav to analyze and lecture on this unique tragedy and period of Jewish suffering. Although the Rav refers to the Shoah he does not provide his students with a comprehensive explanation of this horrific period. To explain the Rav's understanding of the evil of the Holocaust one must read his views on evil and suffering in Jewish history, and extrapolate from these writings, lessons for the Holocaust.

In his most extensive work on suffering, *Kol Dodi Dofek: It is the Voice of my Beloved that Knocketh: Theological And Halakhic Reflections On The Holocaust*, edited by Bernhard H. Rosenberg, Ktav Publishing House, Inc., 1992, the Rav says that one cannot comprehend the nature of evil, because individuals do not have the full understanding of the world. He provides an example of one who cannot see the full beauty of an ornate rug, because he is viewing it from the wrong side.

He unequivocally affirms that evil does exist. Any effort to romanticize evil, is not intellectually honest. As a matter of fact, I happen to have a copy in my brief case, since I was referring to it over the weekend.

The Rav writes: "Judaism, with its realistic approach to man and his place in the world, understood that evil could not be blurred or camouflaged, and that any attempt to downplay the extent of the contradiction, and fragmentation to be found in reality will neither endow man with tranquility, nor enable him to grasp the existential mystery. . . . Whoever wishes to delude himself by diverting his attention from the deep fissure in reality, by romanticizing human existence, is naught but a fool . . . (p. 53).

"When the impulse of intellectual curiosity seizes hold of a

person, he ought to do naught but find strength and encouragement in his faith in the Creator, vindicate G-d's judgment, and
acknowledge the perfection of his work" (p. 63). People have an
obligation to recognize that evil exists, but understanding its essence, is beyond human intellectual capacity.

How can one struggle with the question of suffering? The Rav
elaborates further on the idea of evil in his work *Fate and Destiny: From Holocaust to the State of Israel.* (Rabbi Joseph B.
Soloveitchik, Introduction by Rabbi Walter Wurzburger, Ktav
Publishing, 2000). The Rav states that the distinction between
the two is where the answer to suffering lies. Rabbi Dr. Walter S.
Wurzberger, a prominent disciple of the Rav, writes:

"The Rav employs this distinction in discussing the problem
of evil. He maintains that it is senseless to raise the metaphysical
question of why there is evil in the world. The human mind is
simply not equipped to tackle this problem.

To engage in theodicy is an exercise in futility. Instead of looking for an explanation of our fate, for example, why a particular
evil has struck us, we should ask ourselves how we can respond
to evil in a manner that will enable us to emerge from this experience as better moral and spiritual beings" (p. VII).

"Fate," the Rav says, "is an existence of compulsion against
your will you will live out your life" (Avot 4:29). (*Kol Dodi Dofek,
Theological and Halakhic Reflections on the Holocaust*, p. 52).
The man (or woman) of fate has no free will, nor ability to choose
his own life's path. Things happen to this person, without his
involvement. The fated existence is passive, and arbitrary. Destiny, however, is a different form of existence. The Rav characterizes it as "Against your will you are born and against your
will you will die, but you live of your own free will" (*Kol Dodi
Dofek, Theological and Halakhic Reflections on the Holocaust*,
page 54). An existence of destiny is a life of choice, innovation,
strength, and action; one engages with his surroundings.

The Jewish approach, says the Rav, is to transition from a
fated life, to a destined life (*Kol Dodi Dofek*, p. 54). In our "fated
lives," evil happens to us. We suffer, and we have no control.
In a life of destiny we do not focus on the tragedy that befalls
us. "What must the sufferer do, so that he may live through his

suffering?" is the Jewish legal question the man of destiny asks. What obligation does suffering impose upon man? We do not inquire about the hidden ways of the Almighty, but rather about the path wherein man shall talk when suffering strikes, says the Rav. This reaction to suffering and evil is unique. It seems that the Rav is suggesting that people have an obligation, when bad things happen to them to use their suffering in a productive manner. The Rav tells us. We do not inquire about the hidden ways of the Almighty but, rather, about the path wherein man shall walk when suffering strikes. We ask neither about the cause of evil nor about its purpose but rather about how it might be mended and elevated. How shall a person act in a time of trouble? What ought a man to do so that he not perish in his afflictions? The *halakhic* answer to this question is very simple. Afflictions come to elevate a person, to purify and sanctify his spirit, to cleanse and purge it of the dross of superficiality and vulgarity, to refine his soul and to broaden his horizons. In a word, the function of suffering is to mend that which is flawed in an individual's personality.

The *halakhah* teaches us that the sufferer commits a grave sin if he allows his troubles to go to waste and remain without meaning or purpose (*Kol Dodi Dofek*, p. 56). The Rav therefore maintains that it is a uniquely lonely experience to be a man of religious faith. The individual who suffers and keeps his religious faith has the obligation to respond in a positive fashion to repair the world.

In the Story of Job, this is the answer that G-d responds to Job, a righteous individual who has suffered tremendously. In the Biblical narrative, Job struggles, trying to understand why all terrible things happen to him. Eventually, G-d comes to him and informs him how to productively use his suffering.

In Rabbi Joseph B. Soloveitchik's *Days of Deliverance: Essays on Purim and Hanukkah*, (edited by Eli D. Clark, Joel B. Wolowelsky and Reuven Ziegler, Ktav Publishing House Inc. 2007, p.188) the Rav states, "We have lost many; not too long ago we lost six million Jews, one third of our population. But, on the whole, we have emerged victorious. We still maintain our identity; we are still committed to the same goals to which our ancestors were committed millennia ago." He references the suffering (the Holocaust) by mentioning the six million that perished. By commenting on the strength of Jewish identity and the fortitude of the Jewish nation, the Rav implies that the fate of the Jewish people and its destiny are linked to the lessons learned during the Holocaust.

In the publication, *The Rav, The World of Rabbi B. Soloveitchik*, Volume 2, by Aaron Rakeffet-Rothkoff (Ktav Publishing House, Inc., 1999, p.108), the Rav maintains that Anti-Semitism was at the core of the Nazi agenda, and that those who say that Hitler was more interested in other pursuits are foolish. He goes on to say that Hitler taught the world how to destroy and dispose of all the Jews but was not successful (Ibid. p.133). The Rav is emphasizing the revitalization of the Jewish people in the aftermath of the Holocaust – the destiny aspect of life, rather than the fate. The Rav discusses anti-Semitism during the time of Egyptian slavery. As in the *Shoah*, the goal was to oppress the Jew and discredit him in the eyes of the world.

During the historical period of the Maccabees and the rule of Hellenism, the Hebrew word *k'she-amdah*, which means, "that rose up," appears. This specific word in Hebrew connotes deciding an action, and then following through. The Rav compares this Hellenistic time period with the Holocaust. Hitler wanted to destroy the Jewish people, and then did his best to eradicate each and every Jew.

The Rav writes, "During the terrible Holocaust when European Jewry was being systematically exterminated in the ovens and crematoria, the American Jewish community did not rise to the challenge, did not act as Jews possessing a properly developed consciousness of our shared fate and shared suffering as well as the obligation of shared action that follows therefrom, ought to have acted. We did not sufficiently empathize with the anguish of the people and did very little to save our afflicted brethren" (*Kol Dodi Dofek*, p. 97).

The opinions I express to you are based upon my personal understanding of what has been written regarding the Rav's statements. I do not maintain that these are the exact sentiments of the Rav, but I have attempted to explain his position regarding the Holocaust as I understand them. As a child of Holocaust survivors, of blessed memory, and as one whose *smicha* (rabbinic ordination), is signed by the Rav, I have always wanted to explore how the Rav theologically regarded the Holocaust. I entered the rabbinate because of the Holocaust. *Hineni,* is the expression we all should use. We should "be here" to make a difference in the world. Never again should we allow the world to stand idly by while innocent human beings suffer torture, starvation and death. Never again should anyone be an innocent bystander. I fear the world has not learned this lesson. Will they ever?

SAM: Wow! That's a lot of heavy theology. Thanks for bringing all those deep thoughts for us to chew on. Let's all give these ideas some time to reflect, and maybe we'll come back to that theme another time.

BOB: Good thought. I just had a thought about something you said, Don. About making a difference in the world. You know, when I was in rabbinical school, one of our professors, Prof. Mordecai M. Katz, taught a class in homiletics. Each senior student had to give a sermon in the Seminary synagogue on one Shabbat.

One student, who had his turn to deliver his senior sermon the following Shabbat, gave it in class the Wednesday before that Shabbat. He delivered it, and when he was finished, he turned to Dr. Katz, and asked him, "Will it do?" in preparation for giving it in the Seminary synagogue.

Dr. Katz shot back, Will it do WHAT?"

At that moment, I realized that there is a big difference between a *d'var Torah*, a learned talk, and a sermon. A sermon tries to get people to CHANGE. What do you want people to *do*, or *change*? You can speak about Israel, but what do you want your listeners to *do* about Israel? You can speak about poverty, but are you starting a fund to decrease poverty? You can preach about low interest rates on savings and how they affect donations, earnings for retirees, jobs, things that relate to poverty, or finances, and what should be done about it.

SAM: Good thought. I agree. Sermons should have an "action" component. Leave the congregation with an inspiring idea, to go out and help make the world a better place.

DON: You know, all that sounds very practical. But I've changed my thoughts on preaching several times in my career. I used to give these "action" components at the end of my sermons. But then I had a conversation with one of my seminary professors, and he had a completely different idea.

His feeling was that preaching, especially on the High Holidays, are not about telling them what to do! A much greater teaching place is sharing our own struggles, and how each of us learned to deal with them in hopefully more useful ways. This does not have to do with self-confessions, nor ego! For better or worse, the people don't want ideas nor philosophy nor, alas, very much Torah teaching. They want, as my professor said, the sharing of personal struggles. I'm have a feeling that many of our colleagues agree that this would make for the best kind of sermon.

DON: Well, now we have two possibilities. Perhaps we should alternate between the two.

SAM: Good idea!

BOB: I just read something in the newspaper about Reverand Pat Robertson that I want your opinions about. He gave advice to a spouse of an Alzheimer's patient, saying that it was OK to divorce her and marry someone new. This has caused a very strong reaction by other Christian leaders, as a call to violate the marriage sacrament. How do we understand the idea of tossing out a wife, even though she's in this terrible mental state of dementia? This may be grist for a High Holiday sermon.

SAM: I can't believe I'm about to say this, but I want to defend Pat Robertson for a minute.

If you re-read the article, which I did recently, you will find what he said, in context, and it's much more nuanced than "divorce your spouse with Alzheimer's." What he actually seems to be saying is that he understands the need for love and companionship. In a situation where one spouse is totally "gone," he likens it to death. He never says anything about abandoning anybody. As I understand it, he seems to be saying that in a case where one spouse is unresponsive, once all the custodial and care arrangements have been made, he wouldn't judge somebody who made the choice to divorce rather than commit adultery. From the actual words of his statement, I agreed with him, I wouldn't judge somebody in that situation for that choice either. But read it for yourself, it's really not "just go ahead and divorce."

I think Robertson is getting attacked for something he didn't say, and this is equally grist for a sermon about someone getting judged on the basis of rumors and *lashon hara* [gossip]. I hardly love Robertson's influence and outlook but in this case, I think he's getting a bum rap.

DON: There was an interesting case some time ago in Israel, maybe ten or fifteen years ago. A young woman in her early twenties was in a car accident, leaving her in a coma. Her state was best described as vegetative. No physician gave her any chance to recover. Her husband, also early twenties, wanted to do the best for their child. He applied for a *heter meah rabbanim* [a special dispensation in Jewish Law, in which one hundred rabbis sign a paper permitting a man to marry a second wife under unusual circumstances, such as dementia, etc.] to wed again as she couldn't accept a *get* [Jewish divorce].

He volunteered to arrange for all her care and would visit her, and bring the child, with proper professional guidance. He eventually married and had more kids – lost track, don't know how many. His first wife, as far as I know is still on life-support. This seems a similar case as one with Alzheimers. How would we respond to such a request? In this case I know that a family was saved by it.

BOB: Fellas, I have an emergency phone call on my cell. Be back in a minute. . . . . .

[Five minutes later]

BOB: Oh, my God. I just heard that a daughter of a congregant was involved in car crash on her way back to college. She walked away with scratches but she was driving with her roommate, who sadly was killed. The daughter of my congregant was driving, a deer shot out from in front of the car, the young woman swerved, lost control of the car and crashed. The roommate was killed instantly. To make this an even sadder tragedy the young woman who died was the only child of a widower. The survivor is now suffering from horrible guilt. Any of you who has dealt with such tragedies and has advice to share, I would greatly appreciate some advice from you. The young woman is a friend of my daughter, and we are very close to her family. Very hard all around, for the father of the young woman killed, to the young woman who survived, and for her family. Oh, what can I say???

SAM: You know, when a complex tragedy like this occurs, what can anyone say? We have to agree with our colleague Harold Kushner, who says that such things are part of a random universe, which we mortals can hardly fathom.

DON: Bob, I think you'll do best by trusting your intuition. When the time comes for you to meet with the survivors, the words will come. Or if not, just being with them in silence is often the best step to take. As time passes, and specific issues arise, come back to us and we'll try to be of help.

Let me change the subject, while Bob collects his composure after that tough phone call. My board decided that they want to do a congregation-wide evaluation of my performance. Frankly, while most of the people like me very much, there are always the few cranks who will find a few things to kvetch about, and nitpick. I'm not really in favor of it, but they may just go ahead with it anyway. What do you guys think about it? Have your boards ever talked about it, or actually done such a thing?

SAM: I think that surveys simply invite feedback which can often be more damaging than helpful. They help foster the impression of 1,000 bosses, or the folks who have the do-it-my-way attitude, and might open up a forum for complaint.

That being said, surveys that are focused, and cover the entire range of congregational matters, not just the rabbi's performance, might possibly be useful. For instance, in trying to determine whether or not to lengthen Youth Services, it is helpful to know if people with children WANT them lengthened. The parking lot conversations only help so much. In addition, in today's world, people appreciate the opportunity to comment. Everybody wants to have his two cents heard.

There are things that we do not include on the survey because, with all due respect, we're not going to change it regardless. So, we ask questions about elements that we ARE willing to discuss, and, in that regard, the survey is great. It provides valuable input for us and a sense of being heard for the community. That would be one of my big caveats with surveys: only ask questions where the response might dictate a change. If you're not going to change anything, then don't ask it!

BOB: If I were on the level of the late Steve Jobs, I might also eschew focus groups and opinion surveys. However, I regard myself lucky if I can figure out what I want for myself, let alone what other people want for themselves. As far as I can tell, what made Steve Jobs remarkable was not just that he had confidence in his vision, but that his vision for what people would want was so consistently excellent. Mine is not. Our congregation never had a culture of inviting feedback through surveys until we were required to do so to evaluate some grants we received. Now it is an indispensable part of our synagogue's life. Of course the website *surveymonkey.com* makes it easy. The survey responses generate lots of great ideas, and they help us to see what is resonating with the community, and which ideas that we thought were great, are truly flopping. Every so often there are comments that sting, but for our community the benefits have so far outweighed the problems. We start with the assumption that we need to take the responses with a grain of salt, and that the most important aspects of synagogue life are not market-driven. Meaning we will happily consider and then reject the advice that the survey gives us if it is clearly contrary to our vision for the community. But at least this way we have learned that we need to do a better job getting the community to buy into specific parts of our vision. We do not do a post-High Holiday survey per se, but would consider one for the future.

DON: Granted, I represent an older generation of rabbis, but I do not think these surveys are valuable. They feed into the "new" vision of the synagogue as a religious institution which should satisfy the consumer. The rabbi is the agent of that satisfaction. This, in contrast to the synagogue as a religious magnet, with the rabbi as the energy behind that magnet, who leads and does not just satisfy. A caterer gives people what they want. A rabbi-educator gives people what he thinks they ought to have. Surely, I am overstating and exaggerating the difference, and yes, we need a membership base to pay for the services of the *shul* and pay the rabbi's salary. Indeed, we all both lead and cater. But that being said, these surveys simply lend themselves to the latter and not the former.

SAM: In support of Bob's position, remember that the late Steve Jobs, on whose technology we rely on so much today, eschewed focus groups and opinion surveys, preferring to show people what they want, even before they knew they wanted it! I bought my first iPad, and another one since then, having no idea what I would do with it, and now I cannot fathom life without it. Jobs set a good example for us in this regard!

DON: I'd like to change the subject again, unless any of you have more to say on this issue of evaluations. A few weeks ago, a *Sefer Torah* fell off its holder, and the congregation asked me if they should fast for forty days. I'm curious as to what you two would do in a similar situation.

BOB: Many years ago, a *Sefer Torah* fell in my *shul* on Yom Kippur afternoon. Actually, to put it more specifically, the person carrying the Torah tripped coming down the *bimah* steps. It was a jarring, upsetting experience, for those who witnessed it, and even for many who subsequently heard about it.

The following morning, I went to my office and started searching for the source of the "forty-day fasting custom," namely, the rule that the community must organize a forty-day fasting rotation. But, alas, to no avail. Finally, I called my Seminary professor, Dr. Goldberg, who told me that he'd heard of the "forty-day rule" all his life, but that he'd found no credible, classical *halakhic* source for this rule. He said that the practice of fasting for a fallen *Sefer Torah* is not found in the Talmud or *Rishonim*.

So Dr. Goldberg gave me the following guidance: We should give *tzedakah*, study Torah, and fast for one day. I subsequently wrote a letter to the congregation, relating what had occurred and indicating that the following Sunday morning, in place of our usual post-*minyan* breakfast, we would have a study session. When the Sunday arrived we did just that. We circulated the *pushke*, we studied *Hilkhot Sefer Torah* ["Laws Relating to a Torah Scroll"], and I invited those who were so inclined, to join me in fasting for the rest of the day.

We had a large crowd that morning, including many of the people who had been in *shul* on Yom Kippur afternoon, some people who had heard about the incident and felt somehow traumatized by what had occurred, and the woman who fell while carrying the Torah – who then had a cast on her broken foot. It was, I think, a surprisingly intense experience for the community: an opportunity for us to do some communal *teshuvah* – although almost nobody actually blamed the woman who had fallen – an opportunity for us to heal from a painful experience that we had shared.

Overall, it turned out to be an excellent learning experience, and an emotional catharsis as well.

SAM: Let me move on to an email I received the other day. A colleague in a nearby community, who is a hospital chaplain, sent the following message as an email blast to a bunch of area rabbis:

"You might have noticed that your congregants' hospital stays have grown shorter and less frequent over the years. For years, people who work in hospitals have been predicting 'the phasing out of acute care hospitals.' That's always been the rumor. I attended a recent conference for chaplains. The purpose of the conference was to develop a strategic plan for doing pastoral care, when the acute care hospital is phased out. It's important to be aware:

1) Hospitals will never disappear altogether. They will always be used for trauma, such as car accidents, and ICU – probably with a dollar cap on how long a patient can stay on ICU. Years ago, the majority of people receiving health care were in hospitals. In the future, due to changes in reimbursement and advances in technology, that will not be the case. Most, but not all, patients will be treated elsewhere.

2) This change is not going to happen overnight. Having said that, a change in Medicare reimbursement practice recently, significantly decreased the number of patients at many hospitals. It's happening immediately enough that my colleagues all over the U.S. see it reflected in a lot of empty beds. It's "real" enough that our system is moving from lunchroom prophecy to strategic planning.

3) There will always be sick people in our community who need pastoral care and congregational support.

4) The Business of Health Care will still make money. Surgeries will take place in surgery centers. Home health care nursing will grow very large. Long term care facilities will still exist. Groups like Blue Cross/Shield will own and make money off of all of those things. Right now, the primary model for congregational pastoral care is: 'The rabbi will visit you in the hospital. Please let the rabbi know that you are in the hospital, so that s/he can visit.' Synagogues and congregational rabbis might want to start thinking about other models. I do not have the answer for how you can best meet the needs of congregants in the brave, new world that we're entering. But it's something for congregational rabbis and *bikkur cholim* [pastoral visiting] committees to think about. At the local Board of Rabbis meeting, I responded to some questions about 'Why, this trend?' (Changes in financial reimbursement and technological advances) 'Is it good or

bad for patients?' (Both good and bad– it depends). 'And what does the plan for hospital chaplains look like?" (Probably, we will carry caseloads and the car will be our 'office' . . . no longer dividing labor by hospital or unit). I won't use email as a forum to answer in greater depth than that, but feel free to approach me with questions."

I have certainly noticed the change, and I realize also that I have been slow in adjusting to it. Of course, I know how to visit people in convalescent facilities as well as in hospitals, but, reflecting on this email message, I realize that, perhaps unconsciously, I regard the former situations as less urgent, and I may not be giving people as much attention as I should. What is your experience of this phenomenon?

DON: Like many of our colleagues, I still tend to treat people in non-hospital situations as less serious. But that is not always true. For a number of years I've been trying to ask people, or call the facility to find out just how immediate it is. Most of the time I get a pretty good estimate and plan accordingly. It definitely has meant more driving, especially since I used to be in smaller places with a wide geographic distribution. Of course, unlike big city rabbis, I didn't have the kind of traffic they have. My short exception was my few years in the East coast, where I often found myself with both a longer drive than most and had more traffic. Once, relatively new to a place and not knowing any of the small roads, I found myself on a tight schedule and having to wait for a train. As I later learned, there weren't too many alternatives short of taking an entirely different route. Sort of like the short-long road versus the long-short road dilemma in the story. If you don't know the story. In short, a rabbi asks a kid at the fork in the road how to get to the city he can see ahead. He takes the short-long road and finds it stops short of the city so he must turn around and go back to the fork and take the other road.

SAM: There are lots of changes taking place in terms of medicine, medical insurance, health care, etc. We'll have to keep our eyes on the new developments, and share them with each other as they arise.

I have another issue I'd like to raise, which comes from a member of my congregation who asked me about his obligation to a relative who was not such a kind person. To be specific, he wants to know, "Does Judaism tell us we should be saying mourner's *Kaddish* for this person? Do we remember and acknowledge their *yahrzeits*? Do we say *Yizkor* for a person like this?" The prayers, as I read them, remember "loved ones." The prayers remember people as righteous, loving, caring. . . . What do we say for those people in our lives who were less than righteous, not as loving, and not as caring as we would have wished?

He wants to know if there is anything he can read that would help him as to what our religion instructs us in these circumstances. Any help or guidance you can provide would be greatly appreciated.

BOB: Interesting issue, Sam. I think that it is important to point out to this congregant that the actual Hebrew text of *Yizkor* does not contain the language recalled by this congregant.

The prayers do not remember people as "righteous, loving, caring, etc." The language of the text asks God to recall the souls of those whose names we insert. All we need acknowledge in the text is the name of the person and, if we so wish, their relationship to us – father, mother, etc. We do not need to describe them or their characteristics beyond that. Thus, the language often suggested, such as *Avi mori*, ["My father, my teacher"], does not need to be inserted. And we therefore would not need to add such substitute language as, for example, "*Avi*, that loser." Another aspect of the *Yizkor* prayer is the pledge to *tzedakah* connected with the remembrance. The congregant can understand this as an opportunity to express compassion for others even though s/he felt that compassion was not forthcoming from the relative who has died. We thus show that we are able to care for others even though we may feel that we were not cared for properly.

The question of the *Kaddish* recited during the thirty days or eleven months of mourning can also be answered along similar lines. If, for example, the *Kaddish* is viewed as playing a role in assisting the soul of the one who has died pass through whatever punishment it must go through, saying *Kaddish* can be seen as the same type of expression of compassion as I mentioned before. If, on the other hand, the *Kaddish* is not seen as connected with easing the punishment, it can be seen as giving one an opportunity to consider and process those feelings of anger and hatred and disappointment that grew out of the relationship with the one who has died. Failing to say *Kaddish* during this period may be seen as an expression of continuing to allow those negative feelings to remain as active forces in our daily lives. This does not, of course, mean that we must now transform those feelings to love of that person. It does mean that we can come to a place in our own lives in which we can live independently of the one who has died and that we are no longer controlled by the one who has died.

The *Yarhzeit* observance for parents can allow us to recall that we cannot always have everything we might wish for from those who gave us life, but that we still must acknowledge the fact that we owe the fact of our existence on this earth to our parents. We can use the observance of the *Yahrzeit* to remind us that we wish to leave not a *bitter* legacy but a *better* legacy to those who follow us.

I hope that you find these thoughts helpful.

SAM: Bob, you always have such a wonderful understanding of human nature. I knew I could count on you for a seasoned, mature, and reassuring reply. Thanks so much!

BOB: We've been discussing such serious matters. I just recalled a humorous experience that a senior colleague related to me about Prof. Lazarus, our Talmud teacher.

In Dr. Lazarus's Talmud class many years ago there was a student who was perennially late and he would give Dr. Lazarus a fit. One day he walks in late and the professor says to him, "the next time you walk in late, I will mark you absent."

Sure enough, the guy walks in late for the very next class and Dr. Lazarus says, "Chaim Yankel, you are absent." About forty-five minutes into the class Profs Lazarus says to him, "Chaim Yankel, it's your turn to read." And the student replies, "I am sorry, Professor, but I am absent." And Dr. Lazarus responds, "Then read in absentia!"

DON: That reminds me of something funny I say to parents of babies. I tell them that I can put any baby to sleep. I hold the baby, rock back and forth, and start intoning, "We learn in this week's *parashah*. . . ."

SAM: I guess we all have funny experiences like that, either from student days, or from our work in the congregation. I once asked a pre-Bar Mitzvah student where his family was on the *Shabbatot* they weren't in *shul*. They are in *shul* every week except for once a month. He sheepishly answered that sometimes they just like to stay home and sleep. I quickly and adamantly replied, "That's what the sermon is for!" Interestingly, he misses fewer services now.

By the way, it's a better conversation than the one comedian Rabbi Bob Alper tells of the woman who approached him after *shul* to tell him, "Rabbi, your sermon was super . . . fluous." She added that, "Each one is better than the next."

BOB: Thanks, Sam. OK, you're batting 1000, let's see if you or Don can help me with this one. A congregant's daughter married into an Orthodox family, and wants to know, since his daughter is pregnant, if she can attend a funeral. The husband's family will probably listen to their rabbi, who says that pregnant women should not go to the cemetery. I never heard of that one before. Is there such a law?

DON: There are those who think that the evil spirits which roam the cemetery might harm the fetus. But, of course, that's a superstition. Whether a person wants to be sensitive to whatever spiritual or mystical issues, might be behind it, or not. There is also the practical element of the ground being typically uneven because of the earth sinking on account of the graves. There are also the gravestones themselves that can make a cemetery an obstacle course. The point is that one would not want a woman who is pregnant to fall with a resultant tragedy. The possibility of tripping isn't so far-fetched. I heard that once a rabbi in Charleston died as a result of a head wound he received when he tripped and fell at one of the cemeteries. So the real question might be, aside from any custom or superstition, is it worth the possible risk?

In addition, a colleague of mine is from Syria, and he says that it is very *haram* [forbidden] for pregnant women to attend funerals.

SAM: Don't apologize for being dismissive of this ridiculous superstition. I think we should be absolutely condemnatory of it! I still bristle when I hear this old chestnut. About ten years ago, when I was a new assistant rabbi in Houston, one of the first people whom my wife and I befriended was a gracious, elderly lady who at the time was recovering from heart surgery. Her recovery became complicated, things went bad, and in a few months she was dead. By then, my wife was visibly pregnant with our first son. It was as important for her to attend our friend's funeral as it was for me. At the cemetery, numerous old biddies descended upon my wife with this garbage: "What are you doing here? You shouldn't be here! You'll lose the baby!!"

Obviously this was a very upsetting experience for my wife. Come to think of it, it was upsetting for me as well. Young pregnant couples are vulnerable enough, with all of the uncertainty of impending new parenthood, without "buttinskies" behaving so insensitively toward them. I remember thinking at the time: How would these women have reacted if she had lost the baby? Maybe some would have felt "vindicated."

I've never taken the time to search for any "classical sources" for this so-called *issur* [forbidden custom]. I hope they don't exist. But even if one could cite some traditional or quasi-traditional source, like a kabbalistic notion, I would still reject this as superstitious nonsense, and hurtful at that. No amount of transvaluating can, in my opinion, restore this notion to respectability. We should be encouraging Jews, including pregnant women, to fulfill the *mitzvot* of *halvayat ha-met* [accompanying the dead], *nihum aveilim* [comforting the mourners], etc., rather than discouraging them.

BOB: Here's a logistical and *halakhic* question for both of you. Someone asked me yesterday if his family is leaving their house on Wednesday at 3:30 to go to the airport to fly to Israel, and they can't light candles at the airport or on the airplane, and will get to Israel around twenty-four hours later after a layover in Europe, when should they light Hannukah candles?

DON: I had the same question recently. I told them that they would probably be able to light the *hanukkiah* in the Admiral's club at JFK.

BOB: Here's another question. Our newer Conservative movement publications leave *Adonai* untranslated in English, where we previously would have found "the Lord." What is the rationale for that practice? Is it that *Adonai* doesn't have an apparent gender in English? Is it that *Adonai* is not an English common noun, as the Tetragrammaton is not a Hebrew common noun?

SAM: Liturgy in the Reform movement has a similar trend. Both of the reasons you list are true and play into the conversations that we have in our movement, but, if you ask me, I think that the primary reason is the realization that many of our congregants do not have access to the Hebrew, surely not to its meaning and often not even to read it, so that, at the very time that we are maintaining the Hebrew prayer service, they are effectively praying in English. When they recite the silent *Amidah*, it is in English, which *halakhah* allows, of course. In my opinion, God's name, *Adonai*, provides those praying in English a more immediate connection with God, and a greater feeling that they are fully participating in the congregation's prayers. We should at least allow our congregants to call on God by His name.

DON: I've been leading a service at a home for assisted living where many of the residents can't follow the Hebrew, so we do have responsive readings. I join in the feeling, and my view is that *Adonai* in an otherwise all-English context is extremely awkward. Indeed, I wonder if those who aren't familiar with Hebrew or traditional texts aren't also uncomfortable or, at the very least, asking themselves: "Who is this Adonai guy?" As far as why the change was made, I think the reason behind this may be that, for some, "Lord" is a masculine term. I respect that, but I confess I don't like saying *Adonai* in English.

SAM: I wonder if one possible reason is to make the clear distinction between what Jews mean when they say *Adonai* and what Christians mean when they say "Lord." For Christians, "Lord" connotes "Jesus." Not translating the word avoids such a possibility, especially when Jewish texts are readily available to the general public.

DON: Since I am not comfortable with *Adonai* in English, I use the English word "Eternal" instead of "Lord." It is gender-neutral and conveys a deeply Jewish understanding of YHVH. I adopted this from the French translation of the *Humash*.

SAM: I know we've discussed this general issue before, but I've never received a very convincing answer to my dilemma, and that of my people. Purim is not that far off, and I'm beginning to get questions by folks who are troubled by the description of the violent reactions of the Jewish community to ostensibly innocent Persians described in the last chapters of the *Megillah* of Esther.

Obviously, these chapters should be considered in the context of other morally disturbing texts. For the moment however can anyone suggest studies, articles, scholarly essays, or *divre* Torah that address the issue, and perhaps illuminate it?

BOB: I think one has to take the biblical Book of Esther in its *sitz im leben* [life setting], just as we take various parts of the *Humash* that talk about wiping out the locals. That it did not happen is clear from the later chapters of Joshua and Judges. You should read Adele Berlin's JPS Commentary on Esther. She sees the book as a comedy or a farce; hence many exaggerations. Robert Gordis in his commentary on Esther published by the RA some years ago, but now, sadly, out of print, points out that the harsh verse 8:11 is actually a quote of a similar verse in chapter three. I cannot be more specific as my copy is on loan to someone preparing a course on the Women of the Bible.

I don't have the text in front of me, but the old Prayer Book Press version of the *Megillah* solves the problem by simply leaving out these lines from the English translation. It reminds me of the troubling passages in the *Musaf Amidah* where the *Shabbat* offerings are not translated, just a citation given in the Silverman *siddur*. What you can't translate won't hurt you!

The problem exists when we take the book of Esther as history, which it clearly is not. I would recommend Elias Bickerman's *Four Strange Books of the Bible*, as an interesting book to consider. I remember Professor Gerson Kane once remarking how wonderful it is that while other people actually take out their worst aggressions through war and destruction, we have managed to do this through literature instead of actually destroying and killing.

SAM: Anyone watching the news lately? I am furious at China and Russia for their veto of the resolution against Syria, for their mass murder of their own citizens. Would there be any interest in calling for a boycott of travel and purchase of goods from Russia and China based on their incredulous veto of the UN Resolution on Syria? While Syria is no friend of ours, the wanton and reckless murder of thousands of innocent people and the inability of the international community to do anything leaves me disturbed and angry. I'm very curious about colleagues' thinking on this matter.

BOB: I think not, for several strong reasons:

1. Divestment is an issue regarding divestment and boycott of Israel. I believe any boycott would legitimize the boycott of Israel.

2. Why be selective of Syria? Somalia, Darfur, Saudi Arabia, on and on, are all countries noted for their inhumane treatment.

3. It seems to me protests are going on in Russia. China is noted for being inhumane. Why be selective? The numbers should not be the fulcrum to boycott. The loss of one life, or one tortured soul from abuse, is a wrong, which needs to be addressed.

4. If we boycott China, we will not have the funds to borrow to pay our debts.

5. Why not boycott GE? They are investing billions to create jobs – in China!!!

6. We supported Libya, Egypt, etc. in the overthrow of their governments. We now see the same tyrannical regimes ruling. Libya has the same torture usage. The rebel troops were barbaric and as cruel as was Kadaffi, and our government has not even whispered a protest. But then, when we listen to odious calls from Abbas to massacre Jews, we "hear" the "sounds" of silence. I think selective boycotts are not the way to go. I have questions too, about boycotts in general. The innocent victims in the country who are hurt by our boycott.

DON: I agree with Bob. I generally think that boycotts are a bad idea. I always have in mind the boycott of Israel by Arab states post-1948. My feeling is that a people – Jews and lovers of Zion – should not use a weapon that was used against us. And I hold this view whether I think a proposed boycott will be effective or not. In my humble opinion, in this case your proposed boycott is not likely to have any effect.

SAM: Well, I think I'll drop that idea. What else is on your minds?

BOB: I have a question that will tickle your fancy, as the expression goes. Someone in my congregation actually asked me this, and I have no idea how to answer it. The question is: Do Orthodox Jews have sex through a hole in a sheet? We have all heard this old chestnut. It is, of course, a myth. Or is it? Clearly, if it has any truth to it, it isn't normative. Has any pietistic group somewhere or at some time ever advocated this?

DON: Interesting question. One of my people asked me the same question. I did a little research, and here's what I came up with. I'll do my best to recall the sources, probably paraphrased:

Jewish Law is concerned not only with the frequency of the act, but with the manner in which it is performed. The Talmud recommends nudity. The Talmud, somewhere in Tractate *Ke-tubot*, says something like this: The phrase, "Her flesh," implies close bodily contact, namely, that he must not treat her in the manner of the Persians who perform their conjugal duties in their clothes. This provides support for a ruling of Rav Huna who taught that a husband who said, "I will not perform conjugal duties unless she wears her clothes and I mine," must divorce his wife. The myth that religious Jews are required to make love through a hole in a sheet is nonsense. Pleasure was a concern of the rabbis. They understood that it is enhanced by nudity. In fact, if one of the partners does not wish to have relations in the nude, it is considered grounds for divorce. This is from the *Shulhan Arukh, Even ha-Ezer*.

A tension exists in Rabbinic literature between what the rabbis regard as modest and proper on the one hand, and what they know will maximize a couple's pleasure on the other hand. Modesty requires that scholars of the law not be with their wives too frequently, like roosters. This comes from Tractate *Berakhot*. Yet even a scholar is responsible for maximizing his wife's pleasure. Rabbinic teachings reflect this tension in their discussions about intercourse by day or night, proper positions, and natural or un-natural relations.

According to tradition, relations should take place at night and in the dark. The Talmud forbids relations during the day or by the light of a lamp. Maimonides teaches that, although intercourse on the Sabbath is a special mitzvah, if the Sabbath light has not yet gone out and there is no separate room to which they can move, the couple should wait. In fact, midnight was considered the ideal time for intercourse.

Behind this law stands the principle in Leviticus, "Love your neighbor as yourself." The rabbis were concerned that a man might see his wife's blemishes and that she would then become undesirable to him. However, there are exceptions. The commentator Meiri, on Tractate *Niddah*, teaches that although intercourse was reserved for the night, if because of one's nature one finds himself forced to sleep at night and ought not be aroused or excited, or if the woman's nature is such that she is overtaken by sleep at night and is not receptive at that time, one is permitted to have intercourse during the day, with due modesty, in order that intercourse be performed with acceptance and love and not by force.

BOB: The idea of sex through a hole in a sheet may have come from Rav Nahman of Breslov. He was not one for pleasure within sex. He wrote something like this: Copulation is difficult for the true *tzaddik*. Not only does he have no desire for it at all, but he experiences real suffering in the act, suffering which is like that which the infant undergoes when he is circumcised. This very same suffering, to an even greater degree, is felt by the *tzaddik* during intercourse. The infant has no awareness, so his suffering is not so great. But the *tzaddik*, because he is aware of the pain, suffers more greatly than does the infant. I think I read this in *Shivhay HaRan*. In any event, there were some mystics who emphasized minimizing pleasure from the act.

SAM: Interesting stuff. Let me share something less *halakhic*, to go from the sublime to the ridiculous. This is an anecdote I couldn't resist sharing with you. About a week ago, one morning, as our post-*minyan* breakfast was breaking up and I was about to go into an hour-long meeting with my *shul* president, vice-president of ritual, a congregant came up to me with my least favorite question, "Do you have a minute, Rabbi?" "Actually, Wayne, I don't," I said. "I'm about to go into a meeting." I don't, of course, usually respond that way. That was unbelievably more abrupt than I ever speak. But I was hassled, and frazzled, and not looking forward to my meeting, and I knew that it would not be cool to start my meeting late. I immediately regretted what I had said, and told that to Jerry, the president. I quickly ascertained that it wasn't a pastoral matter that he wanted to speak to me about and then said, "Look, Wayne, I obviously have a minute, but unfortunately not more than that. And I said what I said because my experience is that such matters rarely take only a minute."

"Sure, I understand, Rabbi. But I only need a minute, really!"

"So tell me, what's it all about?"

"Well," he said, "I would like to bring a controversial speaker to the *shul* – someone whom I've heard is really, really good. He can speak about Israel's defense needs, and the challenges it is now facing from Iran, and the need to increase American Jewish support for Israel, but I would first need your approval to bring him here."

"Great question, Wayne. As you probably know, we're in the midst of clarifying our policy on how to determine which speakers to invite to the *shul*, and which ones not to. In general, we're trying to distinguish between educational programs and political advocacy, permitting the former and refraining from pursuing the latter. It will be hard to figure out what to do in this case before learning more about this speaker's qualifications and how he generally presents his views."

"Oh, he's not going to present his views, Rabbi. He's going to present the facts."

"Right, Wayne, right. But I have to get the sense whether this is going to be an academic presentation or would fall into the category of advocacy."

"This guy's a scholar, Rabbi. Not a professional scholar, but someone who I understand knows quite a lot."

"Right, Wayne, I get it. Can you send me some information about him? I'd love to look into it and get back to you."

"Sure, Rabbi, no problem."

"Great, Wayne," – at which point I couldn't resist adding, "So you can see why I was wary of beginning a conversation that I knew wouldn't take only a minute."

"Oh, Rabbi," he said. "I didn't say that it would take you only a minute to figure it all out. I just meant that all I needed was a minute for my side of the conversation!"

The moral of the story: You've got to love Jews.

SAM: I have an interesting issue emanating from our Israeli colleagues. You may be interested in a new criterion that Israel now has for organ donation. If you have made the commitment to be an organ donor, you will be higher on the list for receiving a transplant, in case, God forbid, you yourself need a transplant. My Israeli cousin showed me the back side of his EDI card [organ donor card] which quotes the *Mishneh Torah, Hilkhot Sanhedrin*, which uses the language of *Mishnah Sanhedrin* 4:5. The initiator of the program, Dr. Jacob Lavee, discussed recently, in a *New York Times* article, a conversation with two *haredi* [ultra-Orthodox] Jews he was treating. Both were willing to receive a transplant, but were unwilling to ever donate an organ, in the event of their demise. This decision was, obviously, for religious reasons. Dr. Lavee operated on both patients, saving their lives, but the paradox bothered him. Apparently, this conversation led Dr. Lavee to suggest non-medical criteria for the transplant procedures in Israel. The author of the article believes that Israel is the only country in the world that invokes non-medical criteria when it comes to receiving an organ transplant.

If this is the position of all *haredim*, then it demonstrates the moral emptiness of this position. You can save my life but I won't save yours. This was infuriating for this Israeli to accept, especially when they share the lion's share of the tax burden and defense of the country vis-a-vis the *haredi* population. With the meteoric rise in birthrates amongst the *haredi* Jews, the problems will only get exacerbated.

BOB: Why is this surprising? They refuse to serve in the army, meaning that you send your kids to save our kids' lives, but we won't do the same. You send your kids to school to learn how to earn a living so our kids won't have to. We'll take your organs so we can live, but you guys can drop dead if it's our organs you need. They are in my opinion *porash min hatzibbur* ["set themselves outside the community"], and Israel needs to take dramatic steps to correct this ticking bomb in their society. The *haredim* already know that the days of not working and not serving are coming to an end. They need to serve in some capacity and they need to work. Schools designed for them, separate classes for men and women and professions that will allow them to maintain their religious lifestyle without too much conflict, are already beginning to pop up. My niece teaches *haredi* women enrolled in a Beer Sheba university class as they pursue a degree so they can work. She is teaching them English and they are eager to learn. They travel very long distances to come to this and other courses as they aren't readily available around the country. The idea is not to punish them, but to train them. And that must include cutting back their subsidies and particularly ending the support for schools that don't teach math, science, and other languages. This would not have happened if it wasn't for the coalition form of government they have.

SAM: Hopefully, the Israeli government will figure out a way to involve the *haredim*, something that will be acceptable to everyone.

But here's another question, which a member asked me this week. What is the reason, or origin, for eleven months of reciting *Kaddish* for a parent?

DON: I can answer that. It was Rabbi Moses Isserles, known by the Hebrew acronym, Rema, who spoke about the *minhag* of reducing the twelve month period of saying *Kaddish*, customary in earlier days, to eleven months, in order "not to ascribe wickedness to parents." The original recitation of twelve months was supposed to redeem a parent from going to hell. In other words, if a son recited *Kaddish* for the full year, the parent would be spared this fate. So he suggested that one recite it for eleven months, to show that the parent was not evil, and did not require twelve months to be redeemed for wicked acts.

BOB: I learned another reason, not the traditional one. Even though this is not a traditional explanation, but it makes a lot of sense to me. It occurred to me about twenty years ago when I was completing a CPE [Clinical Pastoral Education] unit at Memorial Sloan Kettering Hospital, and heard a lecture by a psychiatrist who specialized in cancer patients, who spoke about the course of grieving. She said that the period from eleven to twelve months is very, very difficult. As the *yahrzeit* approaches, she didn't use that word, the same season, the same length of day, the same circumstances as those that characterized the death approach, it is very challenging for those who grieve. Keeping that in mind, I see the final month or two of the year as a bookend. Just as the first month of the year is a bookend – a period of intense grief – so too is the last month. Refraining from *Kaddish* during that last month or two of the year is brilliant. We have grown accustomed to saying *Kaddish*. *Kaddish* is our friend. It brings us close to our beloved. And now it is taken away from us. This small gesture can have powerful consequences for people. It can reproduce some of the feelings of loss that were felt during the first month of the year. It's a very good way to prepare for the *yahrzeit* – and the second year, a year during which there won't be any opportunity – save Yizkor – to say *Kaddish* for one's loved one.

SAM: Talking about death and burial, here's another question for you guys. Are there any congregations that you know of which have an accommodation in their synagogue cemetery for intermarried couples, such as a separate interfaith burial section? I'd also appreciate knowing how the interfaith section is set apart from the main cemetery. Thanks!

BOB: As we have a large group of inter-marrieds, we are considering doing something akin to that. Our cemetery has three sections separated by walkways and our third section is as yet unused. We would use it for inter-marrieds, with the proviso that no non-Jewish markings go on the stones, nor any non-Jewish clergy, including Jews for Jesus, officiate at such burial services. I think it's an issue that will be facing more and more congregations as time passes.

DON: Not that I want to encourage such a thing, mind you, but I can tell you that a Reform synagogue in the next community from ours has a section in their cemetery set aside also for this purpose. The layout of the grounds allows this section to be on the other side of a small roadway that enters the grounds. I agree that this issue will continue to grow, but less so, of course, in my congregation.

I think it's time to break, folks. Let's meet next week.

Week 4

᪣

BOB: Nice to see everyone again.

OK, my turn to bring up a question for my distinguished colleagues. We have just hired a new secretary who is not Jewish, and I realize that we never fully clarified our expectations regarding the food she'd like to bring in to the synagogue for lunch. For a long time we had a non-Jewish secretary in the office, but she always "ate at her desk." In many years, I don't ever recall her eating anything other than an orange! I didn't give this much thought, because I figured that she'd bring a lunch box and eat her food at her desk. But just the other day, we had a long discussion about *mar'eet ayin* ["how things appear to outsiders, regardless of reality"], and she then turned to me and said: "Since I don't have kosher dishes, should I not be bringing in my food in Tupperware?" She has only brought in dairy sandwiches, etc., but still, the question fascinates me. I'm curious what policies colleagues have adopted not only to maintain the *kashrut* of their congregational, or staff, kitchens, but also to address the *mar'eet ayin* issue. Needless to say, with Pesach coming, this took on added urgency, but she won't be bringing anything at all during Pesach.

SAM: Our *shul* kitchen is kosher, and we just ask that any staff member who brings lunch should eat it at their desk, or outside at a picnic table. That seems to have solved our problem.

BOB: I'm sure you're right, Sam. If it becomes a problem, I'll bring it up again later.

SAM: I want to raise an issue related to interfaith relations. I recently received an offensive email that had been sent by the Muslim representative on our local Interfaith Council to all the members of our Interfaith Council. He was portraying Iran as a moderate nation and that Israel was the warmonger. . . . etc. Rather than respond to him as my emotions would have dictated, I thought carefully how I might respond. Here is what I came up with. I'll read it to you, and then his reply. I hope you find this interesting and revealing of one Muslim leader's views of his values and objectives and conscious thoughts.

I would imagine if these questions would ever be put to you, my colleagues, you would be able to answer them without a moment's thought, and with many examples. Also, for your information, I told the Muslim representative, Yahya, that he has two weeks to answer my questions.

Salaam Yahya,

I'm teaching a class on heroes and values of our neighbors and the proudest achievements and teachings of our religious neighbors. I'd like to ask you if you could please share with me accomplishments of Islam and Muslims of which you are most proud, and the leaders who espouse the values you hold most dear. Who are your heroes and what about them inspires you or your faith community to be inspired by them? Please answer these questions any way that speaks to your heart. I will be sharing these thoughts with students in various classes I teach.

Thanks for your help. If I can be of similar help to you, please feel free to call upon me.

All good wishes,
Sam

Here is Yahya's reply:

Shalom Sam,

I will be happy to do this for you if you can give me a few days to develop my thoughts on this. It is an interesting view and I have never really gotten my thoughts together on this in an organized way. So it will prove a useful exercise for me as well. Can you give me some idea of how long I have to do this?

Wa Salaam
Yahya

"(Since) good and evil cannot be equal, repel (evil) with something that is better. (Then) you will see that he with whom you had enmity will become your close friend."

"If God had so willed, He could have made all of you a single nation. But He willed otherwise in order to test you in what He has given you. Therefore try to excel one another in good works. Ultimately you shall all return to God. Then He will show you the truth of those matters over which you dispute."

The Holy Quran, 5:48

The Prophet Mohammed PBUH said: "Every act of goodness is (a form of) charity."   Sahih Muslim, Hadith 505 & 496

"A wise man makes his own decisions, an ignorant man follows public opinion."   Chinese Proverb

DON: Your experience with the Muslim representative on the interfaith council should demonstrate the futility of dialogue with Muslims. He starts out with a patent falsehood, namely, that Iran is moderate and Israel is the aggressor when, from the start of the Khomeini revolution in 1979, Israel was denounced as the "little Satan" and unambiguous calls for its utter destruction were made by Iran's new leaders. If you want to get an overview of Iranian aggression, you can find it conveniently in the chapter on Iran in an excellent book, *Jihad and Genocide*.

Since Yahya was spreading a pernicious falsehood, there is no way that you can have a productive dialogue with him. He's not interested in the truth of the matter. He certainly won't admit that the Jews could be right and the Muslims wrong. Please note the verses from the Qu'ran with which he ends his response. The verses are only relevant to the issue of who is the aggressor if you start with the premise that Islam alone is the true religion and

Judaism and Christianity are in one degree or another false in spite of their being "religions of Abraham." The more you argue with him the more he wins. He starts out with a patent falsehood and he will only build upon it. The best thing you can do is to break off relations. The more you continue the worse it will get.

SAM: A good thought, Don. I believe you're right. I appreciate your frankness.

BOB: Allow me to change the subject. Here's a question about Pesach, which is coming soon. It's a question my wife asks me every year, and I ask it too. So here goes: Is Pesach about food and utensils, or about freedom? I think the 60:1 ratio applies. If we worry more and talk more, and discuss more than 60:1 about the glass plate in the microwave than about freedom and what it means to be a Jew and how to keep our children Jewish, I think we Passover(ed) Pesach. Just my wife's humble opinion, and my phrasing.

SAM: Bob, I humbly agree with your wife! Pesach has become all about minute details of laws which weren't even hinted at in the Torah. And don't get me started on the "*narishkeit*" of *Kitniyot* [legumes, which Sephardic Jews eat, but Ashkenazic Jews do not]! It is not an accident that the Mishnah in Tractate *P'sahim* says, *EIN LADAVAR SOF!* ["There's no end to such a discussion]. I don't think they were really talking about mice and crumbs of *chametz*, I think they were talking about all the rules and regulations we have allowed ourselves to become slaves to at this time of year. Pesach has become the antithesis of freedom. When OU says not to use the first towel on the roll of paper towels because it was held to the roll by starchy glue that may contain *kitniyot*, then we understand what *EIN LADAVAR SOF* means.

And it's not only about Pesach that our zeal to follow the law has led to "passing over" the real importance of the holiday. See how the mayor of New York has taken his own *narishkeit* to the point of prohibiting food donations to homeless shelters: The New York Post said this recently: "So much for serving the homeless. The Bloomberg administration is now taking the term 'food police' to new depths, blocking food donations to all government-run facilities that serve the city's homeless.

"In conjunction with a mayoral task force and the Health Department, the Department of Homeless Services recently started enforcing new nutritional rules for food served at city shelters. Since DHS can't assess the nutritional content of donated food, shelters have to turn away good Samaritans."

May common sense once again return to our planet.

DON: Personally, I sometimes think that you Reform and Conservative folks undervalue the importance of rituals, even minute rituals. But that's a discussion for another day.

BOB: I have an interesting issue to raise today, and hope you fellas can give me some guidance. For many years, in the spirit of *kiruv* [reaching out to non-Jewish spouses of members], I have tried to integrate the non-Jewish partner of a Jew into the religious and educational life of the *shul*. Several non-Jewish spouses regularly attend my classes. A few have converted. At a bar mitzvah ceremony I encourage the non-Jewish spouse to rise in his or her seat and read a psalm in English, and also to ascend the *bimah* and help drape the *tallit* on the child while the celebrant recites the appropriate blessing over the *tallit*.

I have reasoned that, after all, these non-Jewish spouses are willingly and lovingly raising their children as Jews, not a small matter in this era of indifference and disaffiliation. Many rabbis do the same, as far as what I hear.

Now the conundrum. Some of my most involved, and observant families are asking, in good faith, why not be more welcoming towards our youth group, USY, United Synagogue Youth? Aside from the official USY rules, why can't a non-Jewish friend attend USY? What is the rationale for stopping *kiruv* [outreach] at the USY door? I know the dating rationale. Many people fear that meeting a non-Jew in synagogue, may lead to forming a relationship, and possibly getting married. But that is flimsy in an age when even religiously observant teenagers meet, and even date, non-Jewish friends. It seems to me that accepting a non-Jewish friend into USY, and accepting a synagogue members' non-Jewish mate as a member of the synagogue is kind of the same. It seems to me that both situations have to be viewed as the same based on the concept of outreach (*kiruv*). So I'd like to know how you are dealing with this issue.

SAM: My hunch is that Don and I disagree on this issue, for a change. I agree with you, Bob. I don't see any difference between non-Jewish spouses, and non-Jewish kids joining our youth groups. I'm sure this will continue to be an important issue for synagogue boards in months and years to come, as so many of the issues we're discussing.

I have another issue that's related to what we've been discussing.

An intermarried Jew asked the following questioned. So Rabbi, you are doing so many things to make non-Jewish spouses feel welcome. Why can't my supportive non-Jewish spouse, who is raising our children as Jews, stand next to me when I have an *aliyah*? Just call me up to the Torah and say: For the third *aliyah* we honor Chaim Jones accompanied by Mrs. Jones. It is clear that I am getting the honor and that she is just accompanying me. What are your thoughts?

Our custom is not to have a non-Jewish spouse accompany a Jewish spouse for an *aliyah*. Non-Jewish bar and bat mitzvah parents are seated next to me when their Jewish spouse has an *aliyah*. The non-Jew then joins their spouse in reciting the Parent's Prayer.

SAM: Don, I guess we're leaving you out of this discussion, since you don't have dual-*aliyot*, with two people having one *aliyah*, and you also don't have women taking *aliyot*. But let me tell you what we do.

The *minhag* that I started in my congregation is exactly that. I call up the Jewish parent and have the non-Jewish parent stand beside them. Actually the Jew places his or her *tallit* over the shoulder of the non-Jewish parent. My reasoning has been that often the non-Jewish parent has been involved in their child's Talmud Torah education in a myriad of ways, and that they have willingly given up passing on their own religious heritage, opting for raising their child in a tradition not their own. In this day and age where only one in four religiously mixed households chooses Judaism, this can become a key moment to recognize that sacrifice on their part by the congregation, and let them share a little *nachas* by standing beside their daughter or son, even if we make clear they are not the parent being called up for the honor, as having accompanied the family on this Jewish journey.

That being said, I certainly understand that other communities might prefer to find another way to honor the non-Jewish parent in a more spectacular fashion.

BOB: Let me move on to yet another issue. I have a congregant whose mother may, let's say, pass away the first day of *Hol Ha-Mo'ed*, when official mourning is not permitted. So the question about *shivah* has come up. There are two options that come to mind.

1. Do the burial, and then delay *shivah* until after the festival is over, essentially beginning Saturday evening, in this year's case.

2. Do the burial, and then do a shortened *shivah*, ending on Thursday morning.

This came up in my congregation this past *Sukkot* as well, and I guided my member to do Option #1, while her sister's rabbi guided her to do Option #2. Option 1 led to a prolonged *shivah*, because they still received comforters during the festival, but for the Option 2 sister, she felt denied a fuller experience.

I checked with a colleague who researched the matter, and this is what he came up with. In the event of a death and burial once Pesach and Sukkot begin, the *shivah* is postponed. *Shivah* observance begins after *Yom Tov*, but the *Yom Tov Sheni* that is the eighth day of Pesach or Simhat Torah is counted as the first day of *shivah*. *Shloshim*, however, is counted from the time of burial.

People can, however, visit the home of those who suffered a loss, even during *Hol HaMo'ed*, but those who suffered a loss should *daven* in synagogue during *Hol HaMo'ed* and *Yom Tov*. There is a *Teshuvah* [responsum] from the CJLS [Rabbinical Assembly's Committee on Jewish Law and Standards] addressing an abbreviated form of *shivah* for cases such as yours.

Some years ago, a colleague summarized the essence of the *te-shuvah*, from the 1970s. This is the summary: "In the seventies, the CJLS approved a recommendation by Rabbi Seymour Siegel that in a case like this, where mourning has been going on for a week anyway, the technical duration of *shivah* could reasonably be reduced to three days, that is, Sunday counts as one day, Monday is day 2, and he could get up from *shivah* on Tuesday morning after the token hour that is observed on the final day of *shivah* on a weekday. You may or may not choose to recommend this leniency to him and he may or may not be inclined to accept it, but as a matter of record, we have it as an option."

"The count in your case would be that the eighth day of Pesach is the first day, and we do not observe the outward signs of mourning on this day. Sunday is the second day, beginning, of course, after Pesach ends on Saturday night. And Monday morning is the token portion of the third day. If a death occurs during the first days of *Yom Tov* or during *Hol HaMo'ed*, full *shivah* should be observed for one calendar day, namely, one full *halakhic* day after *Yom Tov*, plus the following evening and morning. Thus, counting the last day of *Yom Tov* as a day of official mourning, without the observance of mourning customs, the CJLS minimum guideline calls for a *shivah* of three *halakhic* days, only one day in duration by the calendar. Rabbis should be advised to permit home visits during *Hol Hamo'ed*, but to encourage *davening* in the synagogue, as home *davening* would carry the appearance of mourning. Similarly, customs such as removing the shoes should be postponed until after *Yom Tov*."

SAM: That sounds very complicated, but I guess, in these modern times, it's a valid attempt to meet the exigencies of our complex society.

Let me raise a related issue regarding death and burial. May a Jewish soldier be buried in a military cemetery? I've done it, making sure to put a star instead of a cross, on the tombstone.

DON: Do you know that with regard to military cemeteries, rarely is one allowed to actually go to the grave site. I have only gone once to the actual burial site. It is rows and rows of holes with excavation equipment. More often than not we go to a staging area. With Jewish funerals they allow us to do military honors first, then give us enough time to do a Jewish ceremony as though you are at a funeral home. In some veterans' cemeteries they try to do Jewish burials later in the day so that we can have more time. Please note they have a specific amount of time that they give you because it is back to back times of about thirty minutes. You need to check with the funeral home you are working with for accurate information regarding your specific cemetery.

BOB: Actually, I just recently received a request for me to do the funeral and burial of a man in a veterans' cemetery. As far as I can tell, there is no Jewish section in the cemetery in question. I believe that the choice of cemetery in this particular case is largely due to the fact that the family is of very limited means, and the man can be buried at little or no cost. I have looked at the Rabbinical Assembly law committee records, which does not list any official *teshuvah* on the matter, but does list several opinions of the committee chairs over the years which discourage the burial of a Jew in a veterans' cemetery, and discourages rabbis from performing funerals in mixed sections. When I raised my concern with the funeral director he said that they do several funerals a year at the veterans' cemetery, and that they have even had Orthodox rabbis perform them on occasion. So the upshot is that "each person does what is right in his eyes," as the good book says.

SAM: As long as we're on the subject of "death and dying," let me raise the issue that probably every rabbi faces in his or her lifetime – that of Masonic funerals. Should we go along when a congregant requests one for a deceased loved one, prior to the Jewish funeral?

BOB: There are a few *teshuvot* from the various streams of Judaism which have been published, one of them by the Conservative movement, which prohibit Masonic funerals. I believe that this prohibition is in error. It may be based on information which might be true in some cases, but not all. I am not an expert on the subject, but know enough to have serious questions about a blanket prohibition.

The gist of the prohibition is that the rites have Christian elements. I can tell you that in my experience, this is not so. Many Conservative as well as Reform Jews are Masons, and also many rabbinic colleagues in both movements are, or have been, including many distinguished ones. Freemasonry is a very complex subject. Suffice it to say that there is no single Masonic liturgy. The masonic funerals I have seen in New Jersey, New York, and Pennsylvania have no Christian elements. I cannot vouch for all Masonic funeral services everywhere, but given the complexity of the subject, and the dizzying number of Masonic groups, subgroups and related groups, I cannot believe that the authors of these responsa did an exhaustive survey of the subject, which would prove almost impossible. No "critical edition" of all Masonic liturgies has ever been compiled. Nor could it be, given that Masons are pledged not to publish these details.

That being said, Masonic "secrets" are not secret. These have been "exposed" and published for centuries. There are, in print and on the internet, various "Monitors," namely, unauthorized versions of the Masonic liturgy. These are not exhaustive and would hardly be helpful to anybody who wanted to "crash" a lodge, for reasons I will explain. Masons are not disturbed that their "secrets" are public and can easily be learned by non-Masons, but no Mason of good standing will break his oath and reveal them. What is important is not the liturgy, but the oath. Here is a summary of the subject, short and sweet. The basic institution of Freemasonry is the local "blue" lodge, which averages about one hundred and fifty members each. These are chartered by a Grand Lodge, which is usually national, although it is organized on a state level in the U.S. Each Grand Lodge has its own liturgy, based on the original English one. They are similar to one another, but not identical. The funeral services are conducted by the local "blue lodge" and seem to be late in origin and therefore vary considerably. None that I have seen are Christian. I cannot vouch for all of them.

The "Blue Lodge" awards only the first three degrees of Masonry: Entered Apprentice, Fellowcraft and Master Mason. Once, that is all there was to Masonry, but the fraternity expanded in scope. There are, as I mentioned, many, many "appendent" bodies in Freemasonry, which may or may not be recognized by the Grand Lodge, depending on local usage. These include The Scottish Rite, which awards degrees 4 to 32, and on occasion the honorary 33rd degree. Also, there is the York Rite which, itself has several sub groups. One, the Royal Arch, awards four degrees. Jews join the Scottish Rite and also the Royal Arch of the York Rite. They do NOT join the Knights Templar, a subgroup of the York Rite, as this group requires members to be Trinitarian Christians. There are also groups which Masons and their family members may join. These have liturgies. There are many other groups, such as Tall Cedars, Shriners, etc. I am a mason and belong to a group of Masons who are ham operators, "The Gathering." You get the idea. Freemasonry is huge and varied.

Masons must affirm belief in a Supreme Being. They can be of any religion. Much has been written about Masonic concepts of God. "There is no single God concept." Modern Masonry traces its origins to the foundation of the Grand Lodge of England in 1717, which merged several old groups, but there are verifiable documents that prove the existence of Masonic groups as far back as the 1300s. Masonic lore itself traces its origins to antiquity. The influence of 18th century Deism is clearly present, but this would not preclude a Mason from embracing a more classic God-concept, including one who operates through providence, who intervenes in history, reveals the Torah, speaks to prophets, performs miracles, wants us to abstain from *kitniyot* [legumes] on Pesach, etc. In any event, 18th century Enlightenment concepts are not found in earlier Masonc documents and are not binding. What IS binding and very 18th century is Freemasonry's pluralism.

Contrary to what has been alleged in the considerable anti-Masonic literature, Masons do not worship the devil – we [the Masons] really don't. Nor do we control the world. The world, as we know, is controlled by AIPAC in league with the Camp Fire Girls.

My suggestion is this: if you have concerns about the Masonic funeral service, ask about it. It is probably just fine. As the service is public, it is not secret and you will probably be able to obtain the text. Should you have any concern, the local lodge may be able to omit or change an element.

DON: I am aware that several of our Orthodox colleagues do, in fact, permit Masonic ceremonies prior to a traditional Jewish funeral.

BOB: Thanks, Don. Here is my point, in a nutshell. The "prohibitions" in various *teshuvot* are largely incorrect and most certainly incomplete. Further, Jews have Masonic funerals all the time. The general statement that Masonic funerals are somehow Christian is not true. If a rabbi has any doubts or questions, the simple thing to do is to ask to see the text of the liturgy to be used. As the officiant, that is certainly your right, and responsibility. The funeral liturgy isn't "secret," as it is enacted in front of non-Masons. I would be surprised if you found Christian elements, although it IS possible. The liturgy varies from Grand Lodge to Grand Lodge. Check, and you'll see that I'm right.

Of course we are justified in wanting to have some control over the funeral rites. We need to guard against inappropriateness. This sometimes happens when family members speak, and length is a consideration. All I can say is that the Masonic rite is very likely to be absolutely appropriate, and enhance the service, much as military rites do; and provide comfort to the mourners by keeping with the will of the deceased. Regarding time considerations, the Masonic service is usually very short. When putting together the service, weigh this against other time issues, such as requests of family to speak, etc. It can be managed. You can be out of the chapel in a half hour.

SAM: Let me change our focus for a moment, regarding a problem that has arisen in Israel – specifically regarding the singing of *Hatikvah*. Part of the wording is certainly difficult for Israeli Arab citizens of the State of Israel. Is it true that until 2004 *Hatikvah* was not the official national anthem of Israel? I read this in Wikipedia.

DON: I don't know all the facts, but is it an interesting subject. What I do know is that when the Arab Israeli, Salim Jubran, was sworn in as Justice of the Israeli Supreme Court, he refused to sing *Hatikvah*, and Prime Minister Netanyahu came to his defense. I wonder if there wasn't some sentiment through more liberal governments that *Hatikvah* could not be said by non-Jewish citizens, and so they were hesitant to adopt it as the national anthem.

BOB: Forgive me for sounding like the expert on all matters Jewish and Israeli, but I do know some of the history of all this. If you'd like, I can tell you what I think, and some of the information that I'm familiar with.

SAM: *"Y'lamdenu Rabbenu,"* – Let our master expound!

BOB: OK, here goes.
The idea that at some time in the past, Israel was a sensitive, naïve democracy is part of an American, and Israeli, historical nostalgia, which is related to the similarly mythological Israel-as-Jewish-theme-park narrative of Israel-as-socialist-paradise, and Israel before the Six Day War. These are narratives that, again and again, show that general knowledge of Israeli history is truly shameful.

Israel's first "liberal" democratic government was that of Menachem Begin. The governments that preceded it were essentially "state-of-emergency" justified totalitarian regimes with certain democratic window dressing, until the Rabin government, which was a last-ditch effort to save the monarchy. That sounds terrible, but let us not forget that from 1948, the country was run by an Eastern European socialist elite that opposed and actively prevented the enactment of a constitution, and permitted only government-run radio and government-controlled news, strictly censored the press, theater and movies, prohibited the introduction of television, prevented people who did not identify with the ruling elite from obtaining jobs in the civil service or pursuing careers in the armed forces or security services, placed an onerous tax upon foreign travel, and outlawed the possession of foreign currency. During that period, Ashkenazim who did not have the correct political views or affiliations were second class citizens. Mizrahim, from Mediterranean countries, as opposed to Eastern Europeans, were third class citizens. Holocaust survivors were an embarrassment that was largely ignored except for the purpose of robbing them of their pensions. Most Israeli Arabs lived under the direct rule of a military government, created during the War of Independence, and maintained by Ben Gurion, Moshe Sharett and Levi Eshkol even after the Minister of Justice recommended ending it in 1958.

So, which liberal government might you mean, Don? I think it would be absurd to imagine that Ben Gurion, Moshe Sharett, Levi Eshkol, and Golda Meir, who actively oppressed Israel's Arab community, cared a fig for their feelings. So, no, I do not think the reason for not officially adopting *Hatikvah* can be ascribed to any "liberal sentiment" or humanistic sensitivity. I think it would be more correct, as has been suggested, to assume that no one saw a need due to the way the Israeli Government was created. The Executive Council of the Zionist Congress, which had already voted that *Hatikvah* was its Anthem, created *"Minhelet Ha'am"* [governing council] which was headed by Ben Gurion. In Israel's Declaration of Independence, David Ben Gurion unilaterally declared that *Minhelet Ha'am* to be the *Memshalah Hazmanit* [Temporary Government] of the new State of Israel. The Temporary Government then held elections for the establishment of an *Asefah Mekhonenet* [Constituent Council] to draft a constitution. The Constituent Council, apparently without any legal authority, decided not to adopt a constitution, which was its mandated purpose, but rather to appoint itself to be the Legislature [*Knesset*], and elect the First Government, led, of course, by Ben Gurion. So, at no time in the course of the usurpation of power through which Ben Gurion and company segued from being representatives of the leadership of the Zionist movement to becoming the Israeli government, would they have actually felt a need to re-establish *Hatikvah* as the National Anthem.

One of the true miracles of Israel, is that despite the strongly totalitarian leanings of its founders, it became a Western-oriented, liberal democracy. Although many would prefer not to admit it, that is largely thanks to the fact that, as Professor Mordechai Kreminitzer has observed, "Menachem Begin had a liberal-democratic worldview." It was Menachem Begin's fierce devotion to democratic principles and the rule of law that ultimately led to the adoption of the Basic Laws that form Israel's Constitution. See Mordechai Kremnitzer and Amir Fuchs, *Menachem Begin on Democracy and Constitutional Values*).

DON: So would it be correct to say that, inasmuch as the government of Israel understood itself to be inheriting the mantle of leadership of the Zionist movement, *Hatikvah* morphed from being the national anthem of the Zionist movement to being the de facto national anthem of the State, but that this was never affirmed or ratified until 2004?

BOB: Not precisely. *Hatikvah* was voted the national anthem of the Zionist movement at the 18th Zionist Congress in 1933. *Hatikvah* is mentioned as Israel's national anthem in various laws and official protocols, for example, the rules regarding the singing of *Hatikvah* as the National Anthem of the State of Israel were set down in IDF HQ Order 33.0911 of 1 April 1962. It is, however, correct that *Hatikvah* was not directly established as the national anthem by statute until 2004.

I think, therefore, it would be less precise to say that *Hatikvah* wasn't the official national anthem before 2004 than to say that English is the official language of Barbados, Belize, Canada, Eritrea, India, and the Bahamas, but is not the official language of the United States, inasmuch as Congress has not passed a statute establishing it as such. Oh, and by the way, English, along with Hebrew and Arabic, is the official language of Israel under article 82 of the King's Order in Council of 1922, which as the Israeli Supreme Court noted in 1999, remains in force. And, nevertheless, to paraphrase Galileo, it isn't. [The reference is to the statement Galileo reputedly made after recanting his belief in the heliocentric model of the solar system: "*Eppur si muove*," despite affirming that the earth does not move around the sun, "and yet it moves."

SAM: I noticed an interesting article in the papers recently by Bishop Desmond Tutu of South Africa. As is his custom, Tutu comes down hard on Israel and the "occupation." I know that many of you, and other colleagues I've spoken to, think Tutu is an anti-Semite. To call him an anti-Semite based on that article is really a stretch. Anti-Semites don't usually trip over themselves in detailing how painful it is to write negative things about the people they hate. Now, you can dismiss all of his anguish over what he feels he must say, but at least he wrote about his anguish. I haven't exactly heard anguish from Ahmadinejad. Why isn't he concerned about the tragedy of anti-Christian treatment by Muslims? Why doesn't he write pained and anguished articles about Syria? Because he is obsessed with perfection, as many Leftists are. Israel must be perfect, or it is worse than Syria. His accusation that Israel is an apartheid state is not unique to him; it can be heard by leftists in the halls of our very own Congress and in the American press. But his definition of apartheid is hardly the apartheid that existed in South Africa. See Dennis Prager's piece describing the differences.

Look, most of the folks I know on the left are always upset about something not being the way they expect it should be. I think they expect Syria to be evil. They expect Israel to be good, so when it's not, that's what they focus on. I prefer to focus on all the good that Israel does, as I do with all the good that America does. I'm always surprised at how despicable America is portrayed to be by so many Americans. And yet, it's the freest place on earth with the most opportunity to achieve, with hard work and some good luck, whatever one wants to achieve, and I walk around happy to know that I am blessed to live here. The difference between me and those who constantly complain about America is essentially that I'm pretty happy and they are usually upset. Tutu has that smile on his face next to his article, but deep down, I don't think he's a very happy fellow since all he can see is the greatest country in the Middle East – the most moral, sensitive, progressive, and democratic – as a rotten apartheid state. I don't pray that he will meet his maker any time soon. I kind of feel sorry for him, *nebuch*. Just the two cents of a right wing fascist ultra-conservative tea-partying hate-filled would-be evangelical fanatic.

DON: I forget who it was who said that a liberal is a person who can't even take his own side in an argument. Well, that's me. If I feel one way and a reporter says something else, I listen to the reporter. I often doubt my own positions, because I know that I am not objective and get emotional on some issues.

But that means I know how to listen and I know I try to be fair – always taking into account my own subjectivity. But sorry, Tutu is beyond the pale. I know – objectively – that he states only one side of the argument. Hell, I even know Palestinian activists who have a better, nuanced understanding of our side. And more empathy. And let me say this clearly. Ethics are important and even central, but being Jewish isn't just a matter of belonging to an ethical debating society. We are a people, living in a real world where decisions are often difficult and we find ourselves in situations where all choices are bad. I make no apology for saying that survival is also an ethical imperative. We can't just stand around with one finger up our noses and say "ethical monotheism." Sometimes ethics are strategic and they are usually, in the long run, in one's own self-interest.

I am not interested in a life devoid of ethical considerations, but even the prophets of Israel understood that there are nationalistic considerations. They cared about all of humanity and had universal ethics, but to say that this was their sole prospective is cherry picking. Nineteenth century assimilationists preached universal ethics to their empty temples in order to impress the Gentiles that this was really what Judaism was about. They stood in stark contrast to medieval Jews who cared little for the outside world. In time the few Jews who came to the temples began to believe that this simplistic assimilationist line really was Judaism. They drank their own Kool-Aid, and now we are paying the price by producing rabbis who can't even take their own people's side in an argument, thinking that this masochism is the religion of the prophets. Perhaps it is "ethical" and perhaps it is naive. In any event, it strikes me as remarkably bad judgment.

BOB: Rabbi Gerson Cohen, in his second year as Chancellor of the Jewish Theological Seminary, invited Tutu to speak at the Seminary. The next day, in the Seminary dining hall when it still served as the social hall for students and faculty, Gerson bemoaned the fact that because of his ignorance and ego he was duped into inviting this Jew-hater and State of Israel hater to speak at the Seminary. Gerson was livid and quite upset about it. I trust Gerson's and my own judgment more than I trust the judgment of innumerable true lovers of Israel throughout the world – Jews and non-Jews alike. An eternal Jewish problem is that those Jews who are sympathetic to State of Israel haters because they believe their position is the ethical one, and is saving Israel from itself, are totally deaf to rational arguments and empirical evidence, showing how they are in error. I no longer make any effort to change their minds.

DON: Bishop Tutu, and others of his ilk, use the term "occupation," as if Israel is a land-grabber, and the whole issue is of a "foreign power" stealing land from the poor Palestinians. This is why I never use the word "occupation." It is a loaded word, which is always used against Israel. By law, Israel was required to administer the territories seized in a defensive war in 1967 until the time when a peace would be negotiated and borders set. She didn't "occupy" anything. The territories were territories "administered" by Israel.

But so many naive people fall into language errors, and criticisms of Israel that are just total fodder for Israel's enemies. We are duped when we allow ourselves to be used by Israel's enemies. Archbishop Desmond Tutu is an anti-Semite, a hater of Israel and a total liar and demagogue when it comes to Israel, and he should be called out for what he is. He used the word "apartheid" for one reason: to demonize and threaten Israel, and so many have unwittingly given him great legitimacy and material to work with. The rabbis in *Pirke Avot* were right – *Hizaharu b'divreykhem* ["Be careful with your words"]. Wise people should be very careful with their use of language. Words can be dangerous.

BOB: One can be opposed to the occupation, as I suspect many of us are, and still deplore Tutu's use of the loaded word "apartheid." The complete absence of any mention, much less condemnation on his part, of any wrongdoing on the Palestinian side is prima facie evidence that his letter and the recent UMC [United Methodist Church] resolution condemning the "occupation," was, indeed, one-sided. The lack of compassion on his part is remarkable, his arrogance palpable, and his anti-Jewish sentiment obvious. Everyone can see that. I want to see the occupation end. But I have no use for Tutu whatsoever nor for his "moral voice."

DON: OK, fellas. Here's a question that, frankly, as an Orthodox rabbi I've been struggling with. As you well know, tradition requires that there are no festivities, including weddings, from the end of Pesach to Shavuot, a whole seven weeks. Excluding, of course, Lag B'Omer and Rosh Hodesh. I doubt if any of my colleagues would be willing to shorten that period of time, as the liberal movements have, but I myself feel bad that we have to cut out seven whole weeks from the schedule for weddings and other major simchas. What do you guys do in that "Omer" period?

BOB: In our *shul*, we suspend all the restrictions with the arrival of *Yom HaAtzma'ut*, the fifth of *Iyyar*. It is not only a totally unnecessary burden to maintain the restrictions, it is also against the idea that, as the Talmud says, "God has mercy on Jewish finances." How many more days do we want our kosher caterers to go dark? How many more weddings do we want to send to the non-kosher facilities to do since we can't do them in our synagogues? It is totally senseless to me that *Lag B'Omer* can break the mourning but *Yom HaAtzma'ut* [Israel Independence Day] can't. I don't get it.

Some of our learned professors and *halakhic* scholars are regularly coming up with new reasons to spend seven weeks in mourning during *Sefirah*, especially during a time the Torah commands us to be filled with gratitude for the bounty God provides us with. It seems unnecessary, if not a bit morose. Taking the seven weeks of *Sefirah* and adding in the three weeks before

Tishah B'Av, means that Jews are to be in a state of mourning during one fifth of our calendar year. No wonder so many Jews I know suffer from depression! And we're not even sure why we are in mourning! The historical background of mourning during the period of the *Sefirah*, between *Pesach* and *Shavuot*, is flimsy at best. It reminds me of the beggar on the street corner who holds a sign saying, "I haven't eaten in three days," and a Jewish woman walks by and tells him, "Force yourself!" The Torah has given us a mandate, which we actually follow with a *brakhah* that says *Asher kidshanu* b'mitzvotav ["Who has sanctified us by His commandments"] – to offer thanksgiving each day of the harvest and to count down to the advent of the giving of the Torah at Sinai. Is there any other time where we consider ourselves sanctified by the commandments to mourn? Doesn't saying, *"Asher kidshanu b'mitzvotav"* usually lead into something joyous?

In much of the world, springtime, inaugurated by Pesach, begins the time of year with the best weather and the loveliest time to celebrate a marriage. And we prefer to come up with new reasons to be miserable, so we can tell young couples to wait until the blistering heat arrives in June? And make sure not to wait too long because you will run into the three weeks of mourning between the seventeenth of *Tammuz* and the ninth of *Av*? The Torah has given us a mandate to be thankful for seven weeks for what most of us take for granted, our ability to feed our family. In its brilliance the Torah has mandated thanksgiving on a daily basis because God knows that the only way to be happy is if we are grateful. Instead we take the cue from tradition to spend the time being sad and avoiding, of all things during springtime, music! Forbidding music – I know many of us don't, but it's all part of mourning – is taking away one of God's greatest gifts to us, one that can bring pleasure and lighten spirits. What kind of message are we sending our children? Let's spend a few months focusing on death, destruction, massacres, the Holocaust and instead of being thankful for God's blessings, let's just wallow in the misery we've encountered through the ages!

I think the *Teshuvah* which suspends mourning with the onset of *Iyyar* makes sense. After all, how can we not see the establishment of the State of Israel at the fifth of *Iyyar* as important enough to suspend mourning the way a *Yom Tov* ends *shivah* or *shloshim*? Yes, we have a lot to be sad about in our history, and thankfully, there are plenty of folks on earth who remind us 365 days a year about it. We don't need to take weeks and months out of our calendar to be sad. We need to maximize the reasons to celebrate and to be thankful.

SAM: Well, Bob, why don't you tell us how you *really* feel about curtailing festivities and weddings during *Sefirah*? [Laughter]. OK, I think we've chewed that question to death – or to celebration – whichever you choose, so let's go on to another topic.

BOB: I have another question to raise, but before I do, I want to ask you a question. You remember the old Yiddish saying, "Before I speak, I'd like to say a few words." Well, before my real question, here's a logistic question. A female colleague of ours, Rabbi Susan Berkowitz, would like to join our weekly get-togethers. How do you all feel about that?

SAM: No problem.

DON: I won't count her in a *minyan*, or in a *mezuman* [required three Jews to recite introduction to *Birkat HaMazon*, Grace after Meals]. But she can surely have a bite with us, and discuss some matters if she wishes. She might know more *halakhah* than you two ignoramuses! Just kidding, by all means, bring her along.

BOB: OK, I'll bring her to our next week's meeting. So here's my question. Why do some people refuse to say *Adonai*, and say *HaShem* instead? I know it's permissible to say *Adonai* when reciting a full verse from the Torah, but if not that, some folks say *HaShem*. Personally, I'm put off by that.

DON: I actually like to call God, *HaShem*. It started out, of course, as a way of not using God's real name, the Tetragrammaton, the four Hebrew letters – *Yod Heh Vav Heh*, which is not supposed to be recited except by the *Kohen Gadol* on Yom Kippur in the Holy of Holies. It's a way of showing respect to the holy name of God. There is a variety of ways to refer to God in Hebrew that are kosher, such as *HaKadosh Barukh Hu*, the Blessed Holy One, or *Shadai*, the Almighty. But to me this extra degree of care in not utilizing God's real name, as the Torah has it, shows extra respect. I like it. When I hear it, I think the person saying it is a person who has respect for God and the tradition.

SAM: Historically, it seems to me that it arose when quoting Biblical text. Ashkenazi Jews tend to not use *Adonai* in quoting text, unlike *Sepharadim* (Rav Ovadiah Yosef is against using *Adonai*), but even plenty of *Ashkenazim* limit the substitution. Certainly now it is the substitute of choice for mentioning God in casual conversation. That it is a substitute for a substitute is strange, and why we need a fence around the fence is beyond me. I think part of its usage is when Ta"Z objected to combination forms that make no sense, such as *Adoshem*. As other forms became less used, this one crept in. To then substitute it for English, to say *HaShem* in an English sentence, is a whole other story. Then, add to this strangeness spelling it in English – *HaSh-m*. Fences around fences around fences. To what extent will we go?

BOB: I have never been comfortable with using "*Hashem*" and even less "*Adoshem*" not just for *halakhic* reasons, but also for religious/aesthetic reasons. It seems so "*frummie.*" Of course one doesn't want to say *Shem* and *malkhut* [saying *Barukh atah Adonai, Elohenu Melekh HaOlam* . . .] ["Praised are You, Adonai, our God, Sovereign of the universe] unless actually saying a blessing. But I really see no point in saying "*Adonai*" when reading a prayer in English, which is becoming fashionable. In general, I think we need to use English when we're using English and Hebrew when we're using Hebrew. In English, using the word LORD instead of the Tetragrammaton makes perfect sense. It is, after all an accurate translation of Adonai, and it also has four letters and so reminds us of the original word.

Further, we are seeing increased use of the word "*mitzvot*" in English prayers. What is wrong with the word "commandments?" But I am very glad that I'm not the only one who feels this way, *Barukh HaShem.*

DON: Bob, your sense of humor underwhelms me. By the way, some scholars say you should not say "*Shalom,*" nor respond "*Shalom,*" not even in "*Shalom aleikhem,*" to someone bareheaded because *Shalom* is one of the names of God and you cannot say a name of God bareheaded.

SAM: May I humbly chime in with a different perspective? Chaim Nahman Bialik offered the insight that "reading a text in translation is like kissing a bride through her veil." For some Jews, Hebrew is totally indiscernible. The blessings, if familiar at all, are a string of senseless syllables. But sometimes the sense of the Hebrew becomes clear by offering a translation alongside the Hebrew original that preserves some words. This includes words such as *Adonai,* which feels somehow more Jewish than God, less Hegelian than Lord, less Christian than Father in Heaven, even though *Avinu BaShamayim,* ["Our Father in Heaven"] is "ours," perhaps because it is how we say God in Hebrew.

And because this is also how we pronounce God's name when reading Torah or *haftarah,* congregants connect with the idea that they are "speaking to," as it were, the same Creator that our ancestors addressed, in the same way Moses did.

A significant part of what we're seeking, in uttering *berakhot* together, is an authentic feeling of blessing, of connecting to our source and to our tradition. We don't have to be purists about using a foreign language on which we have to mostly lean for intelligibility's sake for our non-Hebrew-speaking members. Why not allow Hebrew where we can? This much of a glimpse into how much richer the Hebrew, in linguistic, intertextual, ethnic, emotional associations, sometimes inspires a desire to learn more, to disentangle the senseless syllables we mumble and to enter into their coherent beauty. It's happened often in my experience.

Meanwhile, offering this much access is a way of welcoming people gently, rather than relegating the uninitiated to total exclusion from the original, the language of our ancestors, the sound and feelings of being intimate with the Hebrew words and all their resplendent meaning and the feeling of removing the veil. It gives people hope, that they can learn more. Why close the doors to that?

After all, there is just so much richness in the word "*mitzvot*," which "commandments" does not convey, not least of which is the ability to begin to recognize related words, the network of meaning in Jewish rites and readings – bar-mitzvah, *mitzvotav* ["His commandments"], *tzivanu* ["has commanded us"], etc.

I recall Professor Minkin teaching too that even though they are Jewish concepts, there are words in English that now have completely Christian overtones, such as salvation, resurrection, providence, Savior, etc.

It seems to me that there are good reasons for both our heads and our hearts to play a bit with the English-Hebrew, to be open to the language that connects us to our Creator, our tradition, our people, and our own ability to navigate the richness of our heritage. That is, for all Jews, not just the fully literate.

DON: Well, like many of our other conversations, no conclusion. But I still like saying "*HaShem*." It makes me feel close to God – maybe because so many of my teachers used it. As I often say at the end of so many of our "debates," to each his own.

A good time to break for the week. All agree?

ALL: Agreed.

Week 5

BOB: Colleagues, I want you to welcome our distinguished colleague, Rabbi Susan Berkowitz, of Temple Rodef Shalom here in town.

SUSAN: Shalom everyone. Thanks for inviting me to your discussion luncheons. I look forward to being a regular part of your group.

DON, SAM: Welcome, Susan!

DON: I'm sure you'll add a significant and alternative dimension to our discussions. I know you have a strong background in Talmud and liturgy, and we'll all be interested in any new insights you have to bring to the table.

SUSAN: I'll try my best, for sure.

BOB: I'd like to kick-off today's discussion, with a query about the way we pray. There are so many physical accompaniments to our *davening*.
  Recently, I had an opportunity to reflect upon the numerous physical gestures and motions that we use to enhance and accentuate our praying, whether in synagogue or privately. So I began to wonder about each of these actions: For how long have we been doing this? And why? Is there a textual source for this practice? If so, what is it? Is it wide-spread? Are there similari-

ties and/or differences among Ashkenazim, Sephardim and Ye-
menites, Orthodox, Conservative, Reform, etc.?

My asking these questions is not intended to criticize or be-
little people who observe these customs or the customs themselves. In fact, I practice nearly all of them myself. My members
frequently ask me about this or that. I want to be able to say
something more profound than *"minhag"* [It's just a custom].

So here follows a list, surely incomplete, of various actions
that can be seen in a contemporary synagogue. Please feel free to
add actions that I have omitted, and respond to questions I have
not asked. Or perhaps there is a good book or website that covers
these matters. Here's my preliminary list:

Barukh she-amar: holding two of the four *tzitziyyot* during
recitation.

Barukh she-amar: kissing the two *tzitziyyot* following.

Bar'khu: bowing at each mention of the words *"Bar'khu"* and
"Barukh."

Kadosh, Kadosh, Kadosh: elevating one's self on tip-toes
three times.

Gathering the four *tzitziyyot* some time shortly before the
Sh'ma.

Sh'ma: closing or covering one's eyes. My understanding is
that the reason is to achieve undistracted concentration.

Sh'ma: emphasizing the letter *dalet* in *Ehad*. My understanding is to emphasize that this is not a *resh*.

Va-yomer: kissing the *tzitziyyot* at the mention of the word
"tzitzit," and at the end add the word *"Kayyamet"* in the paragraph following.

Amidah: three steps back and three steps forward at the start.
My understanding is that this is a practice when facing a monarch.

Amidah: bending one's knees and bowing at *"barukh attah"*
in the first two *berakhot*.

V'kara zeh el zeh: bowing to the left and to the right. Perhaps
only the *sh"tz* (prayer leader) does this.

Modim: bowing.

Modim, during *hazarat ha-shatz* [reader's repetition of the

Amidah]: reading an alternate version during the recitation out loud. My understanding is that, if we recite the basic *Modim* prayer twice, it would be taken as reference to a second divinity.

Berakhah concluding the *ho-da-ah* blessing: bending one's knees and bowing.

Oseh Shalom: three steps back and three steps forward. And is this any different from the same practice at the end of the various *Kaddeshim*?

During the procession removing and replacing the *Sefer Torah*: touching the *Sefer Torah* with a *tallit* or *siddur* or hand and kissing that object. My understanding of the procession is that it is a remnant of an earlier age when the *Sifrei Torah* [Torah scrolls] were kept in a side chamber and were brought in and returned before and following the reading of the *parashah*.

Hagbahah: pointing one's pinkie, or the corner of one's *tallit* at the airborne *Sefer Torah*.

Finally, while not an action, it makes this list: During the *Kiddush*, following the words "*savrei maranan v'rabotai,*" ["Attention, my teachers and masters"] and its variations, responding with "*l'hayyim.*"

Whew! The list is longer than I thought when I began!

SUSAN: Even though I'm a "new-comer," can I start with a couple of sources with which I'm familiar?

BOB: Sure, go right ahead.

SUSAN: *Bar'khu*: bowing at each mention of the words "*Bar'khu*" and "*Barukh,*" – this is in the *Shulhan Arukh Orah Hayim*.

Kadosh, kadosh, kadosh: elevating one's self on tip-toes three times. This is in *Midrash Tanhuma*.

Sh'ma: closing or covering one's eyes. This is also in the *Shulhan Arukh*.

Sh'ma: emphasizing the *dalet* in *Ehad* – also in *Shulhan Arukh*

Amidah: three steps back and three steps forward at the start. This is mentioned in *Mahzor Vitry*.

Amidah: bending one's knees and bowing at *"barukh attah"* in the first two *berakhot* – also mentioned in *Mahzor Vitry*.

V'kara zeh el zeh: bowing to the left and to the right. Rabbi Ovadiah Yosef says there is no source for this custom.

Oseh Shalom: three steps back and three steps forward. This is in Talmud, Tractate Yoma

Three steps back: TB Yoma 53b.

During the *Kiddush*, following *savrei maranan v'rabotai* and its variations, responding with *l'hayyim*. This is in *Midrash Tanhuma*.

BOB: Wow – sure am glad we invited you to join us!

SUSAN: Well, I've been preparing some of these things for my *siddur* adult education class, and they happen to be fresh in my mind.

SAM: Did you get most of the answers you wanted, Bob? Can I move ahead with another issue?

BOB: Go right ahead.

SAM: I've been reading in the media lately about several relatives of well-known people, converting to Judaism in order to marry a Jew. I brought along a clipping about the grandson of Muhammad Ali, who just became a bar mitzvah. Here's what it says:

"The grandson of legendary boxer Muhammad Ali became a bar mitzvah at a Philadelphia synagogue.

"Jacob Wertheimer, the son of Khaliah Ali-Wertheimer and Spencer Wertheimer, was called to the Torah on April 28 at Congregation Rodelph Shalom in front of 150 people including the boxer, the Sweet Science boxing news website reported last week in an article by Ali's biographer Thomas Hauser.

"Ali's daughter, who was raised Muslim, told the website that 'No one put any pressure on Jacob to believe one way or another. He chose this on his own because he felt a kinship with Judaism and Jewish culture,' and that it 'meant a lot to Jacob' that Ali was there.

"The theme of the bar mitzvah was diversity and inclusiveness.

"Ali was raised a Baptist and converted to Islam in the 1960s."

DON: And of course, LBJ's granddaughter.

SAM: And don't forget Ivanka Trump, John King, Chelsea Clinton – married to a Jew, Bush 1's granddaughter, John Kerry's brother, Shyne, the Belizean hip hop recording artist, and now Ali's grandson . . . Gosh, are there any gentiles left?

BOB: So, now that we have plenty of examples of how desirable it is to marry a Jew, how do we get the Jews to marry Jews?

SUSAN: If you have an answer for that one, it will be headlines in all the Anglo-Jewish newspapers. If I may, I have a *halakhic* question, one which many of my members ask me. Some synagogues have *mezuzot* on the door, and many do not. Of course, if someone resides in a synagogue, that would make it a "home." But lacking that, does a *shul* need one?

SAM: I just went through this with a very enthusiastic and newly religious parent in our Religious School, a typical ultra-Orthodox guy, who has contempt for us now, but wouldn't think of taking his kid out of our school and putting him into the ultra-Orthodox day school because he knows how superior our school is. He wanted to put *mezuzot* everywhere in our school building which also has a chapel. He wanted them on closets of a certain size, and on all the staircases, etc. We already had one on every classroom and office and the chapel, as well as the entrance to the building. I explained to him that *mezuzot* in a school building or at the entrance to a synagogue are really for educational purposes, as there really isn't a requirement to have *mezuzot* there. But I absolutely agree, I told him, that we need them on all the classrooms, offices and chapel since it is a great educational opportunity. He of course determined that since I am not an ultra-Orthodox rabbi I obviously have no idea what I'm talking about. How could it be for educational purposes? It's there to protect our children! I told him that we didn't actually view a *mezuzah* in such a way, and quoted to him Rambam, who objects to seeing a *mezuzah* as "divine protection." He was sure that I made it up. We allowed the *mezuzot* everywhere except the closets! But when we had the *mezuzah* hanging ceremony with the kids, and we invited him to help put them up since he donated all of them, we did not allow him to speak about the "protection" he was buying for the kids. To this day he doesn't even look at me when he comes into the building with his kids. But it's ok. It's five kids, and they are paying full tuition, while half our students are on scholarship.

DON: Hey, Sam, I wonder if he would like to donate some protection to my kids! Just kidding. In principle a *shul* does not require a *mezuzah*, whereas a *beit midrash* should have one, though some, including Maimonides, are of the view that it should be affixed without a *brakhah*. It has nevertheless become customary to affix *mezuzot* to *shuls*. If the *shul* includes a library or is otherwise used for Torah study, it should have a *mezuzah*. The generally accepted custom nowadays appears to be that it should be affixed with a *brakhah*.

BOB: That the Rambam didn't see or want us to see the *mezuzah* as an amulet is clear. But, to generalize Rambam's view as THE Jewish view is incomplete. And since many ultra-Orthodox authorities draw on the mystical writings of our tradition, they *do* see the *mezuzah* as an amulet for protection, based on the Zohar. My suggestion is that part of the *mezuzah's* function today is the educational aspect of *why* we have it, which leads to a larger question of the role and function of religion and ritual in our lives.

DON: Rambam's opposition to the *mezuzah* being used as an amulet is deeper than the reference in *Hilkhot Tefillin*.
In the *Guide for the Perplexed* Rambam explains why the One

God would allow the use of pagan animal sacrifice in worship when words, or even mere thoughts, would be sufficient.

Rambam answers that the One God understood that you can't change human nature suddenly, so God permitted the pagan custom of animal sacrifice, but without the paganism, instead directing this form of worship to the One God.

This whole lengthy discussion concludes with one, often unnoticed line "and the same is true of *mezuzah, tefillin* and *tzitzit,* and other practices."

What Rambam is saying is that many of the rituals in the Torah were originally pagan practices, including *mezuzah,* but were permitted without the paganism and redirected to the One God. So the Torah is all about the rejection of paganism, such as the original uses of *mezuzah, tzitzit, tefillin,* etc., but the continuation of these rituals with a new meaning.

However, some of our people were never able to completely give up all pagan practices, which survived alongside the belief in One God. Hence the prophets' continuous admonitions against these pagan practices which eventually even saturate the Jerusalem Temple. Take a look at the second Book of Kings, chapter twenty-three, for example.

Pagan practices continued in popular religion throughout Jewish history, through the rabbinic period, when eventually they surfaced, with official sanction from some quarters, as the Zohar. So for some of us, influenced as we were by the *Litvishe,* more rationally-oriented tradition, we reject, for ourselves, the use of rituals as magical protections.

I am reminded of the events of many years ago, when Arab terrorists invaded a school in Ma'alot, in northern Galilee, in 1974, and massacred twenty-five people, including twenty-two children. When the Chief Rabbinate later sent in inspectors they reported that the massacre occurred because the *mezuzot* were not kosher and so failed to protect the children. I think we moderns cannot accept this as a rationale for our rituals.

It should be noted that the Ar"i z"l [Rabbi Isaac Luria, 16th century mystic] was firm about *not* putting a *mezuzah* on the door of the synagogue, which is the custom still followed at the Ar"i Ashkenazi *shul* in Safed. But I was told that the Ar"i refused to have a *mezuzah* on the door to prevent people from sleeping or eating in the *shul*. If there was one, people would then be permitted to sleep or eat there.

SAM: I think we agree that we need to continually remind our folks that rituals and magic are separate, and that any reliance on ritual objects for superstitious, or magical, purposes, is totally alien to our tradition.

So now permit me to raise a new issue, about Jews who convert to another religion, and the practices regarding burial of such a person. How do you folks handle this kind of situation?

The question was raised by a former congregant who chairs the women's *Hevra Kadisha* [burial society]. There is a family of Russian Jewish immigrants in the community. The father, who apparently converted to the Orthodox Church after arriving in this country, is very happy in his new faith, and wishes to be buried as an Orthodox Christian when his time comes. The son is involved with the local *Chabad*, and was told by the rabbi there that regardless of his father's expressed wishes, when the time comes, he should ignore them and see that he is buried as a Jew. My former congregant wants to know: Is there anything that would prevent the son from following the advice of the *Chabadnik*? From our standpoint, should the father's wishes be fulfilled or should we follow the *halakhah*, as stated by the *Chabad* rabbi? Is that in fact the *halakhah* from our perspective? Any thoughts?

BOB: *Halakhically* the *Chabad* rabbi is correct. Morally though, I would never do such a thing. On the rare occasion when someone is cremated I have yet to find a child who is happy with the decision, but they will also not contradict it. What you might consider is a separate Jewish memorial service after the funeral.

DON: It is certainly not a pleasant situation. *Halakhically*, according to the Rema's [Rabbi Moses Isserles, sixteenth century] commentary on the *Shulhan Arukh*, even a father's request that his children should not observe *shivah* has to be ignored. He says there, *Im tzivah sh'lo linhog alav shivah o sh'loshim, ein shom'in lo.* "If he ordered that no one sit *shivah* or observe *sh'loshim*, we do not listen to this order." How much more un-reasonable is a request for a Christian burial? However, the out-come may depend upon the attitude of the surviving spouse and the other members of the family.

SUSAN: Since the working *halakhic* premise is *"Yisrael Af Al Pi Shehatah, Yisrael Hu"* – A Jew can sin, but still remains a Jew. Once a Jew, always a Jew. One should understand that from this vantage point, it makes no difference what the deceased or his family want, but rather what Jewish law requires. That being said, I know that the challenge remains as to what the "right thing" is to do, and is it in harmony with our understanding of *halakhah*? Also, most of the time, we can advise but we cannot dictate. The family, usually the spouse, will decide what to do, regardless of what our tradition teaches us. And if it's up to the kids, they often follow the express wishes of the parent even if it's contrary to Jewish law or their own wishes. Who among us in the pulpit rabbinate has not encountered someone who said "I didn't want to have him or her cremated, but it was their desire and I need to respect that"?

SAM: Of course, this reminds me of the old joke of a Hasidic Rebbe who was dying in the hospital, and as his students are entering the room, they see a Catholic priest giving him commu-nion. The students cry out to the Rebbe "Why would you want to become a Christian after living a life as a pious Jew?" He re-sponds "I know I'm dying. Better one of them than one of us!" Forgive my prejudice, it's just a joke.

SUSAN: Finally, Sam, don't forget that this comes from a FOR-MER congregant. It's not your issue. It seems that this former congregant, whom I assume now goes to Chabad, is shopping for a *Psak* [halakhic decision] because she didn't like the answer of her Chabad rabbi. Here's one in which you could comfortably say "You need to ask YOUR rabbi about that." If she ultimately realizes that his *piske halakhah* are unworkable, or she cannot live with them, then if she returns to you as a congregant, you may be able to help her without triangulating with the other rabbi's *p'sak*.

BOB: This is one of those places where I think our attitude as moderns and our attitude as *halakhic* Jews simply conflicts. The question about the same story with a Christian who converted to Judaism is correct. I cannot justify to myself not respecting someone's clear personal decision on their own religion, even if I hate that decision, and my feelings come more from being a modern American than from the *halakhah*. I would feel uncomfortable not honoring someone's clear expressed wishes to be cremated as well, but at least there we are imposing Jewish Law on someone who self-identified as a Jew.

With *shivah*, I think it is morally very different, because that is primarily for the mourners, and a father does not have a right to tell his children not to grieve! This is clearly an issue where we have to find some convenient way to balance tradition and common sense.

Now, let me raise an issue that we may not all agree on. What am I referring to? The problems of religion, including the institution of the Chief Rabbinate in Israel. A recent issue of *The Jerusalem Post* carries an excellent editorial about the Chief Rabbinate. Here is a letter that I have sent to the Post commending it for its stand.

"The Jerusalem Post is to be commended for its editorial "Judaism for All," calling for "free market Judaism" and an end to the current state-supported Chief Rabbinate. The Chief Rabbinate as an official governmental body is an anachronism that has long outlived its usefulness and instead has been an impediment to the growth of Judaism.

Its actions regarding conversion, especially the conversion of Russian *olim* [new immigrants], its attitude toward the problem of *agunot* [women whose former husbands refuse to give them a *get*, a Jewish divorce, and are thus prevented from a religious ceremony for remarriage], in addition to the incitement against other movements that the Chief Rabbis voiced at the meeting described in the editorial, all shout loudly that the time has come to put an end to this destructive institution. The Rabbinical Assembly has long called for the privitization of the Chief Rabbinate.

Let it exist on its own and let other rabbinic groups exist as well. Let people choose freely which rabbinical organization, which synagogue organization, they wish to support. The government can provide subsidies to these groups on the basis of their membership and the services they offer. For years we used the slogan 'Let my people go!' regarding Soviet Jews. Now we need to campaign to 'Free Judaism from the Chief Rabbinate!'

DON: There's an article in the November 5, 2013 Jerusalem Post by Rabbi Avi Weiss, of Riverdale, New York, about this topic. I happen to have it with me. I cut it out the other day to bring here, because Avi is one of the more open-minded rabbis among the Orthodox world, as you well know. Would you like me to read it?

SAM: Yes, please!

DON: OK, here goes. Its title is "Put an End to the Israeli Chief Rabbinate's Monopoly."

It's painful to have one's rabbinic credentials challenged by the Chief Rabbinate of Israel. But that's exactly what's happened to me.

In truth, it's much more hurtful to the many people I've been honored to serve over the years. In recent days, I have been informed that letters I've written attesting to the Jewishness and personal status of congregants have been rejected by the office of the Chief Rabbinate. I'm not the only Orthodox rabbi to have his letters rejected – there are others.

I have chosen to go public because the issue is not about me, it's about a Chief Rabbinate whose power has gone to its head. As Israel's appointed rabbinate, it is accountable to no one but itself. Nor could the Chief Rabbinate have denied letters from me or other rabbis without input from select rabbis here in America who, I believe, are whispering into the Chief Rabbinate's ears. For me, they'll whisper one thing, for another they will find some other reason to cast aspersions.

This is an intolerable situation. It not only undercuts the authority of local rabbis who are in the best position to attest to the religious identity of those living in their community, but wreaks havoc for constituents whom these rabbis serve.

Penning these harsh words about Israel's Chief Rabbinate is not easy for me. I grew up in a home that venerated the Chief Rabbinate. After my parents made *aliyah*, my father served as rabbi of Shikun Vatikin in the outskirts of Natanya, Israel. There he worked with Rabbi Yisrael Meir Lau, then Chief Rabbi of Natanya who went on to become Israeli's Ashkenazic Chief Rabbi. Over the years I've met with many chief rabbis. I found them individually to be not only learned, but caring.

But for some time, I've come to the conclusion that the Chief Rabbinate as an institution just doesn't work. Built into the very fabric of the institution is the principle of *kefiyah* [coercion], rabbis overlording the citizenry, forcing their religious dictates down their throats.

Indeed, the Chief Rabbinate has become a subject of scorn amongst the grassroots public in Israel.

Spiritual striving and religious growth can only be nourished in a spirit of openness. For this reason, Israel as a State should give equal opportunities to the Conservative and Reform movements. Their rabbis should be able to conduct weddings and conversions. For that matter, civil weddings should also be recognized by the State. As in America, it should be left to the general public – if they wish, in consultation with their local rabbis – to decide whether to accept or reject these conversions and wedding ceremonies.

Such an open attitude is not only important for non-Orthodox Jewry, but for Orthodoxy as well. When Orthodoxy is presented as the only option, when it's forced upon people, it turns people off. A spirit of openness will make Orthodoxy more attractive.

A related reason that the Chief Rabbinate does not work is that it involves centralization of rabbinic power, that is, rabbinic power left in the hands of a select few who dictate religious policy throughout the country.

When the Chief Rabbinate years back questioned American Orthodox conversions, an Orthodox rabbinic organization, the Rabbinical Council of America (RCA) capitulated to the Chief Rabbinate, rather than challenge the Chief Rabbinate and say clearly that it had faith and trust in our rabbis. This imported Israel's failed rabbinic centralized format to the U.S.

And so the RCA established a system where only a select, relatively few rabbis are permitted to sit on conversion courts, undermining the authority of local community rabbis and placing unnecessary stumbling blocks before serious potential converts. In a piece I co-authored a few years ago, I strongly criticized this policy. ("RCA deal hurts rabbis, converts," JTA, March 10, 2008)

I predicted then that this would be but the first step towards further centralization. That it would not be long before a centralized rabbinic body fully usurped the authority of local rabbis, deciding which select few could perform marriages.

And soon only this body will be able to sign off on letters attesting to the Jewishness or the personal status of individuals from across the country. Is this the type of religious authority we want here in America?

The time has come for the government of Israel, its Prime Minister and Knesset, to pronounce in clear terms that the Chief Rabbinate will no longer have a monopoly on religious dictates of the State. This will present challenges. But these challenges pale in comparison to a coercive and centralized system that is vulnerable to abuse. As the motto goes, power corrupts, and absolute power corrupts absolutely.

It's only in the spirit of openness that Israel as a Jewish democracy will thrive. It's in that framework that Israel's citizenry will be able to reach higher heights, spiritually and religiously.

SAM: Wow, he really says it clearly, doesn't he?

BOB: Yes, and coming from an Orthodox rabbi, we can hope that it will carry some weight

SUSAN: Well, unfortunately, Avi Weiss is not looked upon so favorably by his Orthodox colleagues, right Don?

DON: Right, unfortunately.

BOB: So now let me raise an issue which I would love to hear your opinions about – the length of some parts of our service, especially the *haftarah*.

We do a full Torah reading every Shabbat. I pose "pay attention" questions between aliyot, and we have a wide variety of Torah readers. However, I find that the *haftorahs* are basically dead time. The lay readers often stumble and hesitate, I don't have the person-power in the *shul* to work with and check every *haftarah* reader. The bar and bat mitzvah kids are well prepared, but it's often just long and boring. Some people follow in the *humashim*, others simply nap, doubtless in preparation for the *d'var Torah*.

I'm thinking of cutting the *haftarot* to ten or twelve pesukim. Have any of you done this? Have you found a way to make *haftarah*-time more interesting and engaging and competent?

SUSAN: What a wonderful question. I thought I was the only one who found the reading of the *haftarah*, generally, a time of negative energy on Shabbat morning. Very few of the *haftarot* excite me. Sure, there's the climax of the *haftarah* for *Shabbat Zakhor*, and yes, Amos is wonderful, and reading all of Obadiah gives one a sense of accomplishment, but I agree with Bob: even when the *haftarot* are read well, they're seldom read briskly as they are, say, in Israel. Hence, they do tend to drag on and on.

Which brings up another issue: wouldn't it be nice if we could separate the bar and bat mitzvah from the reading of the *haftarah*? What if we could spend four or five months perfecting the reading of Torah, or *davening* skills or researching the *parashah*? I know that we've talked about this before at some point, but I see this as a problem that will not soon go away.

My short answer to Bob's question is that I don't hesitate to shorten *haftarot*. I don't do it too often, but if I hear from our *hazzan* that a kid is having difficulty, I propose a shorter text, and everyone is pleased. I have yet to affirmatively shorten them regularly. But I wouldn't find anything objectionable in that approach.

DON: I know you're not expecting agreement from me, right? But maybe Sam has some views. Sam?

SAM: We actually now have a *haftarah* that works: we read the middle in English. We do the *berakhot* and the beginning and end of the *haftarah* in Hebrew, making sure to chant at least 10 verses. In between, we read the English from the *Plaut Humash.* We're very flexible about how we handle it, so if there's familiar and beautiful Hebrew, I make sure that's read aloud. If the haftarah is especially short, we may just go with the Hebrew.

I've never been a fan of using English in services, but I've been totally floored at how effective it is, not only for the *kahal* [congregation], but for me. The congregation is now absolutely riveted during the *haftarah.* No one goes to the bathroom, no one talks. The text has come alive for me, too, more so than ever before. And the English works even though we're a very well-educated community, the majority of whom are pretty comfortable with Hebrew. People are used to, and prefer, a service with no English liturgy at all, but the language of the *haftarah* is so often opaque, even fluent Hebrew speakers prefer the English.

Obviously, it's dependent upon the English being read extremely well. We happen to be blessed to have a professional actor in the community, with a magnificent speaking voice, and a beautiful British accent, which doesn't hurt, who is able to really bring the prophet's words to life. Comfort is genuinely comforting, rebuke spine-chilling. It really does feel like the prophet himself is speaking. And the narrative portions are suddenly dramatic, easy to follow and very meaningful. If he isn't there, ideally there's someone else who can read it meaningfully, or I will sometimes chant the English using the *trop* [cantillation notes]. It's never as powerful as when he does it, but it's still much more engaging to the *kahal* than the whole *haftarah* in Hebrew.

We have more leeway on this than many congregations, because the community is very open to experimentation. And being primarily an older community, we have very few *b'nai-mitzvah*. When we do have them, the kids always learn first to chant Torah. The Torah portion is usually much more accessible and meaningful to them than the *haftarah*. Reading from the scroll is far more inspiring. If the kids can also chant the full *haftarah*, that's certainly fine. But if they want to follow what is now our custom and chant only ten verses in Hebrew, reading the rest in English is fine. It enables them to better prepare what they do chant, takes the pressure off them to master so much technical material, and frees their time to focus more on their *divrei* Torah.

On a side-note, we stumbled on this last *Tishah B'Av*, when we did a joint evening service with the Conservative congregation in town. To help everyone feel included, we wanted to do part of *Eikhah* [Lamentations] in English, so I asked our professional actor if he would do the honors. To everyone's surprise what was originally an "accommodation" to facilitate inter-denominational worship ended up generating the most meaningful reading of *Eikhah* anyone in the room had ever experienced, including me. People were in tears. A wonderful lesson on many levels. . . .

Hope that's helpful.

I want to raise something else now. I'm sure everyone but Don has had this problem – of finding a *mikveh* for conversion. Anyone ever advised couples in a town like ours in which every *mikveh* is under Orthodox control, and as far as I'm told, none of the *mikvehs* will allow my congregants in?

BOB: So *halakhah* says Jews must observe the mitzvah of *mikveh*, but the ultra-Orthodox rabbis prohibit non-Orthodox Jews. Present company excluded, of course. Don, if you had a *mikveh* at your *shul*, you'd permit our folks to use it, I'm sure. What Sam is telling us sounds like a Woody Allen joke. On one hand it's a mitzvah, but the most pious among us prevent us from doing the mitzvah.

SUSAN: Before I moved here, I was rabbi in a mid-West town,

and I was lucky enough to have a Conservative *mikveh*, a two-and-a-half hour drive away. But for people who couldn't or wouldn't drive that far, we used a local river or two, or local lakes. Eventually I was able to use somebody's private entrance to a river, so all we had to worry about is if the neighbor was home. The homeowners either made themselves scarce or made it a point not to look out. They weren't Jewish, but obviously very accommodating. *Tosafot* in *Pesachim* mentions using the water in a cave, which of course was dangerous. People sometimes died or were injured. In my other congregation before coming here, we could usually make it in a little over an hour. In a couple of cases, the *mikveh* was communal, and the Orthodox did not have a choice even though they ran it.

DON: I would note that if one skims through the various positions of Orthodox and *Hareidi poskim*, one finds that the general concern of allowing Reform and Conservative Jews to use the *mikveh* is only that of conversion, whereas none appear to question the appropriateness of allowing the use of the Orthodox community's *mikveh* by brides and married women.

Indeed, there are even some Orthodox *poskim* who argue that denying the use of the *mikveh* would be improper, because first of all, it would be a *mikhshol ve-takalah livnot yisrael hakesherot*, ["an impediment for kosher Jewish women"], and second, the non-Orthodox might build their own *mikvaot*, which may not be kosher, and thus women would think they could go to those *mikvaot* for *taharah* ["ritual purification after menstrual period"], and again it would be a *mikhshol ve-takalah livnot yisrael hakesherot*.

Bottom line, while the Orthodox have a problem with non-Orthodox conversions in general, and do not want to be party to them, only the more immoral or abysmally stupid, which characterizes the Israeli rabbinate pretty accurately – Excuse the brief interruption, but I couldn't help myself – only they would prevent a bride or married, or unmarried, woman from using the *mikveh*, since the obligation of *tevilah* [immersion in water] is not open to debate, and if they prevent a woman from *tevilah*, then they are responsible for any subsequent car accidents, financial meltdowns, world wars, etc.

SAM: I know we can count on you, Don, for a bit of humor and sarcasm, though I appreciate the serious thrust behind it. I am laughing and lamenting at the same time at Don's humor!

BOB: There was an Orthodox *mikveh* in Chicago that refused to let known Conservative women use it for any use, including monthly and bridal use. This is what generated the earlier RA *teshuvah* on permitting a swimming pool for immersion for the sake of conversion. The Conservative synagogues in Chicago then funded a *mikveh*. The Orthodox one continued not admitting known Conservative women until Chabad finally took it over, and they eliminated the policy regarding monthly and bridal use. Still it could not be used for conversion, but it was allowed for other uses. Of course by then Conservative women used the Conservative one unless it was closed or not available when they needed to use it.

DON: In the unfortunate situation that you describe, I have advised the person to find a swimming pool that meets the requirements of a kosher *mikveh*. It is perfectly fine for a person to go to the *mikveh* wearing a bathing suit, and I am surprised that someone once wrote me that a bathing suit cannot be worn! Water goes right through bathing suits, so it's definitely not a *chatzitzah* [technical term for a barrier that prevents water from touching the body]. Unless the bathing suit is made of plastic, such that the skin underneath it is dry when you take the bathing suit off after bathing, there can be no problem with it. We often advise people, *lechatkhilah* [in advance, a priori] to wear a bathing suit to the *mikveh*, for various reasons.

BOB: Here's a short question, which I'm sure one or two of you can answer with ease. Are there responsa, outside of *Shulhan Arukh, Orah Hayim*, dealing with the subject of Jews not facing east while at prayer due to the orientation of their synagogue.

SUSAN: The ancient synagogue unearthed in Tzippori during an archeological dig, faces west, apparently because it was built on the lot that was available, which could not be made to face south. Besides, east was the direction of churches. To compensate, the flames on the candles in the floor mosaic face towards Jerusalem. I am certain, though, based on reading and personal visitation experience, that there are synagogues all over the US and the rest of the world that for convenience and expediency, just could not face Jerusalem. It's a mitzvah to face Jerusalem, but if you can't, you can't. Not every property is amenable to that kind of construction.

BOB: OK, another short one. When a couple, married twenty-five years with a valid original *ketubah*, wants a new "artsy" *ketubah*, how do I fill out the new *ketubah*? Do I put the original date, or the current date? What do I do about the *edim* [witnesses]? Is it in any way a "real" document? Can, say, the children sign it as *edim*?

DON: No, it is not a real document in the sense of having legal validity. It is art. That does not mean that is of no value. Symbolism is important. Indeed, I have prepared such artistic copies of *ketubot* as anniversary gifts. They can be incorporated into a "renewal of vows" ceremony like the "special anniversary" ceremony in the *Moreh Derech*, the Rabbinical Assembly's "Manual for Rabbis."

I would add that, as a rule, whenever I use an "artsy" *ketubah* for a real, first time wedding, even one that I have prepared myself, I write on the back "*Pasul. Le-noi bilvad*" [Invalid, for ornamentation only]. I then use a printed *ketubah* as the actual legal instrument. This avoids several problems:

1. You don't have to check the artistic *ketubah* for errors, and mar the art with corrections if errors are found.

2. When the children of the couple are asked by their *Mesader Kiddushin* to bring a copy of their mother's *ketubah*, they will not have to haul the large, framed, decorative *ketubah* to the rabbi or remove the frame to make a copy.

3. It makes it possible for you to use a *ketubah* with the Lieb-

erman clause, egalitarian or other wording that you prefer, even if the *ketubah* artist does not have those options available, or where the couple wish to use a *ketubah* they received as a gift but one which is problematic in terms of wording.

4. It allows you to be very liberal in acceding to any whims of the couple in the wording of the artistic *ketubah*, etc.

BOB: Thanks, Don. That's so helpful!

DON: My pleasure!

SAM: I have a congregant who is approaching the end of *shloshim* for her brother *z"l* next week. I don't have a lot of experience with how one ends *shloshim*, especially for a sibling where that's it, there's no full year of mourning, just thirty days, as the *halakhah* says applies to anyone besides a parent. It's not just a lifting of the restrictions, but also ending *Kaddish*. Obviously I know of the tradition of doing Torah learning on the thirtieth day, and also of visiting the grave. What other *minhagim* do you know about? And, do they end *shloshim* earlier in the day as with *shivah*?

SUSAN: *Halakhically*, there is no special observance associated with the conclusion of *shloshim*, and "*miktzat hayom k'khulo*," [part of the day is equal to an entire day] applies to *shloshim* as well as to *shivah*. However, knowing you, Sam, I am sure you will find meaningful and creative ways to reminisce about your congregant's brother *z"l*.

BOB: Here's a topic which probably doesn't come up that often, but is a very interesting one. We are giving out *aliyot* for a coming bat mitzvah, and we have given *hagbah* and *gelilah* to a husband and wife. The wife has a dog and says she cannot go up the seven steps to the *bimah* without Charlie, her huge dog, to help her. Lots of folks say she doesn't really need him, her husband can walk her up to the *bimah*, and down when they are done. And there are folks allergic to pets who also object. I am looking for *halakhic* sources.

DON: One of my professors wrote on that subject not long ago. He points out that the Talmud's standard for what constitutes permissible behavior in the synagogue is what one would permit to be done in his home. The Talmud states that just as one would not allow a stranger to use his house as a shortcut, so too one is forbidden to use the synagogue as a shortcut. However, just as one would allow a stranger to enter his home, and not require him to remove his shoes, so too one is not required to remove his shoes when he enters a synagogue. Similarly, argues my professor, just as one would certainly permit a blind person to enter his home with his seeing-eye dog, so too a blind person is permitted to enter the synagogue with his guide dog. I assume the woman you speak about is sight-impaired.

BOB: Yes, of course.

SUSAN: I've seen guide dogs in traditional synagogues. It shouldn't pose a serious impediment. Why should we deny anyone an *aliyah* because of a physical handicap? In fact, *ipkha mistabra* [just the opposite], we should encourage them to participate fully in the worship service.

DON: Doggone it, this question has really hounded me. Heck, I wouldn't let a dog in a synagogue on the high holidays unless it had a ticket. One dog claimed to have a ticket, but had buried it in the back yard and lost it. On the *bimah*? Only if they had a Bark Mitzvah. May we all be inscribed for a leash on life.

SAM: Don, what would we do without your beautiful sense of humor? God bless you.

BOB: One of my high school class kids asked me if I believe in miracles. This is what I told him: When I was a teenager like you, I flew from New York to Los Angeles. I was sitting next to a man who I imagine was in his mid-sixties. As the plane lifted off the tarmac, the man looked out the window and said: "Magic, just magic." Then, apparently realizing that he had enunciated his thoughts aloud, and had been overheard by a teenager, he turned to me and said: "Young man, I am a professor of aeronautics at M.I.T. I know Bernoulli's principle, and understand what makes an airplane fly. But, nevertheless, it's magic."

So, I said to him, that's what a miracle is. Something that is totally amazing, even though it follows completely the laws of nature.

SUSAN: I remember a student in Rabbi Brookstein's theology class asking him if he believes in miracles. Brookstein responded by saying, "You know, when I turn a handle in my sink, water comes out. When it's very hot in my house I push a button and it cools off. When I want to know what time it is I just look at something on my wrist and I know immediately. You tell me, aren't those miracles?"

BOB: Great answer! I wish I had thought of that when I spoke to my student.

SAM: OK, folks, I have a question that I'd like your advice on. It's about my *shul*. Next year our *shul* is to celebrate its seventy-fifth anniversary. We have organized a wide variety of programs and are using the occasion to continue thinking strategically about our future. We have created a really attractive logo with the tagline: "Honoring our Past, Building our Future." The chair of our celebration would like to have a large banner to display in our sanctuary for the High Holy Days and for about a year after that. I am not sure what to think about a banner in the sanctuary, and I wonder what you think.

BOB: I have a thing about banners. I myself would be very comfortable with a banner in the lobby, the foyer, overlooking the entrance, etc. But in the sanctuary? I'd feel it a distraction from *avodat Hashem* [divine worship]. I feel the same way about flags. Our American and Israeli flags are in the lobby, not in the sanctuary. Over our ark are the words, "*Shiviti Hashem L'negdi Tamid,*" [I place *HaShem* before me at all times], which to me implies, "to the exclusion of all else." So I guess I'm rather ascetic and minimalist. My sense is that most people would appreciate the sanctuary remaining a sanctuary, and not having its "inde-pendence" compromised in any way.

DON: A student of mine recently posed an interesting question to me, and I thought I would float it out to my lunch group. Why is it that Pharaoh remains unnamed throughout the Torah? In later books of the *Tanakh* different rulers like Taharqa and Necko II are named, for example in Second Kings and Isaiah, but throughout *Bereishit* and *Shemot,* the term "Pharaoh" is constantly used without naming the individual. There seems to be much written about trying to identify who were the Pharaohs who interacted with Abraham, with Joseph, enslaved the Isra-elites, or dealt with Moses, but I'm wondering if you've found anything about why it is that the Torah chooses to just refer to them all as Pharaoh?

SAM: "Pharaoh" means "the big, or great house" in the original Egyptian. It was used much as we use "the White House" as a designation of the President. Earlier, during Torah times, Egyp-tian narratives commonly referred to their ruler simply as "The Royal Palace." Later on, specific names were more commonly attached in narratives.

SUSAN: I can clarify a bit on this subject, too. By the time of Kings there is a greater sensitivity to "history," and to the differ-ent Pharaohs the writers were aware of.

In the earlier stories, each one is merely the pharaoh they were dealing with. There is no need to differentiate different pharaohs whose names are not relevant to the story. We can, with some degree of probability, however, identify some of the early pharaohs.

The pharaoh of the period preceding the Exodus is most likely Ramses II, the Great. He ruled Egypt for around sixty-seven years. He was obsessed with building, for example the city of Ramses, and monuments. But not pyramids, the last one having been built over a thousand years earlier. He was the pharaoh of the oppression (corvée labor, overseen by "*sarai missim,*" which means "officers of the [work tax])."

Upon the death of Ramses II, his son Merneptah, son number thirteen, aged in his sixties, began his ten year reign. Ramses had over a hundred children, but not from the same wife. In his fifth year, apparently believing him to be weaker than his father, Egypt was suddenly besieged from all sides. On the famous Merneptah Stele he describes the Lybians attacking from the west, the Sea People's attacking from the north, and the city-states of Canaan rebelling to the east.

But his father had left Egypt stronger than anyone realized. He claims to have defeated all of them. It is probably during this time of confusion and of greater dangers to Egypt that a small group of resident aliens, the Hebrews, were able to escape.

On that same Merneptah Stele he records the first mention of "Israel" in a non-biblical source. In it he claims to have totally eliminated Israel, which is accompanied by the determinative of a "people without a land." Accompanying the word Israel is a drawing of a crouching couple, a landless people, while its corollary, a mountain with a flag, is a people with their own land.

So is this a reference to the Israelite before they settled the land? Perhaps. The pharaohs of the patriarchal period are not named, but their period is probably during the four generations before Aaron, Moses and Miriam.

DON: Hey, you guys really know your stuff. This is great. Of course they don't teach us biblical scholarship in Orthodox *yeshivahs*. I try to read as much as I can about biblical scholarship, but when it comes to the human origin of the Torah, there, obviously, I usually take a different view.

So who else has a good question, or topic, to discuss today?

BOB: Yes, I have one. My *shul* recently switched from having only morning services, and now they have only evening *minyanim*. Seems like it's easier to get people to come in the evening, after work. We had such a hard time getting ten people at seven in the morning.

So now that we don't have morning *minyanim*, and only evening prayers, and since the month of *Elul* is coming, the question will be coming up about blowing the shofar. Is it permissible to blow shofar in the evening? It would be a shame not to do it, even if we don't have morning *minyanim*. Why should people not become accustomed to hearing the *shofar* blown every day during *Elul*?

SUSAN: I considered this a few years ago, because we have morning weekday *minyanim* only on Sunday. I decided against it after a brief unscientific survey of colleagues from which I concluded that it was just too different from what "everybody else" was doing. Nonetheless, I'm very sympathetic with the practice. After all, it achieves the purpose of arousing the people to do *teshuvah*. Moreover, I see no *halakhic* reason not to follow it.

On the other hand, my understanding is that the original mitzvah of blowing *shofar* in *Elul* applied only to the first day of *Elul*. This was the day that *Moshe Rabbeinu* ascended Sinai to get the second set of tablets, not to descend until Yom Kippur. The idea is that the *shofar* was sounded to awaken people to *teshuvah* and remind them not to once again descend to idolatry. Only later was the practice extended to blow the *shofar* on the other days of *Elul*. How does this cut? Does it support the notion of blowing it at a different time or not? Not clear to me.

DON: Let me share some of my own research on this question. Not because we don't have a morning *minyan*. We certainly do! But because some people can't come to the morning *minyan*, and since they only come in the evening, they want to hear the *shofar*.

The widespread custom throughout *Am Yisrael* is to blow the *shofar* daily throughout the month of *Elul*. The Tur, the commentary on the *Shulhan Arukh*, mentions two reasons for this practice. Firstly, the *shofar* blast hopefully stirs our hearts to *teshuvah* in anticipation of the Days of Awe. Secondly, we seek to "confuse" the Satan by blowing even before the onset of the obligation of *shofar*. This idea is found in tractate Rosh Hashanah. Unlike our practice today, the Tur mentions that the prevalent custom amongst Ashkenazic communities was to blow the *shofar* twice each day during *Elul*, in the morning and in the nighttime. Rav Moshe Feinstein, however, redefines the word "*erev*" [evening] in the Tur. Given the rabbis' assertion that during the nighttime hours, until midnight, God's attribute of justice, rather than mercy, is in force, it cannot be that communities blew the shofar at night. Rav Moshe speculates that "*erev*" here refers to late afternoon, after the *Minhah* prayers, rather than evening.

One could question Rav Moshe's assumption that *shofar* could not be blown at night since these hours are not suitable for appeasing the Almighty. According to the first reason for the practice mentioned in the Tur, that the *shofar* blast stirs people's souls and moves them towards repentance, then there appears to be no reason to distinguish between day and night. The *shofar* blowing serves not as a direct petition to the Almighty, as it perhaps does on Rosh Hashanah itself, but rather as a mechanism by which the congregants will hopefully be inspired to repent. According to the second reason, too, the basis for not blowing at nighttime is less than obvious. Rashi explains the "confusion" of the Satan as referring to our love of the mitzvah. The Talmudic rabbis instituted additional *shofar* blowing beyond the minimum requirement so that we demonstrate our zeal and passion for God's mitzvot, thereby silencing the prosecution against us in the Heavenly Tribunal. If this is indeed the reason for blowing during Elul, then clearly the blowing does not serve as a form of supplication but rather as a manifestation of our love towards the commandments. As such, it would appear, there would be no reason not to blow at night, as well.

In any event, communities today generally blow the *shofar* only once a day during Elul, after the *Shaharit* services. Rav Moshe suggests two possible reasons why the custom developed to blow specifically at *Shaharit*, rather than *Minhah*. Firstly, far more people come to the synagogue for *Shaharit* in the morning than for *Minhah* in the afternoon. In order to ensure the maximum-size audience for the blowing, the custom emerged to blow specifically after *Shaharit*. Secondly, he suggests that the sounding of the *shofar* serves a far more critical need in the morning, just before people leave for work. The hope is that they will be inspired to scrutinize their behavior, and this inspiration will impact their conduct as they go about their business throughout the day. Therefore, blowing the *shofar* in the morning is more important than blowing in the late-afternoon or evening.

Although we do not blow the *shofar* in the afternoon, the original custom recorded by the Tur does yield practical *halakhic* ramifications even today. Rav Moshe rules that should a synagogue for whatever reason neglect to blow *shofar* one morning during Elul, they should blow that same day after /Minhah. Although the original custom of blowing twice daily is no longer followed, it nevertheless remains as a "backup plan," if you will, should the congregation miss *shofar* blowing in the morning.

So, in short, there is no reason why you can't blow the *shofar* every evening at *Ma'ariv* services.

BOB: Terrific. My ritual committee will be delighted to hear about this. Thanks so much, Don!

SAM: I have a tough question for you all. I spoke on the phone yesterday to a woman, apparently unaffiliated, who wanted a recommendation of a *mohel*. I am in transition in that respect, because my first-string *mohel* of many years has recently moved out of town. I gave the woman two other names. A few minutes later she called back asking about yet another *mohel* whose name she had heard. I hemmed and hawed, and when the woman asked me if I had concerns, I told her exactly what I knew: A former member of my synagogue, who is no longer in town, told me that she knew of people who had made use of that particular *mohel*, and that there had been some complications. I emphasized to the woman that my information was third hand, and that the incident in question happened many years ago, but, since there are other *mohalim* in town, I don't recommend that particular person. Do you think that what I said was ethical?

SUSAN: I think you did exactly the right thing, Sam. In fact, from what you're saying, you handled it like a real pro. Your Seminary president would be proud of you. You not only told the truth, which in the case of health I think you have an obligation to do, but you couched it in very diplomatic terms. You told her it was a long time ago, and that the information was third hand.

You didn't outright condemn the guy, but very gently said "there were complications," without specifying what they were. After all, even a superb, well-trained, experienced *mohel* could once in a great while have complications. You couldn't lie to her, but you told the truth in a very dignified, rabbinical, diplomatic fashion. *Yasher koah* to you!

SAM: Thanks, Susan, I feel better about it now.

BOB: OK, Here's another juicy topic. Ready for a fight?

DON: Uh, oh, it's got to be about Orhtodoxy, or something I'm sure to object to, right?

BOB: Well, let's see. Here's the issue. Basically, it's an issue for Conservative colleagues, but I'd like the input of all of us.

Eons ago, it seems, when Shmuel – not his real name – was in elementary school and not the towering young man he is today, we went to a Camp Ramah parlor meeting to get a feel for the camp where we expected to send him for his first overnight summer experience. It seemed like an obvious fit. We belong to a Conservative *shul* and he attended a Jewish day school. Since Ramah is the Conservative movement's network of camps, it would be a place where he could continue engaging with Jewish values and skills, while playing basketball too.

After the camp's director gave his presentation, I asked if campers were expected to wear a yarmulke, and for those over thirteen, *tallit* and *tefillin*, during services. I was surprised when the director said that boys are. Full stop. No mention of girls. So I asked about girls. He deflected, and I asked again. Girls may wear the ritual items if they wish, he said, but they are not required to. When I asked why, he said because Conservative Judaism is a pluralistic movement and not everyone comes from an egalitarian home or synagogue. This was from the director of a camp not in the South or in Canada, where you might expect conservative attitudes from Conservative rabbis, but from the camp designated for New York City-area kids.

That early experience with Camp Ramah came to mind when

reading a recent piece by a woman who discussed her surprise that the girls at a different Ramah camp were neither interested in wearing *kippot* nor expected to. Little seems to have changed in the years since the Camp Ramah parlor meeting. There is much that Ramah camps do well, including teaching Hebrew and engendering a love for Israel. But modeling ideal religious behavior is also part of the job of the Conservative movement's camps, even if that means managing expectations of parents who might object to their daughters wearing *kippah, tallit* or *tefillin.*

Unfortunately, there is still a high degree of ambivalence in the Conservative movement about Jewish women's observance of certain ritual customs. Some of my female colleagues go so far as to say that it reflects a lack of support for women as religious leaders and for developing female lay leadership. Perhaps that's true. I'm not sure, but I do know that when the ambivalence is transmitted from the top, it's not going to change.

The Camp Ramah website says: "The current mission of Ramah is to create educated communities in which people learn to live committed Jewish lives, embodying the ideals of Conservative Judaism." I would argue that both women and men wearing *kippah, tallit* and *tefillin* embodies the ideals of Conservative Judaism, of passion for observance and an understanding of our rituals. Are there challenges facing the movement's leaders at least as pressing as this one? Certainly starting with articulating why someone should choose to be a Conservative Jew. But I see this as part and parcel of the overall challenge facing the movement, and the response ought to include articulating and modeling all of the reasons that it makes sense to identify as Conservative Jews, living wholly as Jews and wholly in the modern world. Teaching attachment to the ritual objects that are part of living embodied Jewish lives is part of that process.

SUSAN: You know where I stand on this issue. If we don't train our youngsters at an early age that these rituals that have long been the preeminent domain of males, then we lose an opportunity to teach them that there's a new spirit in the air, and that women now have all the rights, privileges AND obligations that men have.

BOB: I hope we can convince more of our right-wing Conservative colleagues of your opinion, Susan. It's a very slow process, but I think we're moving in the right direction. But if we don't follow these new ideas and customs in our own movement institutions, like summer camps, we're really being hypocritical.

SAM: Of course you know that I agree. And I'm certain that we'll return to this topic in the future as weeks go by.

In any case, I think it's time to call it a day. See you all next week.

DON: *Le-hitra'ot!*

BOB: *Au revoir!*

Week 6

🦁

DON: Good to see you all again. Let me start off with an interesting question. I think I know how we would handle this at our *shul*, even though I'm not terribly comfortable with it. The question is having a non-Jew stand at the door and open it for seniors and physically challenged people. In your synagogues, do you have any mechanical devices to open doors? We can't allow that, but I wonder what more liberal synagogues do.

BOB: We've actually been discussing this issue, and I'd also like some input from others. Do you use power-assist door openers on Shabbat, or do you use non-Jewish ushers, or what?

I have a member with a movement disorder who cannot enter our building or the bathroom on his own unless there is a power assist door opener. It really bothers me that this very proud man has to struggle to get into his synagogue and has the indignity of needing someone to help him get into the bathroom. He does not want help and wants to be able to open a door on his own. The dilemma I have is if the bathrooms have such openers there will be Shomer Shabbat worshipers who may be offended.

SAM: Even though we are a Reform congregation, we have some older members who are more traditional, and even some young ones who are becoming increasingly more traditional. So what we do is we have power door openers, and this is how I justify their use. Years ago, a neighboring rabbi, very traditional, made a study about Jews with disabilities. H quoted a statement from Rambam to me about attending to *"kol tz'rakhav"* ["all the needs"] of a *holeh* [sick person] on Shabbat, and he applied that statement to include enabling people to participate in public worship. On that basis, I have held that it is permitted to use electrical devices, which we otherwise would not do here on Shabbat, in order to assist someone with a disability. Theoretically, we might be concerned that other people, who do not have disabilities, would use the power openers, and, indeed, I have found that kids enjoy playing with them. However, I think that it is improper to make things more difficult for a person with disabilities because of a concern with what other people may do. Furthermore, I would say that, if someone is offended by the presence of a mechanism which will help people with disabilities, shame on him. If he doesn't want to use it himself, that is another story. At our synagogue, there are also doors with no power assistance mechanisms, so no one has to make use of the electrical device. In fact, the Talmud says, in tractate Shabbat 129a, "*osin lo kol tz'rakhav al y'dei goi*" [we fulfill all the needs of an ill person by inviting a non-Jew to help]. I didn't look it up until now. I guess that I would say that, even though we normally don't use electrical devices on Shabbat, there are those who permit them, and we can rely on those opinions in order to make things easier for a person with disabilities.

DON: Interesting discussion. Maybe some day our folks will come around to the point of view that in order to assist physically challenged people, we'll follow suit. But not for now.

BOB: Don, I'm afraid you won't have any advice on this next one either, but who knows??? So here it is. We've had a Boy Scout troop in my *shul* for a dozen or more years, a kosher and *shomer-shabbat* troop. With the Boy Scouts re-affirmation of their policies prohibiting participation by gays as scouts or scout masters, came a letter from a congregant appalled that, as an egalitarian congregation that supports the RA *teshuvot* of GLBT inclusion, we would continue to hold the charter for a scout troop here in our congregation. I have mentioned to the congregation that, other than urging the BSA [Boy Scouts of America] to change their policy, none of the arms of our movement have made mention of this. I am trying to come up with a way to advise our congregational board as they discuss this issue.

Other than encouraging a letter to be written to the BSA affirming our commitment to ignore their anti-gay hiring and participation policies, I am at a loss as to where to go with this. Personally I would like the troop to stay here, despite the fact that some young families are threatening to leave. Ironically, or not, they would probably end up at the Reform Temple in a nearby town, where a gay rabbi presides, rather than another Conservative *shul* which is not fully egalitarian. For most members who have spoken up, it is a non-issue as long as we ignore the policy. They don't believe a letter should be sent to the BSA.

Any advice, other than somehow splitting the baby in two?

SAM: I think that the pros of the scout troop, the fact that they keep kosher, the positive values of the bonding that takes place in boy scouts, etc., far outweigh what the official position of Scouts is. In no way will it affect your group. If you have a gay leader, certainly no one will interfere.

We live daily with conflicting views in our work, the restaurants we choose, and the organizations we belong to. I'm sure that all Conservative rabbis do not agree "politically." I sort of think so, anyway! And even on *halakhah*. If we worked for Amazon or Home Depot, or Starbucks, the standards of owners certainly would not cause us to quit. We belong to synagogues, and many members do not agree with the acceptance or non-acceptance of non-Jews. My cousin is a Barnard graduate, very liberal, and was professor at a Graduate School, and taught in Catholic Colleges, and did not quit. Her synagogue has a *mehitzah*. They asked her for a contribution. She fought the idea of a *mehitzah*, and lost. She felt the rabbi needed support. Someone bought something for the *shul*. She arranged to give the money for that gift, let the family keep it in their name, and use the money they would have spent for the gift, for the *mehitzah*!

We go to schools and colleges with principles we do not accept in our life. We live in States which have or do not have gay marriages, As Shmuley Boteach and other Orthodox rabbis said, because it is law does not mean it need interfere with our personal choices. I think you can find practical ways in the life of members which they live and are not concerned about issues. I think scouting is important in so many ways. And to have an observant troop is a rare occurrence! I am sure many of the protesting families belonged to your synagogue before gay members were allowed in the Rabbinical Assembly, and, if we go back in time, when women were not treated equally. You get my point.

BOB: Thanks, Sam. You made some good points. Very helpful!

SAM: Here's a problem which we all are going to have to be dealing with more and more as time passes. Namely, the burial of a non-Jewish spouse at a church service. We may have discussed this before, I don't remember, frankly, but it came up yesterday, and I need to give some advice to my board and lay leadership.

Tomorrow morning I will meet with a congregant whose non-Jewish wife's death is imminent. Without coloring the situation by characterizing the individual or the family situation, I'd like to ask your input from your experience. What have you been able to offer families in this circumstance? The closest I've come to this situation was when our longtime custodian died a few years back. I arranged for the hospital chaplain to officiate. I read some psalms and eulogized. The difference there was that the lines were very clear. James, our custodian, was a friend of the congregation and we were close, but he was a Christian and deserved a Christian burial. The family had no congregational affiliation and although the *shul* was the closest thing to a religious connection they had, they understood that I could not appropriately officiate. I have a feeling that tomorrow's meeting will be very different. Any advice you can offer would be appreciated.

DON: If it's your intention to attend the funeral at a church, I think you're doing the right thing as long as you feel comfortable. I have done a few funerals in these circumstances. The oddest one I did was for an employee's mother, neither of whom was Jewish. The mother didn't belong anywhere, and they felt I was the closest she'd had to a clergyperson, and they liked how

I did funerals. I went to a few Christian funerals of spouses of congregants and employees, and if the family wanted and the officiant allowed, I sometimes spoke or read a biblical passage. Otherwise I just went, sat in the pews, and was a "presence." Usually it made quite an impact with the Jewish spouse. Usually, they became more active afterward, though this was not the reason why I did it.

BOB: I think we'd all agree that what you plan is the best idea.

I want to report a conversation I had this morning with one of our colleagues, who happened to mention that he was criticized in the Bush era for advocating impeachment. When he asked what the congregant meant he was told "You read that prayer that speaks of 'just and rightful authority.'"!!! How's that for logic?

SUSAN: This discussion reminds me of the story of the president of the congregation advising the rabbi not to preach about gambling, *kashrut*, Shabbat, adultery, etc. since important members of the congregation will be offended. Just speak about Judaism, he advised. It seems to me that almost everything a rabbi preaches about can be interpreted to have political implications or overtones. Therefore, the rabbi on the pulpit is really limited to the absolute "no no" of not advocating for a particular candidate or Party, especially subtly. At the same time, the question of signing a list of rabbis for this or that cause does not have a black or white answer. Consequently, I think it is advisable not to do so. To me, it is similar to a list of reporters for X, Y, or Z, or pollsters for this, that or the other, etc. It dilutes the rabbi's message.

SAM: Here's a question on *halakhah* and medicine. Which one of you is an authority on this field? A family member who is a *kohen* tore his ACL [anterior cruciate ligament] tendon. The surgeon is considering several options, including but not limited to the use of a cadaver ACL. I've been asked two questions: first, is it *halakhically* permissible to use a cadaver replacement under these circumstances? Second, is it permissible if it's the best option for him, even if there are alternatives?

DON: Rabbi Moshe Feinstein wrote a very long responsum on this question, in *Iggerot Moshe*. He permits a *kohen* to receive a transplant from a cadaver. I would further note that the responsum specifically addresses your precise circumstance of transplanting tissue from a cadaver into the leg of a *kohen*.

SAM: Well, that was an easy one. Thanks, Don!

SUSAN: I want to raise an issue about something I'm teaching in my Religious School. If it's OK, I'll elaborate a bit about what I'm planning.

My tenth grade confirmation class learns about Judaism by looking at Christianity, and a little at Islam. We will "do" theology, history and sociology in a limited number of sessions. I often feel like Hillel needing to teach the whole Torah while standing on one foot. I am also trying to prepare them for college in two years where their roommates and suite mates will be predominantly Christian, besides other faiths. They will engage in conversations where they need a higher level of knowledge of Judaism than can be attained by bar or bat mitzvah age.

Religion is an adult matter and they only have a child's knowledge. That is why continuing solid and intensive Jewish education through the high school years is critical. Our children are a "Jewishly endangered species" by their lack of substantial religious knowledge. It can only be attained as their minds mature in their teen-age years, just like any other subject.

My course is a cram session about Judaism and the faiths they will meet along the way. Maybe, just maybe, they will have a deeper appreciation of the faith into which they are born and maintain an active allegiance into adulthood.

Our conversations are never linear. I also only know the starting point. I never know where it will end up. I take on all questions. They often lead to unplanned directions. So, several weeks ago one of the students blurted out: "Why do they hate us so much?" That stopped the class in its tracks. The "they" in that sentence refers to Christians. The use of present tense indicates the sense that it is still continuing. The context of the sentence drew a direct line between "us" and "them," and maybe indicated some fear and concern for personal safety.

How would you answer this question? Gloss over it? Ignore it? Sing John Lennon's *All You Need is Love*? This question enabled me to run a thumb-nail sketch and abbreviated timeline of the separation of the growing Jewish sect that became Christianity from its mother faith, Judaism. I indicated the need for the new faith to shape its only identity based core issues: do the non-Jewish members need to observe Jewish law, as the born-Jewish members did? Which would predominate, the Church of Jerusalem or the Church of Antioch? What did it mean to be identified as Jews when, particularly after the second rebellion against Rome, the Bar Kokhba rebellion, the Jewish people was loathed in the Empire? What were the implications of the Roman Empire becoming the Holy Roman Empire? Namely, what was the road to hatred of the Jews?

It was never ever that we "deserved it." Rather, to learn to "connect the dots" from Jesus and his students who were observant Jews, to the birth of a new faith, to the Christian persecution of the Jew people through the *Shoah*, the Holocaust, spanning nearly two thousand years. But I assured them that that their neighbors and classmates do not hate them. There is no reason for such fears. The lines between groups in America that cause ignorance that can lead to hatred are being erased by education and meeting each other. I told them about the many church classes that come here to learn about Judaism.

But fifty years ago began the seminal event that changed our world. On October 11th, 1962 Pope John XXIII convened what became known as the Second Vatican Council and would three years later issue the document called Nostra Aetate. It created a sea-change in modern Jewish history. While it finessed the relation of the Vatican to the Holocaust, for the first time in the history of the church, anti-Semitism was bluntly denounced, and most importantly, the Jewish people were not held responsible for Jesus' death, the charge of deicide. While we never doubted our own validity, in the global context, the repudiation of core Catholic doctrines about the Jewish people was and remains critical. This path would lead eventually to Pope John Paul saying that the Jewish people were his "elder brother."

This changed two thousand years of history. In a brief article on the Second Vatican Council I exposed my Confirmation Class to the answer to the blunt question: "Why do they hate us so much?" The church has to change its teaching about us, about our faith, for this to change. They needed to change their preaching from the pulpit and their education in schools. And it took time for it to extend to the far reaches of the church. But Vatican II, as it is better known, did not change their theology. Nor did it change ours. They will read the portion of Gan Eden, the Garden of Eden, and learn from it "The Original Sin." We will learn from it the fallibility of all humanity not to hear the Divine summons, and believe that each soul is born innocent, clean and untainted. They will believe in the need to believe in Jesus as salvational. We will believe that *mitzvot*, the system to implement God's will, and *tzedakah*, will redeem us and save us, individually and collectively.

I said to my class that they don't hate us any more. They once did. We were powerless. Many Jews died in pogroms, the Crusades and the Holocaust. The Second Vatican Council changed the Roman Catholic Church and greatly influenced the rest of Christianity. The real challenge is for people of all faiths to take their theology seriously, to teach about the sacredness of all life, that will lead society to leaven the riches and elevate people from poverty and disability; that will remove guns and murder from the streets; that all will unite in the fight against disease and ignorance; and that will end wars. Maybe then hatred will truly be removed from the hearts of all people.

We will know that the Messiah has come when from the pulpits of mosque, church and synagogue it is taught and accepted, that all roads lead to God.

DON: Susan, I think the kids in your class are very fortunate to have a teacher like you, who can articulate this history of the relationship between Judaism and Christianity so well. *Yasher Koah*!

SUSAN: Thanks, Don!

SAM: I have a slightly different point of view on this matter. Allow me, if you will. Triumphal notions appear frequently in our tradition, and we can't deny it. The *Kiddush*, the *Aleinu*, and the blessings before the Torah, to name a few. They have caused us internal harm and certainly damage to the way Jews are perceived. The Catholic Church has removed many offensive words from its liturgy. It is time that we do the same.

BOB: If you don't mind, I'd like to put my two cents into this discussion. I believe the *Aleinu* is saying that we are unique from the other nations. It is true that others are also unique. We do not teach the exclusive election of the Jewish people. *Tzadikay umot haolam* [the righteous of the other nations] have a share in the world to come. We do not teach that non-Jews are infidels.

We are not hated because of our liturgy. Nor do we live our lives to win the approval of others. We live our lives to please God. To paraphrase Golda Meir: "We will have peace when our enemies love their children more than they hate us." How can mothers celebrate the martyrdom of their suicide "slash" homicide sons and daughters? How can religious people shoot an eleven year old girl for standing up for the education of girls? How can religious people decapitate Daniel Pearl who said he was Jewish? Is this because of *Aleinu*?

We were hated when we were accused of "going like sheep" during the Holocaust, and didn't fight back. We are hated now for fighting back, disproportionately, when thousands of bombs and missiles are randomly shot into Northern and Southern Israel. We were hated for destroying the Iraqi nuclear reactor, and invading their sovereign territory, until George Bush senior, later apologized and praised us for doing so.

We were hated for being communists and we are hated for being capitalists. We are hated for believing in the one God, and we are hated for not believing in their God and for killing their son of God. We are hated for turning Israel into a thriving country and we are hated for being immigrants from Eastern Europe. We are hated for being clannish and we are hated for being in charge of United Way and all the civic and community help organizations. We Jews give more generously to non-Jewish hospitals, universities, and causes than to Jewish causes, and we're still hated.

To fulfill our civic duties and civic pride, we ran for public office, and are hated for controlling Congress. We were not admitted to their medical schools and other professional schools so we created Brandeis University, where we thought we would be respected for our academic accomplishments. We are now a host at last, to quote the title of Abram Sachar's book on Brandeis University, where he was the founding Chancellor. Brandeis had a quota system for Jews so as to allow a mixture of students. We set an example for non-Jewish universities. Now the Jewish professors at those non-Jewish universities are many times anti-Israel and anti-Judaism. I remember trying to recruit a prominent Jewish professor of religion at a local university to help us with our local Hillel chapter, and he refused because he didn't support the particularity of Judaism, only the study of Judaism.

We were hated for only caring about Soviet Jews, when others, like certain Christian groups in America who proclaimed their love for all mankind, did nothing to help any Soviets. Thousands of Soviet citizens were able to leave the Soviet Union because of their connection to Jewish ancestry. Some utopian idealists who say they love all mankind really mean: "We love mankind; it's people we can't stand."

The old Soviet Jewish joke: The Soviet leaders announced in Moscow: "Come to Red Square to get the latest shipment of fresh oranges by 10 a.m." At 10 a.m. they announce in Red Square: "The shipment of oranges is now scheduled to arrive at 12 noon." "Also there's not enough oranges for Jews, so no Jews will be allowed back in Red Square."

At 12 noon, they announced in Red Square: "The shipment is now scheduled to arrive at 2 pm and there are only enough oranges for members of the Communist Party." At 2 p.m. they

announce "there are no oranges at all, they were lost in shipment . . ." to which the members of the Communist Party said
"Those damn Jews already knew by 10 a.m. that they weren't
getting any oranges! Those Jews always get special treatment!"

They hate the Jews because of all the Nobel prizes they
"cheated" to get and won. They hate the Jews because we suck
the blood of Christian children, and use it to make *matzot, ha-
mentaschen*, and many other things.

They hate the Jews for being first responders in Haiti, and
having Haitian children being named Israel. They hate the Jews
in Israel for having bomb shelters and safe rooms while Muslim
children don't. Arafat started the PLO when already in possession of the West Bank and the Gaza Strip. Iran wants to destroy
Israel even though we never attacked her country and millions
of her citizens are suffering as a consequence of sanctions caused
by her crazy priorities.

I heard a lecture by a scholar of Muslim culture who said Islamic culture has "Shame" as one of its key emotional motivators, while Judaism has "Guilt" as one of its key motivators. In
Islamic culture if a child misbehaves, the parents feel shame and
want to kill the child. In Judaism if one of our children misbehaves, we Jewish parents feel guilt, we feel responsible and we
want to kill ourselves.

Islamic culture wants to destroy Jews AND Israel because we
bring them shame. And we Jews respond by saying: "We are responsible because of our prayer, *Aleinu*."

SAM: Well, Bob, I guess we'll have to disagree on this one.

BOB: I guess so! We don't have to bend over backwards to please
gentiles and Islamists. If they want to hate us, so be it. I'm not
about to change the way I pray to try to please them. They won't
change no matter what we do – at least it seems that way, in my
lifetime, anyway.

DON: OK, I think we need a referee here. Let's move on to another topic.

I have a tricky question I'd like to pose to the group. I received a call from a lawyer today, someone who is representing a ninety-three-year old congregant of mine. I'm familiar with the congregant, but she's not really someone I'm close with. She doesn't have any family, other than some grandchildren, a neice and a nephew, from whom she is estranged completely. She lives alone, and is now trying to take care of her estate. The lawyer said that she is looking for someone to be her medical power of attorney, and he would like it to be me. I am obviously a bit leery of such a thing, but I'm also concerned that she doesn't have anyone else. If I don't do this, what will happen to her?

So I'm curious to hear if any of you have any experience with such a thing, and/or if you have any suggestions. I've spoken to my lay leadership, and they are equally concerned that this might be a terrible idea. There is a chance that she might leave her possessions to our *shul* in her will, which makes me even MORE uncomfortable, because someone, including and especially the estranged family members, might certainly say that we were not acting in her best interest, but our own.

So what say you?

SAM: Those of you of a certain age may recall the TV show "Lost in Space." At moments of unknown danger the robot would flail its arms, saying "danger, danger Will Robinson. . . ." You are all welcome for the culture reference. This is such a moment.

I understand you want to be helpful, but this could easily, for some of the reasons you listed, be a terrible idea. Maybe you could compromise and have the lawyer listed as the medical power of attorney, but that you would be a consultant. That way she can be comforted by your input, while you have no legal exposure.

BOB: I was asked to do this once for a widow with no children and without other family close by. We discussed her wishes thoroughly, and while I was not thrilled, I realized she needed the assistance. However, when *she* realized I didn't answer the phone on Shabbat and *Yom Tov*, she decided to ask her attorney.

SUSAN: I have also done this, and I am currently doing it for one congregant who is not married, has no children and one sister from whom he is estranged. I tried talking the sister into doing this for her brother, but she was not interested. So I'm "it" for him. It is so sad for someone to feel that they have no one to look out for their interests. I figure it is the least I can do to help them feel connected to another human being as well as the Jewish community.

DON: Thank you all so much for your help. Not surprisingly, it seems that there are MANY varying opinions on the subject, and there's no clear cut answer. I appreciate that this is generally not a great idea, but I also hear from a few of you that in a similar situation to mine, where this person has no other family, and no one else able or willing to serve as the power of attorney – that it might make sense to do this. I'll keep thinking about it and talking to my synagogue leadership.

Thank you again for all your wonderful help!

BOB: I want to return to one of the very difficult questions that we have already dealt with, and probably will again and again, that of the role of women in the synagogue, the rituals, and the issues of equality.

Like many in our movement, I teach and strive to practice the egalitarianism which celebrates the tension between two points of view. One is that *halakhically* and ritually speaking, men are obligated, therefore so should women be obligated. The other is this: let the *halakhah* evolve by women and for women so they can create *halakhah* and rituals that respect the same Torah and simultaneously respect women's issues.

This approach evolved over three decades of leading "egalitarian" congregations, but came to some articulation through the good graces of our colleague Prof. David Golinkin. A class was taught by Leah Shakdiel who created a wonderful environment to openly discuss the above mentioned tension.

Since I moved here a decade or so ago, I have created an environment where every few months a woman comes to me and wants more information about the use of *tallit* and *kippah* for women. I have taught these women the *halakhot* and rituals of wearing *tallit, tefillin* and *kippah*, and have shared with them Judy Hauptman's insights from her volume of 1998, *Rereading The Rabbis: A Woman's Voice*, but have not been able to create a ritual with them about wearing *tallit* that speaks to them. I have sought insight from the traditional meditations, and from more modern sources, like "Ritual Well" and Vanessa Ochs' writing, but I haven't come up with a "ritual" for women to initiate wearing a *tallit*.

Have any of you done so, or can you point me in the direction of some written material, printed or on the internet, that can help me help these women, literally of all ages, to assume this practice of the mitzvah of *tzitzit* during prayer?

SUSAN: I have a slightly different slant on this question. I really haven't succeeded in creating any rituals, but I have some tension in the congregation on the issue of women's ritual practices.

My predecessor required women to wear a *tallit* in order to receive an *aliyah*. Since the vast majority of women in the congregation do not wear *tallitot*, they are given one upon arriving at the reading table. The majority of women are neutral concerning this practice. However, a significant minority dislike it – some very strongly. We are an older congregation and many of the members don't consider the *tallit* to be a unisex religious garment, but to a greater or lesser extent a male one, although our female cantor wears a *tallit* and *tefillin,* and it is an expectation that *b'not mitzvah* purchase and wear a *tallit* for that occasion. Since the practice remains somewhat controversial, several members have asked that the practice be revisited. So we are doing that. In this particular context, I am happy to make wearing a *tallit* optional. I am wondering how other colleagues have addressed this policy question in your congregation. Thanks in advance for your input.

SAM: Of course, being a Reform congregation we are egalitarian, thus we ask all people to wear a *tallit* if they have an honor. Although we regard wearing a *tallit* as an obligation of all, it is up to individuals to decide to wear it on their own. That is, when they are not in front of the community. When they are representing the congregation, though, by accepting an honor, the individual choice, by men or women, is trumped by the communal expectation.

Perhaps your congregation could purchase some more feminine *tallitot* to help make people more comfortable.

BOB: I've raised this question of women's rituals with some colleagues recently, and one RA rabbi told me something like this: His congregation is egalitarian, and they give women *aliyot* very frequently, including a *bat kohen* for the first *aliyah* on Yom Kippur. They require women only to wear a head covering of choice for an *aliyah*; *tallit* is optional for them. Some kiss the Torah with their *siddur*, others use the *gartle*, and still others borrow someone else's *tzitzit*. Others wear a *tallit* themselves. This is how they do it.

For my congregation, I don't see why it needs to be a requirement to wear a *tallit* to accept an *aliyah* at the Torah. I can see the value of providing women with the opportunity to wear *tallitot*, but I don't see what is gained by requiring them to do so. Given how recently women have been emancipated ritually, if I can use that term, it seems unfair to impose on women the wearing of a garment which for many women and men is associated with *beged ish*, a male garment, rightly or wrongly. What's wrong with allowing the women of a congregation to work out over time what is most comfortable for them? Men have had several thousand years to get used to wearing *tallitot*. Maybe women deserve a few more hundred years themselves.

SUSAN: I hear what you are all saying, but as a woman, I sometimes have a different view. **If we** are egalitarian, and if we require men, then why shouldn't we require women? Otherwise, to be fully egalitarian we should then also allow men who don't wish to wear a *tallit* when called to the Torah to also not do so. And I understand the fact that some women associate a *tallit* with something men wear – "a man's clothing," but it is certainly interesting that *tallitot* did not become more colorful and interesting until women started wearing them.

BOB: I hear you. To me it's all about how new all of this is. Let's face it. Until recently, it was men telling women what to wear and what not to wear. And, Don, correct me if I'm wrong, I think this continues in the Orthodox world. Maybe it's up to women to make these decisions.

I know a woman who has embraced egalitarianism. She *davens*, she *leyns*, she's a part of the heart and soul of the *shul*. She wears a *tallit* with pride. But she doesn't wear a *kippah*. She'll put one on when she comes up onto the *bimah*, because we have a "rule" about that. But she doesn't wear one otherwise. Why? She says "I can't stand to have anything up on my head." "Really?" I asked. "Why?" "You wouldn't understand," she said. "That's just the way it is." And you know, she's right. And yes, I know that *kippot* are not *tallitot*, yes, yes, yes, but the point stands.

So, colleagues, as long as we are discussing women's rights, let me raise a related issue. I am conducting a *shivah minyan* later this week. The son of the deceased requested that I do not count women in the *minyan* in respect to his father. There might be no correct answer in this situation, but just in case we need to count the women to make the *minyan*, what is your advice?

SAM: This may seem a bit passive-aggressive, but it seems to me that YOU won't "need" to count women in the *minyan*. It's not your call. If there are fewer than ten men, that decision will be the son's – how he will honor his father – by not counting women and not reciting *Kaddish*, or by counting and reciting? In short, The *shivah* house makes the call. A Conservative colleague of mine, who I know did not count women in a *minyan* in the *shul*, told me that if the *shivah* house wanted to, he did. His answer was this: we are there to comfort them. They are the mourners. His principle is this: in the *shul* it's my call – in their home it's their call.

On the other hand, I have a Conservative colleague who told me this is the way he handles it: Our policy is to count women and men equally for a *minyan*. Period. If I am in a situation in which this might be problematic for some mourners, I make an extra effort to make sure that there are at least ten men present. So there are obviously a number of possible options.

Personally, my view is that our main job at a *shivah* home is to do what makes the mourning meaningful and less traumatic for the mourners. And for the most part, we do that in a tradition-oriented framework, colored by our own integrity as community leaders.

Who is your congregant? Is the son of the deceased the only mourner? Is he the only one expected to say *Kaddish*? If so, then you can do what he wants. I would ask whether he would prefer not to have a *minyan* or to count women. As the only mourner, it's his decision to make. But he should understand that if your community regularly counts women, then the decision to NOT count them will cause a commotion if you do not have a *minyan* without them. Does he want a brief announcement to explain the situation? Does he want to make it or does he want you to? But if there are other mourners, the question becomes balancing one mourner's needs with another, and it becomes a more difficult decision. I would consider at whose home the *shivah* is – the hierarchy of the mourners – for lack of a better way to put it. Is there a widow? Other children? Siblings of the deceased? And again, who is your congregant? Of course, it all becomes moot if there are enough men.

BOB: Let me share this other approach with you. I ran this by a colleague friend of mine from another town. He replied with an email. I printed it out, and I want to read it to you, just to get another perspective. Here goes:

> My current congregation calls itself "Traditional," which means they use an Orthodox, ArtScroll, prayerbook, and are not egalitarian. When I first got here I'd get concerned on a Friday night when we would have thirteen or fourteen people but only eight or nine were men, particularly when some of the women had come to say Kaddish for yahrzeit. Now I let them worry about it. Either they will find some more men or they will live with the consequences of their decision. Since then we've had more than a minyan of men most weeks and just about every morning. The good thing, I've found, is that it places the responsibility for a minyan squarely on the shoul-

ders of the men, and they take that obligation very seriously, and make a good effort to secure a minyan regularly.

At a shivah house, if the family are members of the synagogue we follow the synagogue's rules and sometimes have to make some phone calls, but if they are non-members, I tell them I have no objection to counting women in the minyan and we have done so when the family does not object. My rule at cemeteries has always been not to count too closely and assume we have a minyan, unless someone calls me on it.

I appreciate your feelings regarding egalitarianism in Conservative *shuls*. While you're fighting for equal rights for women, you might also note that so many of our *shuls* are guilty of ageism as well. They are unwilling to hire older rabbis. People whose contemporaries are retiring have little choice but to apply to congregations that in the past we would not even have considered because they are non-egalitarian. Fortunately for some, this non-egalitarian, so-called "traditional" congregation, where it's ok to come to *shul* Friday night and then go out for pizza afterwards as long as you don't count women in the *minyan*, was willing to offer an older colleague a position with a three-year contract when so many others wouldn't even offer an interview once they calculated the age. Whether or not they will one day become egalitarian is hard to say. The women who choose to belong there do not seem to care and are not urging a change until they bring it up. The older colleague is just happy to have a job. They are well aware that should they wish to become egalitarian they will have no opposition from their rabbi.

SUSAN: You males might not like the voice I offer, but I feel compelled to do so respectfully, because it is my truth as a female rabbi. I find it troubling that that the Conservative movement still embraces non-egalitarian attitudes and *minyanim* both at JTS and in the field, in addition to including wording on job applications that they require only male applicants, now that it's past the thirieth anniversary of the first female rabbi's ordination.

Our values say we embrace tradition and modernity, and it's

time we wholeheartedly embraced the modern part of our movement regarding egalitarianism, and leave the tradition of "all male" anything to the Orthodox. Forgive me, Don, but I have to express this.

Of course the mourner should be comforted and if he has chosen to affiliate with a *shul* that is egalitarian then those are the values of that community. Otherwise he can attend an Orthodox *shul*.

Roughly sixty of the three hundred female members of the RA meet periodically for study, reflection, and support. Someone said that she wonders why we still need to meet as just women. And it's because it seems thirty years later these issues, and others, are still prevalent in our Conservative communities. I know change takes time, but it can be aided by adherence to values that see women along with men made "*b'tzelem Elohim*" ["in the image of God"].

BOB: OK, I think it's time to lighten the conversation. I have a bat mitzvah this coming Shabbat. The young woman is one of our stars in the Religious School. She goes to a Hebrew-speaking summer camp, Camp Ramah. She and her family go to Israel every summer for a month. They have relatives and lots of friends there. The mother was a guest lecturer at Tel Aviv University, and has continued academic relationships with many colleagues. It's your ideal Jewish family. Anybody have an idea for an address to the young lady? It has to be something traditional, perhaps Talmudic, since many of the guests will be Hebrew speakers, or otherwise Jewishly involved.

DON: I have the perfect story for you. It's from Talmud, Tractate Ta-anit 5b. I use it in cases like the one you describe. A man was once wandering in the desert, hungry, thirsty, and exhausted with the heat. He chanced upon a tree whose fruit was sweet, whose shadow pleasant, and which had a brook flowing at its base. He ate the fruit, drank the water, and rested in the shade. When he rose to leave, he addressed the tree:

"Oh tree, how can I bless you? If I were to say 'May your fruit be sweet, it is already sweet.' Were I to say 'May your shade be pleasant,' it is already pleasant. And were I to say 'May there be a brook at your feet,' the brook is already there. My blessing will therefore be: 'May all your saplings be like you.'"

I then go on to describe the family, and all the blessings they have, and the fact that they already have them all. I end by saying that the only blessing I can offer you is that all the generations that follow you and your family will be just like you. They love it! Why wouldn't they?

BOB: Wow! That's perfect. I know that story, of course, and have used it under the *huppah*. Never thought of using it for a bat or bar mitzvah, but for this family it's perfect. Thanks!

SAM: I like to tailor my addresses to the *b'nai-mitzvah* to the family. I'll give you a few examples, ones that may bring you some ideas of your own in the future.

One family was named Brilliant. I knew that I had to use their name in the talk. So I said to the kid, we all knew before you chanted your prayers today that you were Brilliant. That is, with a capital "B." But now that we've heard you, we can all agree that your performance was really brilliant, with a lower case "b."

In the case of another family, the father had an uncle who was closely involved in astrophysics to the SuperString Theory. So I began by explaining that once you become a bat mitzvah, you are now, of course, obligated to perform the *mitzvot* of the Torah, and to verify that you symbolically accept the obligation to wear a *tallit*, whose fringes represent the 613 commandments of the Torah. This is because in traditional *Gematria*, or "mystical numerology," the Hebrew words for fringes, "*tzitzit*" adds up to six hundred. And if you count the number of fringes, plus the knots, that's an additional thirteen, so you have six hundred and thirteen. So wearing the *tallit*, accepting the *mitzvot*, is Judaism's "SuperString Theory." That got a great cheer from the crowd, many of whom were in the field of astrophysics, and even those who weren't knew that this guy's uncle was famous for being involved in that famous theory.

Oh, yes, and one more. I like to use the name of the family, wherever possible. I once officiated at the bar mitzvah of a family whose last name was Ganz. His whole family had gathered for the event, from all over North America. So I said to the kid, "I know your entire family has come from near and far. Do you know how one says 'the whole family' in Yiddish? The *GANZ mishpocho!*" Which means, in Yiddish, of course, 'The whole family.' That got a big laugh out of the congregation. People love it when you make your talk very personal. And using their name, or some characteristic which everyone knows, is always a winner.

SUSAN: OK, friends. Thanks for the "*homer l'drush,*" [sermonic material], which always is useful and welcome. But right now I want to turn to another issue, one that women and men who believe in equal rights for all, should espouse. Inspired by the arrests of our sisters and so many others, a group of other women and I have organized so far a double *minyan,* twenty people and counting, who want to stand up for religious freedom for women at the Kotel. We are planning an outdoor *Shaharit* service on the morning of the next *Rosh Hodesh,* the month of our liberation, and of our first becoming *B'nai Yisrael, Rosh Hodesh Nisan.* Precise time and location TBA but likely 8:30 or 9 a.m, hopefully at Union Square, New York, and possibly other places around the country. We may even be able to organize a similar one here in our town.

If anyone you know in the New York area would like to join in Manhattan, please let me know. We definitely want to keep you up to date about the precise time and place. The bigger the group, the greater the impact of this pray-in!

I have this photo from the home page of the *NY Times,* noting that the resigning Pope was praying at the Kotel, wearing his religious garb, unhindered. It is customary, each day and especially as we welcome each new month, that people gather to pray at the Kotel, the Western Wall in Jerusalem. The beginning of the month of *Adar,* in which Purim falls and joy is traditionally the greatest – be happy, it's Adar! – is celebrated. Notable among groups who specifically come to celebrate at the Kotel is *Neshot haKotel,* Women of the Wall. It is a group of women who have the idea that they should be free to engage in Jewish worship at the Kotel, including wearing *tallit* and *tefillin.* There is a "separate but equal" area of the Kotel where women are "supposed" to gather, not at the main western area with the wide plaza, but around the corner and down some stairs, at the Southern side, called Robinson's Arch. That is the same "separate but equal" area where Conservative groups of both genders are also supposed to worship, so as not to disturb the sensibilities of the Orthodox Jews at the main area of the Kotel, since the government of Israel, in concert with Israel's rabbinic establishment, have designated the Kotel, liberated by Israel in the Six Day War in 1967, as an "Orthodox prayer site." And of course, I use the words "separate but equal" advisedly. In 1898 the U.S. Supreme Court decided in the case of Plessy v. Ferguson that segregation, characterized by the court as "separate but equal," should be the law of the land in the U.S. It was not until that court reversed itself and decided Brown vs. Board of Education in 1954, in which our government even began to acknowledge that segregation should not be the policy of our country.

Unfortunately, this has not yet happened in Israel. With increasing regularity, women who gather to pray at the Kotel to welcome *Rosh Hodesh*, the beginning of the month, have begun to wear a *tallit*, as many of us do – and take for granted – in defiance of the Israeli law that prohibits them from doing so, because they are women. Over the last few months a few women have been arrested for doing so. Usually it is a number of Israeli women, and occasionally a Reform rabbi. Yesterday, it hit much closer to home when two Conservative women rabbis, including one whose congregation is near New York, were arrested for the crime of wearing a *tallit*. So what do we do as we stand, possibly, at the cusp of possible change? There is a possibility that the new government, for the first time in many years, may not include *Haredim*, the religious parties, which might allow for some changes in the way the government involves itself in excluding Conservative, Reform and even some Modern Orthodox rabbis, from Israeli religious life.

Some of my colleagues have proposed that they organize an egalitarian *Rosh Hodesh* outdoor prayer service in celebration of our religious freedom in this country and as a statement of encouragement to those who do not yet enjoy that freedom, hopefully attended by many Jews. As the new Israeli government forms, and we celebrate the next *Rosh Hodesh* in a few weeks, welcoming the month of *Nissan*, biblically, our first month, and the month of our liberation from slavery, we shall not continue to remain silent.

BOB: Although I want to be supportive of the WOW, Women of the Wall, and our colleagues and others who have been arrested for walking their talk, I want to know if the WOW stands for "inclusiveness" or "separate but equal." When the organization was first launched some years ago, Leah Shakdiel, a name we have not heard in many years, addressed the RA of Israel, which I heard on a tour during that time, and she asked for support. When we asked whether or not we could count on the nascent WOW to support mixed *davening* at the Kotel, she indicated that that was not a possibility as they viewed themselves as an Orthodox albeit feminist organization.

That may still be the agenda of the group despite its support from a cross section of North American Jews since the mission statement online states: As Women of the Wall, our central mission is to achieve the social and legal recognition of our right, as women, to wear prayer shawls, pray, and read from the Torah collectively and out loud at the Western Wall.

While I agree fully with that mission, it does not speak out for all Jews to enjoy equal rights at the Kotel. It is asking us to support separate but equal – which seems to me to be out of step with most Conservative Jews and certainly Conservative rabbis.

So now that we are being solicited for public demonstrations of support on *Rosh Hodesh Nissan*, see the invitation on FB, which some of us have received in the mail. I would like to clarify whether or not we will be championing the cause of pluralistic Judaism or pluralistic Orthodoxy in Israel.

SUSAN: Please rest assured that I am one hundred percent in favor of egalitarian Judaism. One might consider this event a hybrid, as it will be a public exercise of egalitarian Judaism, in support of those who don't even enjoy the right to *daven* separately at the Kotel, some of whom may want full rights and some who may only seek limited rights. It is long past time that we find a way to put aside our differences on this important issue and find a way to support the incremental progress of others, even if it is not the full expression that we seek for ourselves. What is the other choice? Is anyone publicly rallying people for mixed, egalitarian *davening* at the Kotel? Is that really our most successful first step? But if someone wants to do that – hey, I'll be at that event too, with bells on.

As a rabbi, with many friends who are attorneys, I am all too aware of the hazards of "separate but equal." Yet we need to start ending these abhorrent practices – all the more so – when it is our own colleagues who are now being taken away by the police. If not us, who?

The group is now in New York, with a spinoff in DC, and I hope in other places as well. They are planning the following for *Rosh Chodesh Nissan*. A pluralistic *tefillah* event, with maybe a couple of speeches and songs at the end. It looks like we will have very substantial attendance, by all four denominations. Those who would feel more comfortable doing so may BYOM, bring your own *mehitzah*, though mixed *davening* will be the predominant mode. The *Shlihot Tzibur* will be two women. The Torah reading is also anticipated to be done by women. There probably won't be many Orthodox men present, but so be it. It's all part of starting the process somewhere. We've made huge progress this week and expect hundreds to attend. Rabbis and cantors will be bringing congregants, day school kids will come, and of course, many, many lay individuals.

WOW has said they will support us in this. And we are supporting them – and religious tolerance. Hence the name, "Wake Up for Religious Tolerance." It is hard to imagine that this is controversial, but sadly, we all know that it is. I am looking forward to a number of more organizational and synagogue supporters this week, including those beyond our denomination.

On the particulars, we are waiting on a permit, so the exact place and time TBA but probably about 9 a.m. in an outdoor public place in Manhattan.

So, are you in? If you're excited, as I am, by the prospect of hundreds coming together in a public place in New York, to *daven* soulfully together, Conservative, Orthodox, Reform and Reconstructionist, in support of those who are subjected to these retrograde and wrong policies in Jerusalem, come with us and Wake Up for Religious Tolerance! And those of us who cannot get to New York, let's encourage colleagues to do this around the US and make our voices and *tefillah* heard!

SAM: I have no issue with the Women, but with the Wall. Since the Six Day War the unbelievable attention to the Kotel has been a distraction from the spiritual needs of the State of Israel and the Jewish People. How did the Kotel gain such importance among Jews in Israel and abroad?

DON: Obviously, there are many historical reasons. Once we regained control of greater Jerusalem, including the Western Wall, there was so much excitement, with chief chaplain of the IDF Rabbi Shlomo Goren blowing the *shofar* and pronouncing "*she-he-heyanu*," and then Prime Minister Levy Eshkol, Chief of Staff Yitzhak Rabin and Minister of Defense Moshe Dayan, marching to the Kotel [now a famous photo] . . . it suddenly became a national shrine.

SAM: This has been a very valuable discussion. Right now I have a different question for you folks. *Pesach* is not that far off, and I've been thinking about some of the new customs that people have been adding to the *Seder*, to give it a more contemporary flavor. I am prepping a new *haggadah* for a family *seder* and wondering how and when you incorporate Miriam's cup. I have spent time going through a bunch of *haggadot* and they all do it in different places for different reasons. If you would share your customs I would be grateful.

BOB: My custom is to exclude it. Why? First, I think it is actually silly and demeaning to women to have to add this just to feel equal to Elijah. Just because he has a cup doesn't mean we need to somehow stick in a symbol of a woman's cup! Equally as important, if not more so, is the fact that the *haggadah* goes out of its way to exclude Moshe. So we go against a very strong tradition by trying to insert Miriam with this invented modern addition. Frankly, the best way to include women is to add some commentary on the pages by some of our more interesting female scholars. So it seems to me. What we do in our home, and in *shul* when there's a community *seder*, is place an artistic tambourine on the table with a picture and quote "And Miriam arose. . . ." Though we do not include it in any ritual, unless someone wants to play it while we sing.

SAM: No other thoughts? OK, let's go on to the next subject – membership.

We are beginning to explore two issues related to membership – recruitment and retention.

First of all, retention. We have had an issue of long-time members who move out of their homes into a care facility or elsewhere, and decide they don't want to maintain their membership. We make every effort to convince them to stay connected. You know, "cradle to grave pastoral care." We try to explain that even if they can't make it to *shul*, we, both clergy and volunteers, come to visit them at home, etc., even expressing to them that if there is a financial need, we will work with them. The problem then arises, what do we do if such a person refuses to stay a member and wants me to do the funeral when he/she dies? Our policy is clear: they are not entitled to such services for five years post-resignation. I do not receive personal honoraria for life-cycle events for members. Anything they do give goes into my Rabbi's Discretionary Fund. I personally feel bad about such situations, but I can understand that there must be credibility for the value of membership for those who do maintain their membership. We have such members who even live full-time out of state, but maintain their membership.

We are looking for ideas on how to change this situation in a manner that we can keep those who do want to resign, yet expect such pastoral services down the road, without totally eroding the value of membership of those who stay.

Then there's the second, related issue, of recruitment: Aimed at our pre-school families, very few of whom are also members, even with the member discount on pre-school tuition. Yet, they want to have a place to attend for the high holidays. We do not sell tickets to non-members, with the exception of guests of members. Like most of us, membership is not required until the oldest child enters third grade, but we want them to continue from pre-school into our K–2 religious school program, which they can do as a non-member. There have been various incentives in the past, such as even larger discounts on tuition if a member has several children in school. Or age-bracket dues structures, which we eliminated many years ago since so many of the children in age-bearing families aren't starting families to age thirty.

So, any ideas or systems that work for you based on the concept that if we can get them in as members during pre-school we are more likely to retain them, not just hope they come back when the eldest child enters third grade.

DON: We have almost exactly the same problems. As far as recruitment goes, my feeling is that you simply have to do what is right. That means doing the funeral, even if they are not members. More people will be angry at you or the *shul* if you do not. I think the five year rule is silly. Those who feel loyalty to the *shul* stay, those who don't, won't care until confronted with a death, and then will spend the time talking to everyone they can about how callous and unfeeling the *shul* is.

As far as retention goes, this is a generational problem that we have yet to crack. People with young children have been getting a lot of free things in their lives, such as an education, a trip to Israel, their wedding, maybe from wedding gifts a down payment on their house, and don't want to pay money to synagogues to become members. I have no real solution, other than what you may have seen about "voluntary" dues. We also have an active PJ Library group, which is also free. We will see if that has any investment value. Who knows? These are tough questions, especially in a difficult economic climate.

SUSAN: Let me share what we're trying to do. We will put people who are on fixed incomes, or who are in care facilities – on very reduced, or even no dues memberships – if it's clear they would be members if they were physically and mentally able. For people who just don't want to pay anymore, but are perfectly physically able to come and financially able to pay, we do not officiate at their funerals.

We have about two hundred kids in our early childhood center, between half-day, pre-school and full-day daycare. However many families that translates into, maybe about sixty. About a third of these families are *shul* members already, whether because they have an older kid, or just are those kinds of people who join *shuls*. A few are members of other *shuls*, or are not Jewish. But for all the Jewish unaffiliated families, we are offering one year of free membership, starting from July first, the beginning of our fiscal year, which will include all the benefits of membership, including High Holiday tickets. After that, people will have to opt out of becoming members, and no longer receive all the e-mails, the mailings, the bulletins, high holiday tickets and services – everything. They will have to actively opt out of becoming members after that first year, and our hope is that a whole bunch will take the path of least resistance – and not opt out, but just maintain the status quo of membership, of course, now paying for the privilege. The plan is for new families in our ECC to get one free year of membership going forward. I can't say how this will work out in the long run, but we're trying it.

SAM: Friends, along the lines of synagogue administration, let me ask this: I am interested in what pulpit rabbis have in place for their professional review by the congregation. Do you have particular forms? Who does the review?

DON: I don't actually believe it is appropriate for congregations to evaluate their spiritual leaders. First, because there's really no way for a committee to be able to evaluate the many transactions you have that must remain confidential. But more than that: once the *ba'alei batim* take on the role of evaluating the rabbi that steps over a boundary. You are their spiritual leader, and as such, you are charged with pushing and pulling them to where you believe they need to head. It's not the job of the followers to evaluate the leader in a faith community, and indeed, trying to do that makes the job impossible. Moshe would have fared miserably in an evaluation by *Am Yisrael* in the desert.

That said, feedback, properly channeled, is good. It should happen in your regular weekly meetings with your president, and it should not be specifically about your performance. It should be about the *shul's* performance, the organization you and the president are charged with leading, and what needs to be done to get to where the *shul* needs to go. That could mean a changed priority in your schedule, or even a fix of some flaw in you, but it could also, and more likely, mean changes in staff support, in budgets, in volunteer activity, or in a host of other variables.

I know the corporate evaluation model from my brother who works in a corporation. It usually is dysfunctional there, and it certainly has little value for a congregation; maybe, but only maybe, for a nonprofit if you are an agency head instead of a *shul* rabbi.

The American Jewish community, about which I worry very much, will not be saved by someone telling you to polish your shoes more often. Our energies are better directed to the real issues, and we need to lead our congregations to a recognition of this.

SUSAN: I will second what Don says. If you are trying to build community, regular feedback with the president or a few key congregants can be very helpful. But an evaluation of performance will not lead to building trust and securing communal bonds. Not for nothing is *tokhehah* [criticism] the toughest mitzvah, and that is when it is constructive. But *ba'alei batim* have many issues and many ideas of what they want in a rabbi. Evaluation based on what criteria and whose scale?

Plus as Don rightly points out – our goal is not to do the will of the congregation but to lead them and teach them. It is a tricky thing for the individuals you are encouraging to push themselves spiritually to now evaluate if the rabbi is doing a good job in their estimation.

SAM: Thanks, guys, for all this input. It's very helpful. So who has another issue to raise?

BOB: I do. A congregant of mine, who is not Jewish, but married to a Jewish woman, is a retired police officer and got spooked because of the killing of police officers by Christopher Dorner. He asked me if I could officiate at the service if he died because he does not practice Christianity or feel any connection to any church. He attends services more often than most members, and helps out in a host of different ways. In short, he feels that my *shul* is his community, but he has not converted. Has anyone had any experience with this issue? What would you do in similar circumstances?

SAM: I once did do such a funeral. The man was poor. I led a plain, vanilla type of funeral service. I read some psalms, gave a brief eulogy at the funeral home. I did not go to the cemetery, but I probably would have, if they wanted me to. You know, when a non-Jewish diplomat, or high-ranking government or community leader dies, we are sometimes invited to read a psalm, or say a few appropriate words. Right? How is this different?

SUSAN: I have officiated at funerals for gentiles; someone I knew; someone who worked for our *shul;* a person without his own strong faith tradition; or a pastor who was an acquaintance. It was a very moving experience. So I would urge you to consider this gentleman's request positively.

DON: Doesn't a *mohel* do *milah* for the British royal family, who are, of course, non-Jews? Or is that report just a *bubbe meiseh?* Isn't that a similar situation, where a Jewish clergyperson officiates at a ceremony for a non-Jew?

SAM: No, it's not a myth, it's true! Prince Charles was the last in the family to have it done. And yes, it was done by a *mohel.*

BOB: Well, since we're in agreement, I see no reason why I

should refuse. I'm sure he'll be very pleased. OK, I guess that does it for today. See you all next week, same time; same place.

DON: So long.

SUSAN: Bye, bye.

SAM: Au revoir.

Week 7

BOB: I'll start off today with a *halakhic*, or if you will, a family-type question. Is there any appropriate reason to change the grave of a corpse already laid to rest? That is, to remove the coffin and place it in another gravesite.

DON: I'll give you a bunch of reasons, Bob. They aren't really *halakhic*, as such, but I think many of them are good reasons. Whether it's *halakhically* sound to do so, I'd have to do some research. But here'a list, to start with:

1) In the frozen north, people are buried in graves previously dug before the perma frost prevented the ground from being opened. In the spring, the bodies are exhumed and buried in their proper place.

2) A new cemetery may not have been completed. The body is buried in the older cemetery until the new plots are ready.

3) An unidentified corpse is buried and later identified and moved to a family plot.

4) Not a fitting reason but it happens: If the deceased had a previous marriage and plots were pre-purchased. The second spouse had the body buried. The family of the first spouse had exhumation to fulfill the deceased's burial wishes. It happened to me twice.

5) Also not a fitting reason but . . . A family could not finish paying for an expensive plot. The cemetery exhumed the corpse and relocated it to a plot which the family could afford.

6) A member of my congregation was buried in Georgia. He had died in a tragic car accident. The family moved to Missouri,

and exhumed his body to be buried with the rest of the family.

7) If there is something wrong with the spot, for example if there's a waterway there and the ground became too wet.

8) If you want to send the body to Israel.

There are, I am sure, lots of other reasons, some legit and others by family choice. Of course, the rabbi doesn't always have the last word.

Take your choice.

I really prefer never to do it. It's always a mess, and it usually ends up in hurt feelings between me, the *shul* and the family.

BOB: That's quite a list. Thanks.

SAM: I've had a few experiences that may fall into some of Don's categories. For example, on one occasion, a family moved to a different city, and wanted the grave close to where they lived, so they could visit often.

Then there are two other examples:

One, the family members got angry with each other, and had some of the family members moved to a different plot.

In another instance, a person was buried in our *shul* cemetery, but the other members of the family belonged to the right wing, ultra-Orthodox synagogue. When his wife died, they had not yet paid for the husband. They promised they would bring the money that was due to the cemetery at the funeral. They "stiffed" the synagogue. And, I might add, this is a wealthy family! Later, they wanted both bodies exhumed to bring to another cemetery. Why? Because they did not want their parents buried in a Reform synagogue.

I told the family, "sure, we will do it." "And," I said, "I will have both of your parents dumped on the steps of the *shul* you belong to." You might tell that I was steaming mad. Forgive me, but at the time, I was fuming, and couldn't control my temper. For some reason, their attorney called me. He said he must have heard me misquoted. I said, no. I told him that I said they wanted their parents to be in a "true" *shul* like Bet Kitzonim – not the real name, of course. So, I was being helpful, I explained.

"And," I said, "I need to first see that they pay our synagogue, and then, their rabbi will need to show me where it says that a body must be exhumed because the synagogue is Reform. If not, we will hire some workers we can find, and leave the bodies on the steps of the 'good' *shul*!"

I do not recall what happened after that.

Again, forgive me, but this was once when I really lost my cool. Can you tell?

SUSAN: Alright, my turn. To change the mood a bit, I want to read to you an email I received from a friend and colleague, who saw in the news that the Pope resigned, and that there will be a new election very soon. So she drew up a list of her credentials, to run for Pope. Yep, you heard me! Rabbi Dorothy for Pope! I laughed heartily when I read the first few lines. But after that, when I saw how serious her platform was, I no longer laughed, but cheered. I only wish we had a Pope, a Chief Rabbi, and a Chief Imam, whose platforms resemble that of my friend Dorothy.

Here's her platform and campaign promises:

1. I believe in a "yes/and," not "either/or" religious stance.

This means that all religions are equally sacred. No religion is totally "right" or "wrong." If you choose to believe in no god, one god, three gods or any other combination, we Catholics will lovingly welcome you and invite you to join us under our big tent.

2. The highest goal of Catholicism will be what our holy ancestors the Jews call "*tikkun olam*," repairing the world so that God is satisfied. When we have done that, the Messiah will come, and I do not care what she is named. It really will not matter.

3. Men and women may be ordained for the priesthood, they may marry or not, as they choose. They may officiate at all sacraments, as their community will accept. There will be different and differing church traditions depending on each church and community, and God will be pleased by the diversity of those who gather to praise the Holy Name.

4. Any priest who has any type of sexual relations with a minor, will be immediately defrocked, and their name will be submitted to law enforcement agencies. God would accept no less, and neither will we.

5. We will no longer try to proselytize anyone. Rather, we will invite our neighbors to accept our Catholic traditions. Gaining new Catholics through intimidation has not worked, it has tarnished the Holy Image in which we are all created, and has diminished us as a religion. Attempts at conversion will immediately cease. We will first focus our efforts on our own flock, who now stay away from our churches in droves.

6. We will support the distribution of birth control devices and information in schools, colleges, and even inside our own churches, to ensure that every child is wanted and loved, and has been created by its parents in a pure and spiritual way. Abortion will be sadly allowed, for the sake of the mother's physical or emotional health. The difficult decision whether to end the lives of deformed fetuses will be made by the parents after due consultation with doctors. We will not judge their decision. We will, rather, support them in dealing with their loss.

7. We emphasize that all life is holy. Our Catholics may choose to believe that life begins at conception or that life begins at birth. What is more important is the quality of that unborn child once it is born, and we will do everything possible to bring that child into a world of peace, love and acceptance.

8. God created each and all of us in the Holy Image. Therefore we fully accept the diversity of gender. It will no longer matter whether you are created straight, gay, lesbian, bi-sexual or transgender. It never mattered to God, it will no longer matter to us. What matters more is that each child of God will attempt to repair this world to the best of their ability. Everything else is simply detail, not important to God or to us.

9. We will have diplomatic relations with all nations of the world. The only exceptions are those nations which murder their own citizens, or those that proclaim that they will destroy their neighbors. This is extreme blasphemy, and it is unacceptable to God and to us.

10. The belief in Heaven and Hell remains an individual choice. Some may believe in a physical locale, others may believe more in a spiritual one. As your Pope, I will do everything possible to help you live a faithful life which will be rewarded by your leaving a legacy for those who remain. Our actions on this earth will

determine our destination after we leave. Mother Teresa is in Heaven, Adolph Hitler is in Hell. I need no "proof" that Heaven and Hell physically exist. God's acceptance is the only reward I seek. You are free to disagree. I welcome the conversation.

I shall retire at the age of seventy-five, in the hope that someone younger will be chosen after me to finish the work I have begun.

This is my platform, and I hope you will support me.

SAM: Please tell Rabbi Dorothy that she can be my personal Pope.

BOB: Amen!

DON: I not only love that platform, but I might use it if, Heaven forfend, I ever have to interview for another rabbinical position.

(Laughter).

BOB: Well, now that we've solved all the problems of the Catholic Church, let's try and figure out some of their theology. I've been studying chapter 53 of Isaiah with my adult study group. You know, the one about the so-called "suffering servant." I've been trying to compare our translation and commentary with that of Christianity.

My question is regarding the tense of the many verses in the chapter. It seems to me that many are in the past tense. That is, referring to the Jewish people in Babylonian exile. But others say that it can be read as present tense, thus bolstering the Christian argument that it refers to a person, and not the historic exile of the Jewish people. Can any of you biblical scholars help?

DON: The final word that I read from the Talmudic rabbis on the problem of suffering is "we don't know." See Talmudic Tractate *Berakhot* 5a–b and 7a. Many solutions are proposed and left on the table, an indication of the inscrutability of the problem. The idea of a *tzaddik* suffering to atone for the sins of the many is, to be sure, not a definitive, dominant trope, but remains one among many – as in the notion of the *lamed-vavnikim*.

BOB: With all due respect, I don't think it matters what the prophet thought when he talked of the suffering servant. I certainly can understand seeing the servant as the whole of Israel. And I do not have a problem with seeing an innocent person suffering on behalf of the collective. Doesn't this happen all the time? I think of Billie Holliday's song "Strange Fruit." I think of it every time someone suffers because others have sinned.

SUSAN: My recollection, from reading the commentary in the Anchor Bible on Isaiah, is that the prevailing opinion appears to be that Deutero-Isaiah is referring to himself. The question that troubles me about the "suffering servant" is where did Isaiah come up with this idea of an innocent person suffering on behalf of the collective? The idea seems to be a retrogression from the biblical concepts of reward and punishment, free will and personal responsibility, and the ideas inherent in the *Akedah*, of the repudiation of the sacrifice of an innocent, and the resort to animal sacrifice as an expression of a human, rather than divine, need. Not surprisingly, the idea did not resonate with *Hazal* [the Talmudic rabbis], but was perfectly suited to the needs of Paul.

BOB: Well, I must say, that while there are many occasions when the group has helped to solve a problem, or at least point one of us in the right direction, this time I feel like I'm left in the middle of a lake without a paddle. And likely my students will be too! But, I guess I can say that since no one else can figure out, or identify this metaphor of the Suffering Servant, with any certainty, that is, then I am in good company. Even the ancient rabbis were stumped.

SUSAN: Hey, Bob, that's as good an excuse as any I've ever heard. Just say, like Rashi used to say, without embarrassment, "*Aynee yodaya*." "I don't know the answer."

BOB: OK, since no one gave me a satisfying answer for that question, I'll try another one.
We have recently become aware of a family in our congregation which has always presented itself as Jewish, attends syna-

gogue regularly, has children in religious school and is active in holiday observance. But as it turns out they are also involved in a Messianic Church. They have never made any attempt to proselytize. Their mission apparently is not to Jews but to Christians, to bring them to the Jewish messiah, and to have them observe Jewish traditions while believing in Jesus. They want to show them that they are Jews who believe in Jesus, but they don't go after Jews. They go after Christians, and bring them to observance of the Jewish rituals while believing in Jesus.

We don't know if they are actually Jews or have just lived their lives as Jews, and they do live their lives as Jews, as I pointed out. We will soon sit down with the parents. Our thought is:

a) Get them to admit that they have a different spiritual life outside our synagogue which includes worshipping Jesus as the Messiah.

b) Indicate to them that they are of course always welcome in the synagogue, but that they cannot receive honors to the Torah any more, or bring their youngest to the Torah for a bat mitzvah.

If they were in any way involved in going after our people we would probably ban them from the synagogue. I'm not sure exactly how we would do that, but we would look into it.

We're not sure if we want to tell others about them. We assume that if we did, that would be the end of it, and they would stop coming to our synagogue. Ultimately my feeling is that would be best in the final analysis.

Any ideas? Anybody have an experience like this with this type of messianic Jews?

DON: You know where I stand. Smoke them out, tell them that your *shul* is for Jews, not fake Jews, and politely as you can, usher them to the door.

SAM: Oh, Don, don't be a fuddy-duddy! They sound like nice, but misguided folks. Bob, why not send them to my synagogue? He could probably be president of the congregation, and she'll be president of the Women's Guild.

SUSAN: Hey, Sam, don't be a smart aleck! Bob has a serious

problem. Again, Bob, I think you're going to go home emp-
ty-handed again. I sure don't know what to suggest. Maybe send
them to a nearby Jews-for-Jesus operation.

BOB: OK, I think I should have stayed home today. Two strikes.
One more and I'm out of here.

DON: Now, don't be a spoiled sport. Believe me, if there was an
easy answer, we'd be more than happy to suggest it.

BOB: Alright. Let's go on to another issue.

SUSAN: I'm looking for information, either articles or *teshuvot*
that come from the Orthodox world dealing with the issue of a
Kohen marrying a *giyoret* and a *gerusha* [divorcee]. We just had
a very high profile wedding in my *shul*, which I ended up doing
by default. It involves a Venezuelan couple who live in Panama
but married in the States. He is a *Kohen* and she is a *giyoret*
by an Orthodox Sephardic rabbi, but doing the *huppah* in Ven-
ezuela was not good for political reasons. I'm certain that the
family was afraid to go to that country as they were active in the
anti-Chavez world, and not hold the wedding in Panama because
they would have made their lives miserable. So they came to the
U.S., where they have a lot of family. And I did it because no
other rabbi was available.

It was being discussed in my Melton class since some of them
are of that community, and they couldn't understand how the
marriage could have taken place, since their rabbis tell them it
is absolutely forbidden, and no Orthodox rabbi would do it, and
they should be forced to divorce. I have, in some ways, quite a
lovely community, very welcoming, as you can see. I explained
that first of all we permit it in our movement, and I explained in
summary why – that we are not sure who is really a *Kohen* today,
and we don't want to box in *Kohanim* from marrying any Jew
they want. And second, the fact is that decades ago these marriages were often performed by Orthodox rabbis – quietly – and
almost no Orthodox rabbi, even if he wouldn't do the wedding,
would ask them to divorce, or in any way reject them in the com-

munity. It was for all practical purposes a non-event in those days. I also said that even today many Orthodox synagogues accept these weddings post-facto, and some even let the *Kohen* continue to receive *Rishon* [first *aliyah* at the Torah, normally given to a *Kohen*]. But they would not give *Rishon* to their children, who are *hallalim* [children born to a woman forbidden in marriage to a *Kohen*]. The second teacher after me in Melton is a young and superb Orthodox rabbi, who didn't challenge me. He had already entered the room, but expressed great surprise and wondered if there is any 'documentation' of this.

So I'd like to see if there is something out there. I personally knew of such cases in the Orthodox world, very close to our town, but something anecdotal is not what I'm looking for. I'm looking for either an article or a *teshuvah*, or some kind of discussion in the Orthodox world about how the issue was, and now is, dealt with.

DON: Looks like today is the day that nobody gets a good, complete answer. What I can say is not an answer to your question, but you may find it interesting that in Israel the *Rabbanut* will not perform a wedding between a *Kohen* and a Jewish woman who is born to a non-Jewish father. Yes, you are hearing this correctly. I can check with some of my colleagues, and see if they have heard of anything like this, and if there is anything written about what you're asking. But I have my doubts.

SUSAN: Oh well, I'll just have to tell my class, "*Aynee Yoda-at*," as Rashi would say.

BOB: I will be doing a funeral on Sunday at which the family has requested Masonic burial rituals be performed prior to the traditional Jewish burial service. I recall having witnessed this Masonic rite exactly one time and feeling very uncomfortable as I watched it unfold. To those who may have more experience with this rite, if you have experienced the same discomfort I have felt and have found some way to lessen it by the timing or manner in which the Masonic burial rite is carried out, could you please share your advice with me?

SAM: I am an active Mason. This question comes up from time to time among colleagues. There are several issues.

Firstly, is the Masonic burial service compatible with Judaism? That depends on the service. There are many variants. Most are fine. Some are distinctly Christological or Trinitarian. You should check that out. Don't make the mistake of asking the Masons who will be doing the ceremony if it is in sync with Judaism. They may think it is, but not recognize Christian elements which might be in there.

Secondly, logistical questions. How long will the Masonic ceremony take? You'll need to ask that as well, but generally the Masons are experienced in dealing with the sort of time constraints that apply to modern funeral services. It shouldn't be a problem. But you will need to know how long they will take. They should be done before you even begin your portion. They aren't likely to go much over ten minutes. Length of eulogies and additional readings may need to be adjusted.

Thirdly, professionalism. Will they do a good job? Will they bring dignity to the service? Most of the Masons who are tasked to this sort of thing do excellent work and may even excel at declamation. But on occasion, some won't. Those who are invited to lead these services are usually very good at it.

Should you allow a Masonic service at all? If the above considerations are all addressed, I would think so. It honors the wishes of the deceased, and brings comfort to the mourners. Freemasonry is remarkably varied and can be profound. From time to time Jews will need to navigate aspects which might be a problem for us. But, for the most part, Masonry is oconsistent with the *Sheva Mitzvot Bnai Noah* [The Seven Commandments of All Humanity], and the very concept of Noahides is part of the corpus of Masonic lore. It advances a core agenda which is very Jewish.

I hope that this helps.

BOB: Couldn't be more helpful, Sam! Crystal clear. I made notes while you were talking, and I'll check out timing, possible Christological elements, their professionalism, and all the things you mentioned. I think by covering these bases, I'll be OK with it.

DON: Here's something I'd like to share with the group. It doesn't need an answer. It's not a question. Just a life experience that if I tell it to you, you may crack a smile. And that will make me happy.

I faced an intriguing challenge this afternoon. The local Chabad rabbi's daughter is engaged and my wife and I were invited to an engagement party. I happen to know the daughter, who is all of about twenty years old, and she is a sweetheart. She teaches at the local Chabad day school. I believe this is the fourth of his ten children to be married. I once asked him how many children he has and he answered "a Conservative *minyan*."

Anyway, I went to the local market to find an appropriate engagement card to include with a small gift. The cards were almost all inappropriate. Those that speak about how they found each other do not include when Daddy finds the groom. Those that speak of walking hand and hand in the rain do not realize that these two will never walk hand and hand anywhere, at least in public. I found one with a lovely poem about God bringing people together, but it ended with a quote from the New Testament. Not exactly appropriate. I was ready to give up when I found a simple card that simply says "The best story is the one you write together." Even young Chabad couples write stories together. Just thought I would share this.

SUSAN: Thanks for sharing it, Don. It sure made me chuckle. One never knows what new experiences are coming down the pike.

I have a *halakhic* question for you guys. Ready?

A family in my community is celebrating the birth of a baby girl, born to the Jewish mother, conceived from a donated egg from a non-Jewish donor. I know that the CJLS *teshuvot* by Elliot Dorff and Aaron Mackler on this issue, from 1994 and 1995, indicate that maternal identity in such a case is determined by the gestational mother, not the source of the egg – so that in my case, no conversion is necessary. Whereas conversion would be necessary in the case of a non-Jewish gestational surrogate carrying an infant born from an ovum from the Jewish mother. In this case, this family has heard, perhaps from Orthodox relatives, that there has been a reevaluation of this issue in recent years and that now the prevailing Orthodox practice is to have a *giyyur le-humra* ["conversion just to make double-sure"] in the case of an egg donation if the donor was not Jewish.

My questions:

First, is this an accurate description of the prevailing Orthodox practice today?

Second, does the position of the CJLS now remain as it was some two decades ago, indicating that absolutely no conversion is necessary or advisable when a Jewish woman gives birth to a baby born from an egg donated by a non-Jewish donor?

DON: Here is a copy of a brief *Wall Street Journal* article about reevaluation of who is mother among Israeli *Haredi* authorities. Susan asked me to bring any ideas I had about this question, so here are a few lines from the article.

> Traditional denominations of Judaism believe that faith is passed down from mother to child. Until recently, Orthodox rabbinic authorities widely recognized the birth mother as the parent who confers religious status on her offspring. But at the January conference in Jerusalem of the Puah Institute, Rabbi Mordechai Halperin said that the pendulum of rabbinic opinion has swung toward conferring maternity on the egg donor. . . . .
>
> One of America's most prominent Orthodox rabbinic arbiters, Rabbi Moshe Tendler disagrees. He believes recent rulings out of Israel are misguided: "Genetics provide only the blueprint, and for the next nine months the work is done by the gestational mother," Rabbi Tendler says. "While the gestational mother is in labor, the egg donor could be on the beach in Miami." Still, Rabbi Tendler says he performs a handful of conversions every year of babies born to Jewish women using non-Jewish eggs; just so there's no doubt about the child's religion.

I believe the respected Orthodox posek, Rabbi Nachum Rabinovitch — even though he did call Yitzhak Rabin a *moser* [traitor, for being willing to give up parts of the Land of Israel], and is considered by some a radical in the settlement community – holds that the birth mother is the mother for all purposes. As you heard in the article, Rabbi Moshe Tendler, of Yeshiva University, also disagrees with the new opinion.

So to answer your question, Susan, the stricter Orthodox in Israel hold one opinion, and the somewhat more modern Orthodox rabbis here in America, have the opposite point of view.

SUSAN: Par for the course, as they say, right? That's the old joke about two Jews holding three opinions.

DON: Right! Throughout Jewish history you have sects and groups of all kinds who make their own decisions, and people in another country, or another continent, disagree. Anyway, at least you have some parameters of the argument.

SUSAN: Yes, thanks, Don. Helpful, even though not a full answer.

DON: A close friend and colleague of mine spent *Pesach* this year in Israel helping his nonagenarian parents cope and finally agree to accept full time help, which should hopefully enable them to remain living in their apartment for the foreseeable future – however long that foreseeable future is.

From the reports after his return, it is such a different experience being in Israel for a *Yom Tov*, as compared to being in the States. Both as it relates to the issues of the day and to the experience of the *hag* itself. I want to comment on the latter only.

There is something profoundly different about celebrating a *hag* that has two days of *Yom Tov* and five days of *Hol Hamoed*, as opposed to a *hag* that has four days of each. Throw in a Shabbat, and the days of *Yom Tov* and Shabbat overwhelm the days of *Hol Hamoed* in the States. I have long been an advocate inside my *shul* of two days of *Yom Tov*, in spite of many of my most educated – including rabbinic colleagues – and articulate folks providing well-reasoned arguments for eliminating the additional days of *Yom Tov*. But it is not the extra day that is the problem, it is the message attached to the Festival with the de-emphasis of *Hol Hamoed*. Seeing a country alive during this period, one comes to fully appreciate just how significant *Hol Hamoed* can be, even for those who have no connection to the "religious" elements of the *hag*. I know this has been addressed by many over the years. But as we are seeing with the *kitniyot* [legumes] discussions, and the impact that Israel has had on changing the practices of the observant American community as a result – including the OU now providing a label for such products in America – I believe that in the coming years we will begin to see a similar type of movement related to *Yom Tov Sheni*.

While it was fascinating to see some *frum* American Jews walking the streets of Jerusalem on *Yom Tov Sheni*, as if they were in *galut*, the vast majority of non-resident Jews who cared deeply about their Jewish lives, were done with *Pesach*. By the way, the Mayer Rabinowitz *teshuvah* on what we are to do in Israel on "*Yom Tov Sheni*," namely, that visitors to Israel during a festival should observe only one day of *Yom Tov*, is spot on. In fact flying home after the *hag*, he sat next to a YU rabbi and he told him that he wanted to come home on the eighth day of *Pesach*, according to the Diaspora calendar, but his wife didn't want to drive up to their home while the neighbors were still having *Yom Tov*. The long term dye is cast, in my mind. Long ago there was a *teshuvah* in the Conservative movement to reconcile the calendars and to eliminate *Yom Tov Sheni*. It clearly was not the time to do it, and few congregations took to the idea. But the zeitgeist of the Jewish people today is quite different. The impact of Israel is different today. I wonder if there is room to begin a serious discussion about this, or if, like *kitnyot*, it will simply happen operationally. People will just begin to follow the Israeli calendar. In truth we stand to benefit much more if we begin the conversation ourselves.

BOB: As always, Don speaks eloquently and thoughtfully. Having spent *Pesach* in Israel just a few years ago, I take to heart his feelings and experiences. *Pesach* is meant to be spent in Israel! It is not just the expression we recite at the *Seder* and at the end of Yom Kippur, "*L'shanah ha-ba-ah BiYerushalayim*," ["Next year in Jerusalem"] but the logical conclusion of *Dayenu*. Five days of *Hol HaMo'ed* to two days of *Yom Tov* is a much better score! Four days of *Yom Tov* to four days of *Hol Hamoed* is a tie, without a winner. Sorry, but baseball is on my mind. The Cubs are two to one today. I am therefore completely in agreement with the idea that celebrating a *hag* in Israel trumps celebrating it in *galut*. It is the second idea that I have a problem with.

Last year at the Hartman Institute, I was able to study with a well-known American Jewish scholar. It was a wonderful and enlightening experience. But one evening, he was on a panel with two others talking about their views of Israel and Zionism. What he essentially said is, "I love Judaism, but Israel is not really much more special to me than any other place where I can express my Judaism openly and freely." Of course, he did not mean that we don't have a history in the land, or a special relationship with Jerusalem, but what he meant to say, I think, was that being in Israel does nothing for him Jewishly that he can't find elsewhere. Indeed, at times it is even more problematic!

I profoundly disagree with that. I don't want to be that kind of Jew. There is something different and more natural about being a Jew in the land of Israel. Indeed I assume that is why Don's parents moved there to begin with. There is no more profound reminder of this in the Diaspora than *Yom Tov Sheni*, which is simply short for *Yom Tov Sheni shel Galut* [the second day of the holiday observed only in exile]. I am the last person to say that one cannot live a full Jewish life in the Diaspora, or that all Jews must move to Israel. Yet I think it is of great importance, as Don himself recognizes, to understand that being a Jew in Israel is – perhaps even radically – different from being a Jew outside of Israel.

There we win five to two, here it is a tie. Besides, like you, thanks to *Yizkor*, I had a much nicer crowd on the eighth day than the seventh. And who doesn't enjoy an extra day of not sitting in the office, visiting hospitals, etc.

I remember many years ago sitting in the *shvitz* at the Concord Hotel, where we used to have annual RA conventions, hearing one rabbi at a prominent synagogue talk proudly about how he had gotten rid of *Yom Tov Sheni* at his *shul*. One of his neighbors sitting next to him remarked, "I know. All of your people come to me on the second day."

SUSAN: I've been following this thread with deep interest. A few years ago I affirmed the oft-unrecognized authorization of the CJLS to abolish *Yom Tov Sheni* for my left-of-center congregation, and my family's personal practice. To my knowledge, only one of the *shul* regulars attended *shul* elsewhere. He went to be with his father at the Orthodox *shul* of his youth. The regulars all affirmed that it made sense for a variety of reasons. The "irregulars" likely neither noticed nor cared, and it was embraced easily by the congregation. I have maintained my private practice ever since, and in general it has been a blessing for my family on many levels.

And now, for a humorous and ironic tale. The one inconsistency in our practice has been Pesach. Being back where I grew up means that we have a decent amount of immediate and extended family within an hour's drive. *Shalom bayit* has led us to attend *sedarim* on the first two nights. That was supposed to be the case this year, but the cousin hosting second night had to cancel because of family illness. I was excited that FINALLY I would be rid of the need for the superfluous – in my humble opinion, second *seder*. Our family was coming to our place on the second night, and I planned to invite discussion on the themes of the day, and enjoy some extended singing around the table, sans the formal *seder* itself. My kids revolted. They were adamant that we needed a second *seder*, even as they embraced that it would not be *Yom Tov*. So *nu*, I ended up conducting a *seder* on the second night, wryly appreciating the punch line of the Talmudic story of *Tanur shel Akhnai–nizhuni banai*, "My children have defeated me!"

I look forward to seeing you at Sinai soon.

SAM: Our local Jewish funeral home, Goldberg's, is run by a wonderful fellow and a good friend who is Catholic, and who runs two other non-Jewish funeral homes that have been his family's business for years. He worked as Joe Goldberg's assistant, and bought the business when Joe died many years ago. He has asked me about having music playing as people enter the funeral home. He does this in his other non-Jewish funeral homes, and wants to know if he should add this to Goldberg's. He usually does classical music, softly playing in the background, even at times during the eulogy. He wanted to know if that was ok, and perhaps to use Jewish music. Is this done in Jewish funeral homes?

BOB: I have strong feelings about music, both before and during funeral services. I attended a funeral in New York some years ago, and there was soft, beautiful, Jewish, music before the service. It helped set the tone for the experience, the same way as music sets the tone during a movie – whether it's romantic, a comedy, a drama, etc. Then, during the funeral service, between speakers – and there were six or seven, if I recall – there was a children's choir. The deceased was a teacher, and the choir was made up of some of her students. And then the late Debbie Friedman played "*Lekhi lakh*," "Go to the land that I will show you. . . ." It was incredibly moving. I'm all for music at funeral services.

SUSAN: Let me turn now to a different issue. I have a problem I could use some advice with. Our congregation has been struggling to get ten people at the morning and evening *minyanim*. I've tried hard to maintain the *minyan* for people who have to say *Kaddish* as mourners or for *yahrzeit*. But it's time-consuming, a gazillion phone calls, postcards, and reminders without end. I just don't know what to do any more.

BOB: Here's what we've done: We went down to three mornings a week – Sunday, Monday, and Thursday. We *daven* at 5:15 pm every evening, including *erev Yom Tov, erev Shabbat* and *Minhah* on Shabbat, to make it simple. We *daven* regardless of numbers, and if we don't have a full *minyan*, we say just one *Kaddish yatom* with the *Aron Kodesh* doors open, even if we only have a *mezuman* of three. We tried, quite passionately, to keep the full *minyan* going through the years, even making last minute phone calls and causing others who were on time to wait until someone came. But now almost no one lives in the neighborhood of the *shul*, and it meant waiting for longer than the *minyan* would last for someone to arrive. So I met with the ritual committee years ago and said I honestly didn't think that God counts how many of us are there, and that those saying *Kaddish* have a right to say it. It brings them comfort on a *yahrzeit* or during *aveilut*, and anyone who doesn't wish to respond is under no obligation to do so. Without ten we don't do any other *davar sh'b'kdushah* [sacred liturgy requiring a quorum of ten] during the service. The cantor or I teach a lesson instead of the normal Torah reading when we don't have a *minyan* of ten.

I understand that by relaxing the normally strict rules of *halakhah* in this way I may make it more difficult for colleagues to keep the *halakhic* standard should someone bring back our lenient approach. But I must tell you that our *minyan* is more relaxed and enjoyable than it ever was before. We begin and end on time, we sing together more and mumble privately less, we have regulars who look forward to being there; and those who only come for *yahrzeit* never worry that they may have to leave without saying *Kaddish*. When anyone who wishes to have a *minyan* of ten indicates their desire in advance, we are always able to accommodate those wishes. At *Minhah* we do a shortened Ramah-kind-of-*Amidah*. We begin together, followed by just the *hatimot* of each of the *berakhot* together. It's on cards that have Hebrew, English, and transliteration, and obviously have silent *Amidah* at *Ma'ariv*. In other words, anyone who attends our *minyan*, and we often have many more than ten people, does so not out of guilt, nor out of pressure to be there for someone else, but because they value the time for *tefillah b'tzibur*.

SUSAN: I think you described your system to me once, and I've given it a lot of thought, but for now I just cannot bring myself to ignore the requirement for a quorum of ten males and females, of course. I'll keep thinking about it. But short of any other magical suggestions, somewhere down the road, we'll either have to do that, or just have *minyanim* less regularly, or maybe I'll even give one of my major High Holiday talks about the importance of sustaining a daily *minyan*. Other *shuls* around the country do it, and I don't get why we can't do it.

SAM: I admire your perseverance, Susan, and my guess is that if you keep trying, you'll reach your goal.

SUSAN: Thanks, Sam. That's the kind of encouragement I need. I'll keep you posted.

DON: Let me focus now on something else that's come up. I have a young couple who are about to be married. They love the idea of reciting a version of *Eshet Hayil*, the famous "Woman of Valor" poem from Proverbs 31, each Friday night but would like a different text. Do any of you have alternative versions that you could share with me? They would also like something for the wife to share with her husband – an "*Ish Hayil*" text. If you have something like that, kindly share that as well.

SUSAN: The text in Proverbs of *Eshet Hayil* doesn't mean what in the Orthodox world it has come to mean, and what a great many others seem to think by default, because we haven't absorbed the meaning of the text many of us learned in *Tanakh* at whichever seminary we attended. The "woman of valor" is actually "a woman of (earned) status." She's a professional as well as a family woman, a woman of considerable social and professional reputation that she has earned in the community. *Davka* NOT a stay-at-home wife, whose only praise comes from her husband for being a good modest *housefrau* on Friday nights! Her husband, who is a judge, not hanging out in the *beit midrash*, is acknowledging his entrepreneurial wife as if she were Wisdom embodied, and had those characteristics. And she's equal. She wears *Argaman*, which means her cloak is striped in purple – the other murex dye along with *tekhelet*. Trash *Eshet Hayil*? Not a chance. My husband sings it to me in English. It doesn't scan so well, but it does get the point across.

This is what biblical scholarship is for, not for the sake of erudition, but because it's better *peshat* [literal meaning], which is what we're about, no? Being the *peshat* of Judaism? As well as our own midrash, but none needed here.

DON: I've heard of singing מי האיש החפץ חיים, Psalm 34:13 ff., in response to אשת חיל. An alternative to either or to both might be to read from Song of Songs. Another alternative I've heard is that some people use Psalm 1.

SUSAN: What a beautiful suggestion, Don. They must be special congregants. I'd love to hear ideas and suggestions from the rest of you.

BOB: Thank you so much for this concise commentary. I truly appreciate it and accept it.

There are, however, many things that we know and teach and explain and advocate – only to find that our congregants remain unimpressed with teaching and explanations. Our congregants' emotional reaction to *Eshet Hayil* will govern their response to it for many years to come – some love it and some will never accept it. And there is nothing new about this. This is the way it has always been!

SAM: I would like to call your attention to *Shir Yedidot* which is located in the *Mizmor Shir* Bencher from KTAV. This was a bencher created years ago by about twelve of us who wanted a traditional egalitarian bencher. *Shir Yedidot* was compiled and created by Sharon Bromberg as part of her senior thesis from List College. This is an egalitarian alternative to *Eshet Hayil*.

DON: You guys have given me some great ideas. I want you to know that I've asked some of my Orthodox colleagues about this question. And I brought with me an email from one colleague, that I want to read to you. He says:

> My wife and I have been married over fifty years. I have read *Eshet Hayil* before *Kiddush* every Shabbat eve during that time. Once, our then five-year-old son, who had just learned to read Hebrew, asked if he could now read it. I told him "No,

that's my privilege, you'll read it for your wife some day." He does.

SUSAN: That's so lovely!

I also brought an email, from a female colleague, when I heard that this topic was coming up, I wrote her, and here's what she answered:

> I agree with your reading of *Eshet Hayil*, and your interpretation of the image of the woman therein. What has bothered me about this practice, especially as it continues to be done among the Orthodox, is something a little different, and perhaps a little more subtle: the way in which the procedure of blessing the children and reciting *"Eshet Hayil"* establishes the husband/father as benevolent patriarch bestowing his blessing on the subordinate family members. In our household, where my husband and I both bless our children, it's less of an issue, and though we don't currently do this, if I were to choose something I felt was appropriate to say to him on a weekly basis, such as some of the suggestions that many of our colleagues have made, then I would have no objections to *"Eshet Hayil"* being what he recites to me.

DON: Thanks, Susan, for bringing that. One more point of view heard from. This is really an interesting discussion – especially for me, as an Orthodox rabbi.

BOB: Folks, here's a question that came to me this week. A couple in my congregation wishes to renew their vows after thirty years of marriage on the Sunday of *Hol Hamoed Sukkot*. Since it is not a wedding but a renewal of vows, is there a *halakhic* objection?

SUSAN: We Jews are crazy! We tell people they can't get married during *Sefirah* because it's a time of great sadness – the Talmud says Rabbi Akiva's students perished because God punished them for something akin to bullying – what a lovely thing to teach our youngsters! Even though from my reading of the Torah it seems like a time of immense gratitude and joy, let alone springtime! So that's seven weeks of no weddings, and then we tell them we won't marry them during the three weeks because we need to be in mourning for almost a month leading up to *Tishah B'Av*. So fully one fifth of the Jewish calendar is a time of mourning. Is it any wonder why Jews are so miserable? And then we add to that list *Hol Hamoed*, and *Sukkot* no less, why? Because it's TOO HAPPY a time to have a wedding! *G'valt!*

And, oh, since we're talking about weddings, here's another question: I have heard different things about a bride not seeing a groom on the day of the wedding. Is this a Jewish custom or not, and what is the origin and purpose of it? If a couple wants to follow it, how do they sign the *ketubah* if it is one that is signed by both?

DON: The practice of bride and groom not seeing one another isn't specifically Jewish. I know that it is practiced in the Church of England and there is a reference to it in Downton Abbey! How is that for classical sources?

I suspect it is grounded in the real fear that the bride and groom might "jump the gun" regarding intimacy.

You ask about what to do about the bride and groom signing the *ketubah*. Of course this was never done until recently. Neither signed it. The groom took possession of it, and it was given to the bride under the *huppah*. It isn't only feminist issues at work behind the common practice of bride and groom signing, especially since the groom didn't sign at all, but likely that Westerners can't conceive of a contract which isn't signed by all parties.

You could have the bride and groom sign in different rooms if there is a restriction of not seeing each other before the wedding, or they can sign together. It might be explained that the *ketubah* signing is the start of the wedding and integral to it. The wedding isn't just the *huppah*. It is likely that they had been taking pictures beforehand anyway.

There is absolutely no reason why the *hatan* and *kallah* should not both be present at the signing of the *ketubah* before the *bedeken*. The idea that it is "bad luck" for the *hatan* to see the *kallah* is not a Jewish tradition. Indeed, the very idea that the *hatan* and *kallah* should not meet before the *huppah* is a *minhag shtut* that has no basis in any traditional Jewish source whatsoever. It is a modern hasidic innovation that has been taken to extremes by some *hareidi poskim*.

Thus, while Rav Elyashiv ruled out of thin air that a *hatan* and *kallah* should not see each other, speak to each other, or send notes to one another, R. Ovadia Yosef, whose knowledge of sources is encyclopedic, has said that the practice has absolutely no basis. And, indeed, the practice was not followed by Rabbi Moshe Feinstein or Rabbi J.B. Soloveitchik. Rabbi Moshe Tendler's *kallah*, Shifra Feinstein, took part in the *seudah* following his *aufruf* on the Shabbat prior to their Tuesday wedding, and Rabbi Chaskel Besser, the former head of Daf Yomi, met with his *kallah* at the Kotel on the morning of their wedding. In those days, there was no *mehitzah* at the Kotel, and they were able to talk to one another.

Hevreh, let me turn the conversation to another issue. This came up recently when I saw an article about the ordination of rabbis from some seminary I never heard of – maybe an "on-line" place.

With the proliferation of new rabbinical schools and online ordination platforms, what does a rabbi need to know today? What skills do we need? What makes a rabbi, a rabbi?

BOB: Each movement needs to have its own definition of what it means to earn an ordination as a rabbi. Just as we cannot imagine a rabbi in the twenty-first century not knowing *Tanakh* and the modern approach to its study along with a background in Heschel, Borowitz, Soloveitchik and Kaplan, so too Chabad cannot imagine a rabbi who doesn't know *Tanya*, and the Orthodox can't imagine a rabbi who isn't conversant in *Shulhan Aruh* and a *blot* of Gemara.

The element that we can't measure is that of common sense and an innate ability to teach Judaism as well as model it. You can know and not be able to teach/communicate. But you can't properly communicate if you don't know. And that is where I see the problem. The level of ignorance of some "ordained" rabbis is palpable and plainly embarrassing, at least to those lay people who know something.

You can be a rabbi with knowledge but fail at it because you are a boor, but that makes you a boorish rabbi. But you can be Mr./Mrs./Ms. congeniality, and not know much, and that should disqualify you as a rabbi. You might be a great cheerleader for Judaism and a great actor and performer at life cycle occasions, but that doesn't make you a rabbi just like many cantorial soloists who are great at what they do, but limited and are not *hazzanim*.

But the reality is that the market place will decide who is a rabbi and right now in many communities it is defined by charisma and economics. If you have charisma and you accept compensation below the market place, you are a "rabbi." Very sad.

One other thing. No you can't, in my opinion, become a rabbi online. You can fulfill some of the class assignments for sure, because being a rabbi means learning with and working with people. Online is a way of teaching and learning, and we need to be skilled in it, but it can't be exclusive.

SUSAN: I have a non-*halakhic* question on which I'd like the thoughts of my colleagues.

I'm sure we all agree that "welcoming" is a vital tool – perhaps the most vital – in establishing, growing, deepening, and maintaining synagogue and other Jewish communities, and non-Jewish communities, for that matter.

Some aspects can be challenging, require changing perspectives or habits, or call for transforming institutional culture. And some are so easy that failing to do them defies explanation.

This past Sunday, I attended the morning *minyan* at a vibrant and active Conservative synagogue while travelling out of town. There were perhaps twenty others there – all wearing *tallit* and *tefillin* – and one woman wearing a *tallit* but not *tefillin*. The *davening* was competently led, and those present were comfortable and knowledgeable in the service. To make sure, there was someone calling pages in a pleasant and not overly verbose manner.

I was there to say *Kaddish*, and was the only person from outside of the community present that morning. Not one person present said a single word to me, before, during, or after the *davening*. It was obvious to all that I was a stranger and a mourner. Not a word.

I've posted on my rabbinic listserv about such an experience several years ago, and was chastised by one or two colleagues for not identifying myself as a rabbi or letting the rabbi or administration of the synagogue I was visiting know I was a rabbi, and would be there on such-and-such a date. Although I can't accept that it should matter that a visitor and an *aveil* is ordained when it comes to *hakhnasat orhim* and *nihum aveilim*, I took the *tokhahah* to heart and e-mailed the synagogue office and colleague's assistant in advance of my visit, in the name of confirming that the Sunday *minyan* was being held and the time was correct.

Our new synagogue president has presented all the professional staff and her executive board with copies of Ron Wolfson's *Relational Judaism*. My reaction to every page I've read so far is, "I've been saying this for years!" I suspect the concept is something we all know and on which we concur.

So why isn't it happening in such easy-to-apply circumstances?

SAM: Teaching "welcoming" is an ongoing process. I'll give you an example. A few years ago, our *shul* adopted the practice of having members of the board wear name tags at the end of services on Shabbat morning. That way, people could come up to them and ask about the *shul*. They could reach out to strangers, etc.

At board meetings, board members were routinely encouraged to go up to people at *Kiddush* to greet them. Of course, since we have bar and bat mitzvahs almost every week, it's more likely that a "visitor" is a member of a bar or bat mitzvah family, visiting the *shul* for the first and only time. But that shouldn't make a difference.

Soon thereafter, my cousins visited the *shul* on a Shabbat morning. After *Kiddush*, they munched on *kugel* and cake and sipped some coffee. Because there weren't enough seats, they stood off to the side.

Afterwards, I asked my cousin if any board members had come up to him to introduce themselves.

"No," he said. "All those people with the name tags simply stood and talked with one another."

Teaching people to go out of their comfort zone and, instead of shmoozing with their friends – which everyone loves to do at *Kiddush* – introduce themselves to a stranger. It 'aint so easy. So we must continue to remind people how important it is to do just that.

Hey, before we leave, I want to share with you a bit of humor I came across this week.

In reviewing a book on Jewish humor from the New York Times Book Review, Anthony Gottlieb tells a little joke about Mrs. Morgenbesser, the real-life Jewish mother of Professor Sidney Morgenbesser. She was once asked about her health, and reportedly replied, "Not so good – thank God."

Of course, I have my own Morgenbesser story to tell. Sidney, the son, actually drifted into and out of the rabbinate in the early 1940s. He graduated from JTS in 1944. In the 1940s Professor Morgenbesser was already a fixture there. Because of his Jewish connection, Morgenbesser frequently spoke before the Columbia University Jewish Graduate Society.

At one time, Professor Morgenbesser debated Rabbi Dr. Leo Jung of the Orthodox Jewish Center on West 86th Street, on some topic of Jewish interest. Rabbi Jung, already an older man, suffered a brief memory lapse and failed to recall some minor detail. He apologized. "You know, I'm not as Yung as I used to be!"

Professor Morgenbesser, without missing a beat, replied: "Don't worry. *Morgen vett zein Besser* [Tomorrow will be better]!"

Even Jewish philosophers make jokes – and puns.

DON: Attributed to Prof. Morgenbesser is the classic story about the English Professor stating that while two negatives make a positive, two positives do not make a negative, to which Morgenbesser responded, "Yeah, Yeah."

The Jewish mother's joke that I know is, "How are your children doing?" "They're struggling, *Barukh HaShem*."

Anyway – see y'all next week.

Week 8

❧

SAM: Let me start off today's discussion with a difficult question in the *halakhah* of Jewish medical ethics. I'd be interested in responses to the situation of a non-Jewish surrogate mother who became pregnant with the egg of a Jewish mother and the sperm of a Jewish man. Does this baby have to be converted?

SUSAN: A baby's Jewishness is determined by the birth-mother. The Committee on Jewish Law and Standards of the Rabbinical Assembly, the international Conservative rabbinical organization, approved a paper on this issue entitled "Maternal Identity and the Religious Status of Children Born to a Surrogate Mother" by Rabbi Aaron Mackler, in *Responsa 1991–2000*, the Committee on Jewish Law and Standards of the Conservative Movement, edited by Kassel Abelson and David Fine, New York, 2002, pp.137–145.

Please take into consideration that a baby's conversion is a very easy procedure. It includes circumcision, which the baby would undergo in any case, and immersion, and unless the child expresses his disagreement as soon as he turns thirteen, he is automatically Jewish. If he is not converted as a baby, and you are honest with the child regarding his birth circumstances, and he were to meet a Conservative or Orthodox woman that he wished to marry, he would then find himself in the uncomfortable situation of having to convert as an adult in order to marry her. A distressful situation could be avoided by undergoing the procedure as a baby.

Genetic material is not relevant to *halakhic* rulings. Under

Jewish law since the surrogate mother is not Jewish, she cannot transmit Jewish peoplehood to him.

SAM: Is there really a situation that a person would be expected to produce a conversion document in the future, or am I being ridiculous in thinking this is an important issue?

SUSAN: It may seem counter-intuitive, but that's what the Law Committee decided.

SAM: I can't believe this. But let's do some more research. Maybe there's a Reform responsum that is more reasonable.

BOB: As long as we're discussing Jewish identity, let me ask this question:

Hevreh, do you have policies about kids, non-Jews or of patrilineal descent only, attending both Hebrew school and church? If you do allow them, is there a cut-off age, such as moving from Sundays only to three times a week of school?

Moving to our specific situation: Does the family assume the children will have bat mitzah and then baptism? Obviously, I would not agree to a bat mitzvah, they are aware of this. But is that grounds for asking them to leave?

Our synagogue school committee would like to limit enrollment to matrilineal Jews and those whose parents are in conversion process. Namely, cases where parents intend to raise the child exclusively Jewish and convert the child.

Some parents don't see why kids can't be raised as both Christians and Jews. The kids spend a lot more time at church than *shul*. I would appreciate hearing how others handle matters like this.

DON: This problem is probably becoming more common in your *shuls*. Thank God we don't have such issues.

BOB: You're right, it's getting more and more common.

SAM: We've solved part of the problem by permitting patrilineal descent.

SUSAN: I think this is a problem that needs further study. Let's come back to it at another time.

BOB: Let's turn to a happier topic. June 14, Flag Day, is a day which I always associate with the birthday of Chancellor Louis Finkelstein, *z"l*, of JTS. I believe today is his 118th birthday. As Rashi quotes the familiar midrash about *Yaacov Avinu*, "*Mah zaro b'hayim, af hu b'hayim.*" "If one's progeny is alive so is he." I would like to consider myself one of his spiritual descendants, so to me he is still very much alive.

As a junior JTS administrator, I was privileged to be a fly on the wall in observing the giants of the day. There are many vignettes about all of them. In honor of Dr. Finkelstein's birthday, I will share two.

Many years ago I was Director of Admissions of the Rabbinical School. As this was during the height of the Vietnam War, and everyone wanted a 4D deferment, difficult decisions had to be made to determine the intent of each applicant.

One applicant, however, was already serving in the Armed Forces. As a teenager, he had committed a foolish felony which resulted in his paying restitution and being sent into the Armed Services as atonement for the offense he had committed. I reported, at that time, to Vice-Chancellor Kogen. Rabbi Kogen, *z"l*, was the unflappable administrator's administrator. Even he was at a loss as to how to handle this application. So he sent me to the Chancellor. The Chancellor never involved himself with admissions, so as not to be swayed by potential donors.

We met in the Chancellor's book-lined office. He was pouring over a *gemara* as I entered. He listened intently to the facts of the story, asking no questions and with no interruptions. At the end, he raised those famous, bushy eyebrows and in his distinctive voice asked, "We believe in *teshuvah*, don't we? Do you think he has done *teshuvah*?" On the spot, I thought for a second and replied in the affirmative. "Well," he said, "if we believe in *teshuvah*, what choice do we have but to consider his application along with all the others?" For me, another lesson learned.

The other story about Dr. Finkelstein was told to me by Rabbi Finkelstein's secretary, who never tired of telling me the story at least once annually. She was the grandmother figure in our office for many years. She had very young children, One day, in the midst of dictation, her children's school called. Not realizing that there was any urgency, she said she would return the call soon and continued taking dictation. Later, when Dr. Finkelstein became aware of what had occurred, he admonished her. "Whenever a school calls regarding a child, that has highest priority. Nothing takes precedence over the needs of one's child." Her reverence and respect for him never wavered from that day on.

DON: Beautiful stories. Thank you for sharing them.

SUSAN: Thank you so much for reminding me about his birthday.

Rarely does a day go by that I don't think about Dr. Finkelstein. I had the unique pleasure of driving Dr. Finkelstein to and from the Seminary often in my last year of Rabbinical School. And that year, the respect that I had for him only grew, and I grew to love him. While I either addressed him as "Professor" or as "Dr. Finkelstein," he was always a Rabbi in my eyes – even if he wouldn't give a *p'sak*!

Just this morning an elderly congregant I was visiting in the hospital asked me what he was like as a person, not as a scholar, and the visit lasted a lot longer than I had planned as I shared affectionate anecdotes about him.

One of the things Dr. Finkelstein told me was that his teacher, Dr. Solomon Schechter, said that "the purpose of the Seminary is to expose students to great men." On this day, being his birthday, I recall the letters he would send, taking note of my birthday, my wedding anniversary, and my son's birthday. I always acknowledged his letters with a call. "How are you, Professor?" "I can't complain." You can't or you won't?" And he would just chuckle diplomatically.

But more than anything I recall one brief conversation when I thanked him for always remembering and writing, when he had so much still to do to complete *The Sifra* – and I know I wasn't the only one who received his birthday and anniversary letters! And he said, "Why not, we're friends, aren't we?" I still can't bring myself to say or to think of ourselves as "friends." I was, and still am, so far out of his league. But there have been few times in my life when I felt as privileged as when he called us "friends."

DON: I never met him, but it is very warming to hear these stories. Thanks!

SAM: I have another question for my esteemed colleagues. Do any of your synagogues have a policy concerning dogs in the sanctuary? I'm not talking about Seeing Eye dogs and any dog which is a physical assistant to its master. Most synagogues I assume would let such a dog in. I'm talking about letting a pet dog walk down the aisle during a wedding in the sanctuary. Do any of you have a policy concerning this? As for the background to this: Don't ask!!

BOB: When I had that request for a wedding, I asked the family, "Before I check on the *halakhah* on the question, do you really want your wedding to be remembered as 'the one where the dog walked down the aisle?'" The request was withdrawn, even though the dog was old enough – in human years – to have had a bark mitzvah. As one of our colleagues once remarked: *Kina hora*!

Let me change the subject and ask this question: I was speaking with someone today who told me that her husband has often left money – I imagine coins – on gravestones when visiting Jewish cemeteries. He is Sefardi, of Turkish descent. I've never heard of this custom. Can anyone comment?

DON: Is check or credit card accepted?

SUSAN: Stop being wiseguys! I never heard of leaving money. Sometimes people leave small stones, as a sign that someone was there.

DON: OK, let's get serious. One of the biggest controversies in a long time in the religious world in Israel is the revelation by

Makor Rishon, the most popular newspaper in that community, that many men and women are texting during services on Shabbat and *Yom Tov*. The reactions have been fast and furious and going on for some time. Bottom line is it seems that many are doing it. The summation was a new type of religiosity in our communities, people deciding *halakhah* by what they think is right for them. Wow, does that sound familiar! So I gather by the comments of Conservative colleagues that in general their *shuls* are stricter on this bad habit on Shabbat than Orthodox *shuls*.

BOB: With a cell phone, at least the person usually tries to turn the thing off. Although much of the time they can't find the darn thing, and so they fumble around and make a lot of noise.

But how about babies crying during the sermon while the parent sits there like a *golem*? Several times over the past few high holidays this has happened in my synagogue. The parents apparently think that their babies' crying is the sweetest music on earth.

SUSAN: I would like your thoughts on "live-streaming" High Holiday services. Many synagogues do it for those who are ill, or in the hospital. But now it's becoming more widespread, and for less valid reasons.

The primary concern voiced by those skeptical of, or outright opposed to live-streaming, was that it would discourage attendance at services, and take away the incentive for those who pay membership dues solely for High Holiday tickets.

I bumped into someone yesterday. I said "I was sorry we missed seeing you in *shul*." She said that she stayed home and watched another service streamed on the internet. I know that the only reason was she was too cheap to buy a ticket.

I didn't know what to say. "I hoped you enjoyed it." "I hope it was meaningful for you." "Sorry you were too damn cheap to buy a ticket." "Let me know next year, and I will see if I can get you a free/cheap ticket." Yes I know, it's already the New Year and I am thinking evil thoughts.

On the positive side, she did watch the service.

Personally, I wish a code was required to watch the streaming. A code could be given to those who are house bound, out of town, in the hospital, etc. Of course that wouldn't work when there are dozens of services already online.

Then there is the story of a guy who goes to the rabbi and said the big game is *Kol Nidre* night, and I am torn as to which one to go to. The rabbi says, "No problem. That is what Tivo's/DVR's are for." And the guy says, "You mean I can TIVO *Kol Nidre*?"

SAM: OK, folks, I now have a very serious question, and I'd love your thoughts.

The eighth grade teacher in our religious school wants to speak to me tomorrow because one of her students asked, "If God knows everything, and God can do everything, and God is good, then why does He let bad things happen?"

The teacher wants to know what to say. The teacher said, "Someone came to the synagogue once and said that you can have two out of three." In other words, out of these three, God can only do two: know everything, do everything, God is good. She seemed to like that response, but wanted to give the "Reform movement's position." I have downloaded two pieces by Louis Jacobs, but I want to suggest something which is honest, helpful, and age-appropriate. I could say to the teacher that there is no official Reform position on the subject, but I don't think that that would be helpful to her. I believe that there is no firm, clear, easy answer to the question, and part of my faith is to act as if good is rewarded and evil is punished, even though I don't know if that is really true. I believe that the World to Come takes care of things, but that is no explanation, because I believe that the statement is a tautology. We have no knowledge of the World to Come other than the definition that it is the "place" where the wrongs of this world are righted. I would tell adults about some historical Jewish responses, which is what Jacobs does, and then share with them my own thinking. Can you do this with a twelve year old? I think that I know who the student is, and if I am right, she and her parents have chips on their shoulders. I can imagine her or her parents going around saying that she asked an honest religious question and the teacher and the rabbi refused to answer it. What is the best course to take?

BOB: Sam, your twelve-year-old is asking an honest religious question, so her parents can be proud of her. Isadore Rabi, the Galizianer who won a Nobel Prize for Physics, attributed his scientific success to his mother, who, when he came home from school as a child, would not ask what he'd learned that day, but if he had "asked a good question." May this girl win a Nobel Prize.

But on theodicy – which, before I entered Seminary, I thought was the second of the Greek JK Rolling's Achilles Potter series – she doesn't have a claim to originality. Jeremiah, a pretty righteous fellow who suffered not a little himself, questioned God directly about this (12:1): "Why does the way of the wicked prosper? Why are the workers of treachery at ease?" God responds in classic Jewish fashion, with a question. I recall that the Midrash tells of *Moshe Rabbenu* asking God the same question, but do not have the source available.

And of course, the book of Job is built on this theological dilemma.

Pirke Avot is a great "platform" of Rabbinic thought and it has many statements about the justice in the world: evildoers will be punished and the good will be rewarded, which is consistent with the Deuteronomic outlook on life. We recall it twice a day in the second paragraph of *Kri'at Shema*.

But it also includes the stridently perceptive wisdom of Rabbi Yanai (4:19): Rabbi Yannai said: it is not in our hands to explain the reason either of the security of the wicked, or even of the afflictions of the righteous.

The growth of belief in the World to Come as the forum in which the accounts will be straightened out was evidently a means of keeping faith in a just God and a just world while realizing that the data does not always support the proposition.

So what's the best course to take, you ask, to confirm her parents' view that she asked a good question and that you, the rabbi, does not have a good answer, that you are following in the tradition of generations of Jews and rabbis who have wrestled with this issue, that you ask it yourself every time you recall the *Shoah* or see a young congregant with cancer or hear of people killed in car accidents or reread *As a Driven Leaf* or *When Bad Things Happen to Good People*.

"Life is not fair," Jimmy Carter said years ago, and probably many more before him, or so it seems on occasion. The challenge of the Jew is to recite *Kri'at Shema* twice a day and, at the same time, to remember Rabbi Yanai. I would not be ashamed to admit that I don't have a good answer to the question. It's the people who claim to have one about whom I'm skeptical.

SAM: Thanks, Bob! That's probably as good an answer as I can get.

SUSAN: Excuse me for a minute, folks, I am just getting an important call on my cell phone. Be right back. . . . (A few minutes later): A congregant lost her father. A sibling who's in control of the father's affairs ordered a cremation with no service. Cremation may take up to two weeks till final. The congregant wants to know when to start *shivah*. Should I have her start immediately? I'd appreciate quick responses.

BOB: I would start now. She needs her family and friends now, not in two weeks. By then, they won't be as interested and committed to being with her.

SUSAN: Good advice, Bob. Be right back, after I relay my reply.

SAM: Here's a fascinating question that can only be asked in the twenty-first century. It has to do with synagogue emails that we send out.

I have a question that is both tactical and *halakhic*/ethical. Perhaps like many of us, we send out email announcements to our congregation's email list using an email marketing service. We use Mailchimp and have also used Constant Contact.

Among the benefits of this is that we have a tremendous ability to track people's use of our emails, including which emails they open, where they are when they open each email – if they open it on a mobile phone – and exactly what links they click on.

Presumably most of us realize in theory that whenever we receive an email with links in it, someone can keep track of exactly where we click. And yet, I don't think most people are conscious of this fact while they are reading their email, so our synagogue is receiving a lot of information about people's location and interests that they are not really intending for us to have. There's something quite creepy about this. But sometimes we get what could be potentially useful information.

We noticed, for example, that someone who has not rejoined the synagogue this year, because of a public dissatisfaction with a particular synagogue policy, still opens every email from the synagogue, almost immediately after it is sent, and very often he clicks on links in the email, and especially clicks on the links for synagogue membership information.

This appears to indicate that he continues to have a very high level of engagement with our synagogue community, and could also mean that he is seriously contemplating rejoining the synagogue despite her grievance, though there are other possible explanations too. By the way, that I can so easily obtain this information reminds me how easy it must be for government agencies to get all kinds of info on me.

My questions:

(a) Should we feel ethical qualms about tracking this kind of information? Should we set a synagogue policy not to look at those reports? Should we say that this person deserves that we not be stalking his email-reading and internet-clicking habits? Or should we say that it is well-known that organizations collect info about the links that people click on, so we should have no qualms about it?

(b) If we do say that it's completely ethical to track this info, how exactly would we act upon it? I could just casually call up Mr. X to check in with him, but I can't imagine the conversation would go well if I were to indicate that I know something about her habits in reading emails from the synagogue. And this means that the conversation would be duplicitous. I would be pretending that I just happened to call, when actually my call was triggered by things he did that he probably assumed were completely private.

Any responses? Thoughts regarding the ethical, *halakhic*, tactical, are welcome.

SUSAN: This is a tough one. Let's all do some thinking, and do some research, and return to this issue at a later meeting.

SAM: OK, you're probably right. It's not an easy question.

BOB: Friends, I have a question that I have never dealt with before. Does anyone have a ceremony for an upsherin that they can share? I have been asked to officiate at one, and although I've been to a couple, I have never been in this position before.

DON: I have something from a few years ago. I'll try to dig it up and send it to you. It's fascinating how *upsherin* is growing in popularity. I think it's a perfectly timed ritual, developmentally speaking, and a wonderful way to engage families with young children.

Some of my colleagues who react so strongly whenever anyone ever asks for resources and help with *upsherin*. They might say: Are you serious? There's a Jewish ritual that's growing in popularity, and you want to discourage it because it looks too *frum* or has roots in paganism? As I put away our *lulav* to be used again to search for *chametz* during *Pesach* I'll think more about your objection.

SUSAN: My teacher, and the teacher of many of our colleagues, Simon Greenberg, used to teach that Conservative Judaism represents a non-superstitious non-fundamentalist rational yet traditional understanding of Judaism. One of the foundations of my Seminary was to base our understanding of Judaism on history and scholarship, not ritual that often borders on heresy or idolatry.

I understand the desire of people to hold on to and explore rituals and ideas that seem quaint and meaningful. We have to decide when to disabuse them of an idea that really has no place in modern Judaism, and when to affirm a practice that needs reinterpretation.

Having a ceremony marking a child's first haircut can be meaningful. Affirming that the Satan, or devil, has left this child alone because it was fooled into thinking a boy was a girl – which is indeed the foundation of this ceremony – is at least embarrassing and in my mind perhaps heretical. It may also be quite sexist and let's face it, it belongs with those who still believe in demons.

I am not certain what I would do in Bob's situation, because we want so badly to affirm those interested in Jewish tradition, even when that tradition is probably out of bounds were we to delve into it even a little bit. Yes, we are indeed serious – not because it looks too *frum*, but because it looks too heretical, and perhaps even at the expense of alienating a family we should stand by our principles.

BOB: I have a question that I would guess several of you must have dealt with at some point, given the fact that we need a *minyan* of ten for Mourners' *Kaddish*, and we often have less than the full quorum.

Among those who follow the practice of counting the Torah scroll itself as the tenth for the recitation of Mourners' *Kaddish*, do you allow this for any other part of a the service where a *minyan* is required? I inherited the practice of counting the Torah as the tenth "member" for Mourners' *Kaddish* and to read Torah at weekday *minyan*.

DON: There is absolutely no source for this practice. Whoever suggested it didn't understand the *gemara*, where it is raised as a possibility but clearly and immediately rejected. There is a minority view that you can count one minor as the tenth, but nobody who says you can count a *Sefer Torah*, or the *aron hakodesh*. See *Berakhot* 47b. Instead of reciting Mourners' *Kaddish* without a proper *minyan*, it would be more beneficial for the dead and for the mourner to read or teach a *Mishnah* to those present.

SAM: Your answer is technically correct. I'm just wondering how to say that to the person who has come to say *Kaddish* on the Yahrzeit of her daughter. In that situation I count the Torah. If no one is there to say *Kaddish* we don't.

DON: I must reiterate my earlier reply to this question. I NEVER count a *Sefer Torah* as a tenth person to a *minyan*. If and when the Torah can answer Amen to a *berakhah*, I will then count it, and don't give me any double talk about a Torah scroll being a source of eternal albeit silent witness. An inanimate object, regardless of its intrinsic or symbolic *kedusha* is NOT a substitute for a live person. As to a pre-bar Mitzvah *bahur*, let him come AFTER his coming of age and then he will indeed be counted.

People needing or wanting to say *Kaddish* are encouraged to bring a Jewish friend or family member of age – or more than one – to help ensure that there will be a *minyan* present. Failing that, I have invited those expecting to say *Kaddish* to recite an appropriate psalm instead when there is no *minyan*.

SUSAN: Don, friends can disagree. To me, *Kaddish* is a prayer that transcends its meaning. To learned rabbis it is a prayer of praise recited at various times that requires a communal response. To mourners it is much more personal and they don't really care that there are only five, six or nine people to respond. Indeed I have found over the years that no matter what we say, many people will recite *Kaddish* when they are alone! We always try to have ten, but when there is not we will still say *Kaddish* at the end of the service.

I was opposed to this at first, but I have come to understand how important it is to many people. It is not a *brakhah l'vatalah* [a vain recitation of a blessing], and I am prepared to answer before the *kisei ha-kavod* [the Throne on High] for the times I have said it with mourners when less than ten were present. Indeed one of the most powerful moments for me occurred maybe ten years ago when there was a huge snow storm. I never cancel Shabbat services, so I trudged here in the snow. Much to my amazement someone else did the same who had a *yahrzeit*. I went through the service, announced the *yahrzeits* and said *Kaddish* with him at the end. He left the *shul* many years ago, but I have no doubt that this moment has stayed with him too.

DON: Forgive me for raising another *halakhic* question, but, naturally, these Jewish legal issues obviously bother me more than others. But all of us should be concerned about this.

Are you all aware that if someone wishes to be buried at Arlington National Cemetery there is a wait of several months?! I intend to try to see what I can do to rectify this unacceptable situation, but in the meantime I have a congregant whose father just died. What should be done about *shivah*? How about *Kaddish*? It seems wrong to have him wait several months.

BOB: It IS a vexing situation, and should be legislatively remedied, as it is detrimental to our religious practices, and those veterans who are entitled to burial in a national cemetery should at least have the courtesy extended to their loved ones and family to have the comfort of following the traditions of their faith. After all, isn't that one of the freedoms they fought to preserve, protect and defend?

That having been said, I have been told at one of the national cemeteries in Florida, where services are held under a pavilion on the premises, the family is NOT allowed to accompany the casket to the grave or participate in its burial, that services are limited to ten minutes each, INCLUDING any military honors. Moreover, it is the policy of National Cemeteries that those buried there are buried in the next available grave, not in sections separated into religious areas. Therefore, our Jewish veterans are NOT being buried in consecrated ground, which by our definition, would be in an exclusively Jewish section. By US standards, it's ALL consecrated ground by virtue of the American soldiers who served being buried there. Families are permitted to return and visit the gravesite at the end of the day's burials, if they wish to. This, of course, precludes concluding the committal portion of our service, as the funeral directors euphemistically call it, with the shoveling of earth and *Kaddish*.

I have suggested to our Jewish funeral directors that to counter the lack of consecrated Jewish burial areas, a packet of Israel Earth – you know, the stuff we all sprinkle – be placed INSIDE the casket before it is closed and delivered for the service and subsequent burial. I have suggested that the packet of earth be slit open and placed beneath the deceased's head or neck or under the pillow on which the head rests. At best, this is token-ism, but, in my opinion, better than nothing.

All to whom I've suggested this have thought this was a good idea. Why not? The funeral directors can bill for an extra packet of Israel Earth!

It is understandable but disturbing that there is such a backup for veterans' burials and most of all, the hardship it causes the mourners is heartbreaking.

May I therefore suggest that while we seek some remedy for this grave injustice – sorry for the pun – we suggest that our mourners follow the procedure of reciting *Kaddish* at the conclusion of the FUNERAL service, and begin shivah and *shloshim* immediately upon leaving the cemetery and returning home, just as if burial were to take place overseas. Were this to become a standard practice in these circumstances, much of the hardship caused by these US governmental policies and delays in burial could be ameliorated for the grieving families.

SUSAN: I have heard, don't know if it's fact, that there is long-standing *halakhah* that if the body is being buried away from the mourners, they begin shivah etc. as soon as they turn from the coffin. This would be a valid alternative, and would also reduce the hardship for grieving families.

As long as I have the floor, so to speak, let me raises another important issue.

I just returned from viewing the film "The Other Son" at my *shul*. It is well done and quite intriguing, a story about how it is discovered that an Israeli boy and a Palestinian boy are switched at birth. I imagine many of you have already seen this film.

At one point, Joseph, the boy who learns he is by birth a Palestinian Arab, visits a rabbi to discuss the implication of this discovery. The rabbi tries to offer comfort to Joseph while of course explaining that if he is to be considered a Jew into the future he must go through the standard procedures and rituals for conversion. Joseph then asks if the other young man, Yacine, the one actually born to the Israeli Jewish mother is considered a Jew. Of course we know that the rabbi tells him yes. The rabbi states that Judaism is not a belief, but rather a matzav, translated in the film as "state."

Joseph is incredulous and leaves the rabbi's office bewildered.

Recently, I met with a Jewish young man and his fiancée prior to their wedding. I was not the officiant. The groom's parents are very active in my *shul*, and I know the young couple pretty well. I had heard that the bride's mother converted years ago, under Reform auspices, but several years after the bride was born. The bride had never converted.

When I reviewed this situation with them, I offered to take the bride to the mikvah. They left the office, didn't come to High Holiday services at my *shul* as they had previously planned, and may not return ever. Her understanding of her life as a Jew had been totally invalidated and undermined. No matter how much I might view this as a technicality, it was a monumental disappointment for her.

Was this type of disappointment avoidable? Am I missing something? I know that sooner or later the same questions might have arisen, when they might have children, even if I had not discussed this issue with them.

Should I have not mentioned it to them since I was not officiating?

Am I much different than the rabbi in "The Other Son"? If the answer is no, is that a good thing? If the answer is yes, is that a good thing?

BOB: Perhaps the real "answer" for those who have been raised Jewishly but who are not at present *halakhically* recognized as such by the Conservative movement is, forgive me, to finally admit that Roman Law regarding "citizenship" being determined by the mother's status (a model which clearly influenced the sages of the time), be abandoned in favor of the biblical model. The well-meaning, middle-ages attribution of Jewish status to those who emerge from a Jewish mother's womb, for the sake of kindness and compassion for cases where the father might have been an unknown Cossack or Hun, just doesn't make sense in today's world. In the Bible, Rivkah, Rahel and Leah were from the former family of Abraham, but were no less idolaters than was

Abraham's father until they were married and integrated into the belief/practice system of their husbands.

They "joined their husbands' tribe" upon marriage, and the children born to them are us. Plain and simple. Rabbinic Judaism recognized when times had changed, and new definitions, institutions, and interpretations were necessary to ensure Jewish survival. If we are truly their heirs –spiritually, intellectually and methodologically – can we do any less?!

It's passed time to let go of a model that no longer is cogent, just as the rabbis in their day and age replaced sacrifice with prayer and the Temple with the synagogue.

Sometimes tradition trumps change, sometimes not. If we want to see Judaism continue in generations beyond our own, we have to rise to the occasion, as did our ancestors. Our Sages did what they saw necessary for Jewish continuity and survival. That's why we're still here.

SAM: As rabbis, we encounter people who, for any of a variety of reasons, view themselves as Jews but are not *halakhically* Jewish. They may be Patrilineal Jews or people adopted by Jewish families without *giyyur* [*halakhic* conversion], or they may have other, less common stories. As a teacher and rabbi, I have found it useful to say to such people from the outset something like this:

"Legal systems, like computer code, are binary. They have to define things as yes or no, forbidden or permitted, guilty or not guilty, in or out. As you and I well know, reality is much more complex and nuanced than that. I don't doubt that you are already, in an important way, a Jew, because Jewishness is about who we are in a very profound sense: who we think of as 'us,' what our commitments are, how we view the world. In that sense, you are Jewish, or well on your way to being Jewish.

"But under the up-or-down view of Jewish law, you're disqualified on a technicality. I try to avoid the language of "... you are not a Jew" at this point. It would be an honor and a privilege for me to help straighten out the technicalities to bring you in line with the more complex reality of who you are."

In other situations, that last sentence has to be replaced with a demurral rather than an invitation: "While I have great respect for the sense in which you really are Jewish, as Conservative Jews I have to respect the legal dichotomy. . . ."

I have found that such an affirmation of the unofficial, incomplete, but very real Jewish identity of my interlocutor usually goes a long way toward bringing him or her into the process of *giyyur*, or at least toward taking the sting out of my refusal to offer some formal recognition of the person's Jewishness.

I think framing the situation in the way I have described can be helpful.

By the way, the film that sparked this discussion is very much worth seeing.

I am sure that we can compile a long list of anecdotes focusing on those who considered themselves Jewish only to find out that they were not. In my Seminary days, I taught converts, and once I was teaching a young woman whose fiancé was an attorney. Evidently her fiancé discussed the sessions they had with me, with some other lawyers in the office. One day I got a call from a young woman. She introduced herself and her family name was a very common Jewish surname. She said "Tell me what you told Max [not his real name] is not so." I asked what she was referring to. She said that he mentioned in conversation that if your mother was not Jewish, you were not Jewish.

This was before the Reform movement adopted their patrilineal position. I responded that what I said was true. She responded, and this is an exact quote: "Don't believe it; I never dated a *sheygitz* in my life." It also turned out that she had been an officer of Hillel at the university where she did her graduate work. She met with the officiating rabbi and was assigned to me for instruction. In her personal behavior she was as Jewish as anyone else. One of the rabbi's questions that he always asked at the conversion ceremonies that he conducted was "Do you renounce your former faith?" I had asked him if he would waive the question in this case, but he said that he would not deviate from the pattern he had used for many years. I told the young woman that the rabbi would ask her a question that really did not apply to her, since the only faith she ever had was the Jewish faith, but since she was technically not Jewish even though she had lived a Jewish life, she should respond "yes" to the question. So the situation of people suddenly finding out that although they were raised as Jews they were not Jews according to *halakhah* is not new.

DON: What to do with people raised as Jews but not "technically" Jewish is going to become an increasingly normal occurrence. The problem presents itself before a bar mtzvah or before a wedding. Before a bar mitzvah is more awkward particularly if we need *hatafat dam brit*, but also in case of *mikveh*. Before a wedding is less awkward as they are adults and the rituals are not the problem as much as the idea that they aren't "really" Jewish in our eyes.

Just in the past year I had to arrange one *hatafat dam* and two *mikvehs* for bar mitzvahs and a few *mikvehs* for brides-to-be. The easiest is the status of the bride-to-be, which, for some, is determined by the *mikveh,* while others are ok with her Jewish identity. So to increase the number of those who are ok with the Jewish identity I want you to go to *mikveh* as a bride does before her wedding and say the blessing upon immersion. That goes very well.

We talked with the kids about how people enter this country and become citizens. I ask them also about driving. You took lessons and you practiced, but you just never got around to getting your license. What do you think you should do? It works every time – so far that is.

SAM: I'd like to turn the conversation to a different tone – a really deep, philosophical question.

I have a congregant who is asking for good examples of specific ethics and values that are not purely ritual or theological in nature, yet are "distinctively Jewish." Perhaps an example could be that for Jews the act of giving is an expression of "justice," *tzedakah*, as opposed to charity – pity, or compassion. Or perhaps, as Joseph Telushkin claims, "Judaism does not preach universal forgiveness, but insists that in some instances, to forgive the perpetrator is to malign the victim." Or, perhaps as Yitz Greenberg wrote, "The perfection of the world will not be bestowed upon us by some divine gift. The goal can be realized by nothing less than a partnership, or covenant, between God and humanity." Both pledge to sustain and work for life and full human dignity in every way for as long as it takes. Perhaps some of the specific laws of guarding our speech, do not appear in such a way in other traditions. I was wondering if you have some more good examples, and how you would respond to such a request? I have my own thoughts, but would like those thoughts to be enriched and challenged by yours.

DON: Distinctively Jewish is problematic, if the idea is to find an ethical idea that has no currency elsewhere, even as a non-normative position, because ethics are all about the human condition, and the human condition is common to us all.

But the ethical stance that distinguishes Judaism perhaps most from that which reigns in America is communitarian focus rather than individual focus. The question of morality is always what serves the well-being of the community rather than what serves to benefit the individual. Thus universal health care is a given in the Jewish approach, but has enormous difficulty in American thought. This has manifold ramifications.

Here's another strictly Jewish ethical value, "*gadol ham'tzuveh v'oseh mi-she-eino m'tzuveh, v'oseh,*" namely, preferencing obligation and loyalty to God over personal voluntary behavior.

Another uniquely Jewish value is the attention to details, as in *lashon hara*, gossip. The same "values" exist elsewhere, but have not been thought through so thoroughly by other religions.

One more, though it is less clear if this is an ethical norm or a scientific policy determination; the idea that life begins at conception is decidedly normative Catholic and now evangelical. The Jewish position, that life begins later, at the formation – forty days – or perhaps at birth, or in the best current merger of Jewish thought with modern science – at implantation – about two weeks – but after stem cell harvest from blastocysts.

SUSAN: I think what's really being asked is a question which many Jews have and don't ask out loud, is "why be specifically Jewish?" Our congregants value ethics, not rituals, and believe the purpose of Torah was to bring ethics to humanity, so what does Judaism have to contribute in the twenty-first century, when we already have "Judaeo-Christian ethics"?

In that context, what is uniquely Jewish is not any particular ethical stand, such as abortion issues, etc., but the nexus of ethics, embodied rituals, and study. Everybody believes in *tzedakah*, but the practice of giving a coin every time we *daven* to train our bones to do *mitzvot* – the Slonimer Rebbe says to make our bodies Jewish – is particularly Jewish. Everybody thinks gossip is bad, but I know of no other religion that has thought out the details so thoroughly, such thought being dismissed as "casuistry" or "legalistic." We have developed embodied spiritual practices as well as the practice of Torah study to train ourselves in these universal values.

SAM: Thanks, guys. Some interesting ideas!

Let me change the topic now. I have a request from a Christian pastor nearby, let me read it to you:

"My name is Reverend Smith, and I am the Director of Music Ministries at Methodist Church here in town. In other churches in which I have served, we have invited a *shofar* player to sound the usual soundings for the beginning of the year on the first Sunday of the Christian Advent, which this year is this coming Sunday. As I mentioned, I am hoping that we can do the same this year at our church. We would request the *shofar* for our 11:00 a.m. service, and the sounding would occur right at 11:00.

"I am personally only somewhat familiar with the names of the *shofar* calls and their symbolism, and would love to include a paragraph in our bulletin explaining them. The *tekia gedolah* being the one with which I am most familiar, though my spelling may leave a bit to be desired!

"Thank you so much for your consideration and help!"

This is either appropriate, in the spirit of interfaith respect and collaboration, or inappropriate – co-opting our rituals and ritual objects for their sacred calendar. I'm not sure which. What do you think?

BOB: I would respond positively, in a spirit of interfaith cooperation and good will. In fact, I was once invited to sound the *shofar* at the dedication of a new pipe-organ at a Lutheran seminary, and did so myself, making the donors of the organ, who had suspiciously Jewish-sounding names, very happy.

DON: I have a hard time with this. I love interfaith events, when they are done sensitively. I just think that here we are using a Jew to celebrate the advent of the Christian Messiah. I don't have a problem with the symbol – if done by a Christian. I'd advocate for a Jewish *shofar*-blower training a Christian to do this. Maybe they know a bass player who could pick it up easily.

BOB: Divorce the profound Jewish symbolism of the *shofar* from the purported Christian theology and be a good neighbor. We over-think Christian invitations as an attempt to subvert Judaism and capture or convert Jews. I doubt there would be any Jew present at this service other than the *shofar* sounder, and unless she is so inclined, there probably will be no apostasy involved.

SUSAN: Every so often, I think I've seen it all and heard it all. But here's one for the books:

In the town next to ours there is apparently one of the largest Bucharian Jewish communities outside of Brooklyn in the United States – tens of thousands. I've been at a few of their *simchas*, and they are characterized by tons of food and heavy drinking.

Now, some of the organizers of the Bucharian Jewish Community want to rent our synagogue social hall for New Years Eve, from about 8 p.m. to 4 a.m. I imagine that the rental will be several thousand dollars. Of course, we would build into the cost the expected cleanup. Historically, there's a great deal of drinking and puking in various corners of the building, when it's too hard to get to a toilet.

But here's the zinger. They want to know if they can have a holiday tree. I know that trees are common in Russia even among Jews and they are not "Christmas trees" per se, just "holiday" or "festival trees." I don't like the optics, but in America can one really distinguish between the two?

Also, they seem to have a character who dresses up like Santa, although he's not really Santa, but a gift bearing fellow in a red suit. This actually reminded me of going to an Orthodox cousin's *seder* in Tel Aviv where Eliyahu was dressed up in a padded red suit and a fake white beard. We thought he looked like Santa, but they insisted that this was the way that they've always portrayed Eliyahu.

We may decide that we don't want them here because they are extremely rowdy, and we will be cleaning up all sorts of disgusting things. That's an administrative and financial decision of which I really do not want any part. But I could effectively nix the whole affair if I tell them that neither the tree nor the Santoid are allowed.

We traditionally have difficulty getting a *minyan* on New Year's morning, so I'm half tempted to allow them to hold their affair if we can drag any of the remaining Russians who remain conscious in our social hall into our chapel to help make the *minyan*!

Any thoughts?

DON: I have some Bucharian friends, and in my opinion you might want to pass on this one for many reasons, including liability and *mar'eet ayin* [optics]. But the "Santoid" in question has more in common with Jack Frost than with Santa, despite the similar costume. His name in Russian folklore is "Ded Moroz." He comes with his sidekick *Snegurochka*, snow maiden. All in all, as Chico would say, there ain't no Sanity Clause. . . . I'd think it over before you decide.

SAM: *Hevreh*, I have an issue that many of you have probably dealt with. Our beautiful building has a big social hall – sorry, "ballroom!" – and a full-sized catering kitchen. The idea is that it would make the synagogue an attractive venue for *b'nei mitzvah* parties, weddings, and community events. We certainly have more of all of those than in our previous facility, but with that comes new challenges.

It's become clear that we need to engage our own security personnel to ensure that guests at events and parties stay in the designated areas. Party planners have brought personnel who ostensibly do this, but those individuals aren't looking out for the interests of the synagogue. We don't expect – nor is it fair to ask – our facilities personnel to handle crowd control. They're busy enough during an event.

It would only take a couple of strategically-placed individuals to keep kids, and adults, in the party, out of the sanctuary, school wing, youth lounge, and parking lot. However, those individuals would need to be empowered to enforce those limits. We have a uniformed officer from a private security firm present, but his job is really keeping unwanted individuals OUT.

Basically, we're looking to set up "hotel security" – the kind of guy you'd find standing outside a ballroom in a hotel where a bar or bat mitzvah party or wedding reception is taking place, holding a walkie-talkie and making sure you don't go wandering off where you oughtn't be.

Has anyone dealt with this in a synagogue setting?

SUSAN: In these times, protecting synagogue property from damage and theft is, in many ways, less of a consideration than the safety of guests and the liability of the congregation and the host family. Sad but true.

For example, locking doors would seem to be a logical and simple way of restricting access. However, it is also frequently considered a fire hazard to lock internal doors which would prevent guests from leaving one part of the building – the social hall – where a fire may be, and passing through a safe area – the school wing – to reach exits. That's why our synagogue is looking at strategies which place security personnel in strategic positions to prevent access to off-limits areas.

The challenge is enforcement. If a rambunctious thirteen-year-old, or an inebriated forty-three-year-old, decides to ignore the instructions of the person posted at the door of the sanctuary, or school wing or parking lot, and push past anyway, there needs to be someone legally empowered to enforce the boundary.

SAM: Thanks. I'll mull it over some more.

I have a current political question, and would love your thoughts.

I'm sure that many in the next week or two will want to speak about Nelson Mandela. I'm conflicted. He was certainly a heroic figure and did much for his people. But the more I read about what he said and wrote about Israel, the more obvious to me that he, like most classical anti-Semites and anti-Zionists did two things:

a) applied different norms to Jews and Israel than he did to all other peoples and denied us exactly what he wanted for his people.

b) seemed to know everything about history but when it came to Israel he forgot all the inconvenient truths.

He was not a Martin Luther King who was much more fair and consistent in his application of his philosophy, and quite frankly if the world or America had listened to him Israel would probably not be around today as a Jewish state or even as anything with Jews. So how do we approach this complicated great man who was essentially anti-Zionist. By the way, like others, he cloaks his anti-Zionism in being pro-democracy and just protecting the poor, innocent Palestinians who are victims of the powerful Israelis. He kind of forgot about their refusal to accept an Arab state in 1947, and their desire to destroy the Jewish state and push the Jews into the sea. Just an inconvenient truth for him.

BOB: He may have been a great leader, and moral icon in so many ways, but in my book he's an Anti-Semitic s-o-b. I'd ignore the subject.

SUSAN: I'd like to throw a bit of levity into the conversation, so let me tell you a cute story I heard from a senior colleague, maybe apocryphal, maybe not. If not, it's a myth that has a lot of truth in it.

As *Kohelet* says "nothing new under the sun. "Prof. Max Arzt *zts"l*, once announced at an RA convention, after a particularly rancorous session of complaints about job conditions and lack of observance among congregants etc., that there would be a meeting of all the rabbis who were happy in their jobs in the phone booth outside the lobby. Of course that was in the Concord, of blessed memory, so there were about 1,000 rabbis present. Maybe some of the young colleagues do not know what a "phone booth" is, but if you do, you get the joke. The remark got a big laugh from the crowd.

DON: On that happy note, let's call it a day, and everyone have a great week. See you next week, same time, same place.

Week 9

BOB: First the good news. I am pleased to announce the engagement of our daughter Shira to Gerald Daniels of Rochester, NY. She found a nice guy who enjoys being Jewish. Now the questions. My synagogue just built a beautiful new building. I am already getting word that it is expected that the wedding will be in my synagogue. My daughter wants to take it elsewhere. She claims she already did her bat mitzvah in the synagogue, in our old building. Do I insist, or do I follow her wishes? Or do I divide it, doing the ceremony in the building and a reception at a hotel elsewhere?

Also, who do I invite? Staff? President? Officers? Nobody? This wedding probably will not take place for at least another year. But these are already becoming issues.

Most everyone I've asked so far agreed that it is *her* wedding and *they* need to decide. A few understood how she does not have the same emotional feelings towards a new building. And perhaps the one who put it best said that I can always get a new *shul*, I cannot get a new daughter. Well put. Cost is an issue and I will discuss it with her. Right now we are leaning towards an *aufruf* for the congregation, a ceremony in our new sanctuary, and a reception at a nearby hotel or country club. We will invite a few staff and the major officers, but mostly friends and family. And I have to figure out how to pay for this.

Meanwhile, another issue came up that I forgot to mention. We both love Bob Carlisle's song *Butterfly Kisses* and hope to use it for a father-daughter dance. But for those who know the song, one line speaks of Jesus. Anybody know where I can get an edited version that does not mention Jesus.

SAM: Believe it or not, there's a Sam Glaser version on an album called *Fatherhood*. Everything is out there somewhere.

BOB: Thanks, Sam! That should solve one of the problems. *Nur auf simchas!*

SUSAN: To change the subject, I just thought I would share this. A parent at my school would like to build us a permanent Torah Reading table, and has asked me for an optimal set of dimensions. Bearing in mind that this table will need to be moved fairly frequently, I was curious if anyone has an ideal set of dimensions they would recommend that I give him.

SAM: Since you are looking at this, why not also consider making it handicap accessible, even if there are no such children in the school who could use it now. It would be an important statement to the whole school community.

DON: Susan, call my executive director. We just made one, and it's handicap accessible.

BOB: I recently received an email from a senior colleague that I thought you'd like to hear.
Here's what he wrote:
I entered JTS early enough (1951) to still sit at the feet of two great giants of Jewish scholarship – the Talmudist, Levi Ginzberg (1873–1954), and the historian, Alexander Marx (1878–1953). But they were both already aged and in declining health.
Nevertheless, some tales of their early JTS days, at the turn of the twentieth century, were still in circulation. I don't remember who it was, but one older student passed on to me a legendary account of these two renowned scholars delighting in the first snowfall of a winter season, sometime around 1905. And what did they do to mark the occasion? Why, they threw snow balls at each other – just as we all did when young.

So next time you read any of the great works of these two famous scholars just pause and envision them throwing snow balls. It'll surely help humanize them.

After hearing this, now I understand why Marx and Ginzberg were so accurate when throwing the *hallah* to their guests after the *motsi*, which used to be a popular custom among European Jews.

And while I'm on the subject of stories of the famous, here's another one. A professor of mine at JTS told me this:

I am one of the participants in the weekly meetings of Hug-Gershon, the study group founded by our late colleague Rabbi Gershon Winer. This year we are studying the first part of Isaiah. Each of us presents on a rotation basis. For my preparation, I chose to focus on the commentary of Shadal, Shmuel David Luzzatto, on Isaiah. On checking the history of the family I was surprised to learn that New York's legendary mayor, Fiorello LaGuardia was a descendant of this illustrious family. His mother's maiden name was Coen and her mother's maiden name was Luzzatto. An expanded edition of his sister's book *Fiorello's Sister – Gemma LaGuardia Gluck's Story,* published by Syracuse University Press in 2007, tells of her as well as her daughter's and grandson's incarceration during the Holocaust. Gemma's husband and her son-in-law did not survive. Gemma, born in the United States, lived in Hungary where she was a teacher. She lost her U.S. citizenship when she married a Hungarian Jew in Hungary. The study of Isaiah has led me to discover facts I never knew that have nothing to do with Isaiah. While mayor of New York, he gave a talk at Temple Emanuel on Fifth Avenue. LaGuardia was raised as a Protestant and knew Yiddish fluently. Upon entering the synagogue he put on a yarmulke. When he got up to speak, he noticed that he was the only one present with a yarmulke and he asked "Am I the only Jew here?"

Here's another story from another senior colleague:

In reading the New York Times which I get via the Internet, I saw that the new nominee for the Federal Reserve Chairman is Ben S. Bernanke. For the *Yamim Noraim* of 1966, I had a student pulpit in Dillon South, Carolina. I went alone as my wife was expecting our first child and stayed until after Yom Kippur.

I stayed with the nominee's parents and remember Ben very well. He helped me roll the *Sifrei Torah* and was very interested and involved in everything about the *shul*. He was post bar mitzvah. His parents, Philip and Edna, had a strictly kosher home. They had two younger children, Sharon and Seth. His mother was originally from New England and her parents had relocated to Charlotte, North Carolina, where her father was the kosher butcher. Meat was sent via the bus that traveled from Charlotte to Dillon. Ben's father was a pharmacist and he and his two brothers were the only pharmacists in Dillon. Ben's full name is Ben Shalom Bernanke, and his parents, who I recall as most gracious and kind, told me how they gave him that name. It was the tradition in the South that the first born son received his mother's maiden name as his first name. Thus, in Dillon there were people with the name Smith Williamson and Brown Jones. The Bernankes translated Edna's maiden name, Friedman to Ben Shalom. His grandparents were both physicians in pre-war Vienna. They came just before the war to the states, but their medical degrees were not recognized. As they had to make a living and were too old to sit for exams, etc., and had three children, they came to Dillon where they operated a pharmacy. The area synagogue was located in Dillon since the town had made rooms available to the area Jews to hold services in the 1920s. The synagogue dated from before World War I. They never had a permanent rabbi and were served by numerous JTS students for the *Yamim Noraim* over the years. For many years, Rabbi Murray Alstat, the brother of Rabbi Philip Alstat, served their religious needs when he had a pulpit in Fayetteville, North Carolina. The sisterhood was proud of its support of JTS and was a member of Women's League. I have fond memories of the almost two weeks in Dillon some forty years ago. Just think, the youngster who helped me prepare the *Sifrei Torah* and gave me numerous insider pointers is now the nominee to be Chairman of the Federal Reserve.

SAM: Great stories. Thanks! Here's a very practical question. I was talking last night with a friend of mine in the New York area – non-Orthodox but goes to Chabad – who performs energy audits on commercial buildings. He asked me if I knew whether synagogues are doing energy audits on their properties.

According to him, incorrect billings and overcharges are rampant in the energy industry, and commercial structures can often recoup tens to hundreds of thousands of dollars when a proper energy audit is done because it goes back in time a number of years. He suggested that this would be a no-brainer way to raise – or recover – funds for synagogues, day schools, federations, community centers, etc., at no net cost to the institution.

I don't imagine that most of us have been directly involved in something like this, since normally a Building and Grounds Committee would handle it. However, if you have any experience in this area, I would appreciate hearing about it and whether you feel it was worth the time and effort.

DON: Well, looks like we have no takers, so let's go on to another topic. Perhaps some of us can do some research and revisit the issue at a later time.

BOB: An issue that's been bothering me for quite a while is the slow sinking of the Conservative movement. The latest Pew survey buttresses my concern.

Why are we dying? It's the services! It's the services, stupid!

The Pew survey, with its "death knell" for Conservative Judaism, came as no surprise to me. I see it in the pews: Shabbat morning, I see people in the 50+ group at *shul*, and then walking home, I see all the young Jewish families getting out of their cars after their morning excursion to anywhere but *shul*.

The fact is, the younger generation do not find Conservative services compelling. I would argue that one aspect of this generation gap is the fact that traditional Conservative services are driven by a sense of nostalgia. The conservative Jews of the twentieth century weren't *halakhically* observant, but wanted a synagogue reminiscent of the synagogue they imagine their grandparents attending; one that feels authentic. JTS Chancellor Arnie Eisen points this out in his work on *Rethinking Modern Judaism*. In one synagogue I know of, the martyrology consists entirely of a reading about "my grandfather standing in his *tal-*

lis, crying, reciting the ten martyrs." Ironically, they don't recite the "ten martyrs!" The service is a nostalgic experience for the older generation, who imagine their grandparents being moved, and are themselves moved by their sense of nostalgia.

The younger generation is not moved by nostalgia, and needs something meaningful to them. They need a service which is inherently spiritually compelling – something which moves them, now, in the present. This is more than just the rabbi explaining what the prayers mean; it means creating an experience which helps those who don't know Hebrew commune with God. I can explain what the words mean, and how I personally relate to them, but I haven't helped them connect to God through the prayer experience, which is what they really mean. I would rather spend time deeply explaining and having congregants contemplate one line of the *Shema*, chant a bit and say it with true *kavannah*, than say the entire paragraph in Hebrew from memory. I would rather do one song from *Pesukey D'Zimra* really well, singing our hearts out, than the full set of psalms.

And this is a deeply *halakhic* approach. The medieval *Sefer Hasidim* rules that one should pray in one's native language if one doesn't understand Hebrew, because prayer is the "service of the heart." Fifty years ago, Heschel was decrying passionless services that felt like reading yesterday's newspapers. *Davening* which enflames the heart is a central *halakhic* issue, more important than making sure we say every word of the traditional Hebrew *nusah*, much of which is late medieval *piyuttim*.

Building on this problematic approach to spirituality, education was centered around these traditional services. In one synagogue I know of, they ask kindergarteners to sit still for thirty seconds before the *Shema*, losing many of the children in the room. I asked the Education Director the purpose of such a practice, and she said it was to train them to enjoy sitting still in services. I realized that for her, Hebrew school trains the children to be good Conservative congregants – that is, to sit through traditional services. Many Hebrew Schools don't teach about Shabbat in any depth, about *kashrut* and the ethics behind it, about ethics or values or what living as a Jew really means day to day. The sole focus is the service.

I don't want my child to learn to tolerate a boring kids' service, so that she can later tolerate an adult service that she doesn't connect to, that is passive. I want her to develop spiritually in age appropriate ways, to love coming to *shul, davening*, learning, and playing. I don't want to train her to tolerate the experience of sitting quietly in a service; I want to train her to be a passionate Jew, and as an adult to seek out places with passionate *davening*, transformative study, and loving community.

The Conservative movement put all of its eggs in one basket: the traditional service. In marketing terms, we only offered one product, which it turns out the next generation doesn't want. Can we have the courage to break from that mold, and actually serve the spiritual needs of the next generation?

In one of my jocular moods, I created the following:

Ten Top Signs That the Conservative Movement is Dying:

1. The CJLS [Committee of Jewish Law and Standards] votes to adopt every standard of the Reform Movement, just ten years later.

2. The bush is consumed.

3. The motto of the movement is no longer "Tradition and Change." It's replaced by *Hadesh Yameinu K'kedem* [Renew our days as of old].

4. New ordination diplomas no longer read "Rabbi, Teacher and Preacher," but rather "Rabbi, Cantor, Ba'al Koreh, Religious School Principal and Custodian."

5. JTS, HUC, and AJR Merge and conduct all of their classes in a loft in Soho.

6. R.A. Placement is now on Craigslist.

7. Conservative Rabbis for hire for minimum wage OBO [or best offer].

8. The next chancellor of the Seminary is neither a rabbi nor a Judaic scholar; but an executive from Service Corporation International.

9. All members of the R.A. Executive Council come from "A" congregations because that's all we have left ["A" congregations are under 250 families].

10. The last message on RAVNET [the Conservative rabbis' listserv] is a beautiful, heartfelt *Kavvanah* to be read as we

hand over the keys of our mortgage free synagogues to the local *Chabadniks*.

SUSAN: Cute, Bob, but now I think it's time to discuss some historical ritual. Does anyone know when scarf-sized *tallitot* became common in Conservative synagogues? Has anything been written by Conservative *halakhic* authorities on their use? I am aware of the classical sources, but am trying to determine whether any contemporary arbiters have officially declared them "kosher."

BOB: Regarding the size of the *tallit*, I heard the following from Emunah Katzenstein, the daughter of our teacher Dr. Louis Finkelstein at Rosh Hashanah 5723 (1962) dinner in Jerusalem. There were many guests, most of whom had some connection with JTS. The conversation went from person to person and we learned a great deal that evening. Muni, Emunah's nickname, told us that when her father went to his first pulpit he wore a large *tallit* on Shabbat. Some of the *ba'alei batim* came to him afterwards and told him that it was the custom in their synagogue that the rabbi wear a scarf *tallit* and not a large one. Her father's response was to the effect that he wears a large *tallit*, end of discussion. A few years later when her father left that pulpit, the new rabbi came wearing a scarf *tallit*. After services, the *ba'alei batim* came to him and told him that the custom in their synagogue was that the rabbi wears a large *tallit* and not a scarf *tallit*. After hearing this interesting story, one of the guests asked "Did your father go to JTS?" Muni replied, "Yes." The same young woman continued, "My father also was at JTS, maybe he knows your father. What's your father's name?" When Muni answered, "Louis Finkelstein," we all smiled. So the discussion on *tallit* size goes back at least to the 1910s.

DON: My father tells the story that in his community in Romania only *kohanim* wore big *tallitot* so they could do *Birkat Kohanim*. *Leviim* wore scarf *tallitot* so they could wash the *kohanim* without wetting them. *Yisraelim* wore the shawl type. This also made it easy to give out *aliyot*. So in my dad's community the practice goes back to the 1800s.

[Shawl types are the ones that come down over the shoulders to the elbows and cover half the back. The scarf kind just hung from the neck].

SUSAN: OK, here's another *halakhic* question, for everyone but Don, of course. I have a question about the use of musical instruments on Shabbat. My understanding, from the recent survey conducted by USCJ, is that *shuls* are all over the map on this. I am curious how many places permit musical instruments during *worship* but not otherwise. As I understand it, this is in keeping with the Sigal *teshuvah* on the use of the organ in synagogue on Shabbat. If you, or a colleague you know works in a *shul* with such a policy, I'd be curious to know how reasonable and acceptable congregants find this.

BOB: We have musical instrumentation Friday nights and Yom Tov nights. No other instrumental music on Shabbat or *Hagim*, not at *Kiddush* Luncheon, USY *Kinnus*, etc. Mixed reviews. I believe that it makes the service easier to sing with people mostly unfamiliar with Shabbat melodies, but we have a very small Friday night participation. Some believed this would "revive" Friday night. Hardly. Those who come regularly Friday night – my eight or nine *hasidim* – love the guitar playing and look forward to it, but it has drawn only a dozen or so previously non-involved people which is a good number to have in *shul*, don't get me wrong.

The more traditionalists see musical instrumentation as a sign that I'm a closet Reform rabbi, and that we're heading down a not-so-slippery slope to purgatory, or worse. But it didn't affect them personally, since they self-identified as non-Friday night participants at *shul*.

I used the Dorf-Spitz *teshuvah*, which I am still very disappointed was not passed by the CJLS, as a teaching text. There is not much else in the movement literature. I also taught Joel Roth's *Shvut* article, I think it's from 1986, in *Conservative Judaism* magazine, as a teaching text.

SAM: I can give you plenty of examples, but I don't think you're interested in a survey of Reform congregations.

BOB: Right. [Smiles].

SAM: While I have the floor, let me ask a question that applies to any and all of us. What do you use for your emergency contact needs? We currently have a call forwarding feature on our *shul* phone system, but it is proving to be undependable.

When someone calls in after hours with an emergency and they are looking for the rabbi, currently they are told to "press 2 and leave a message which will be forwarded immediately to the rabbi."

I could replace this message with my cell phone number, but I am reluctant to do that. I am looking for good alternatives. I was checking out "onpage" or similar app-based pager programs. I am open to any and all suggestions.

SUSAN: I think, in my humble opinion, in spite of our desire for privacy, it is impossible not to have our cell phone numbers given out to our congregants. If you are worried that you don't have a dedicated line for your family or close friends, why not get two cell phone lines?

DON: I believe that when you call our *shul* off-hours they give a phone number to call in emergencies. It is NOT the rabbis' cell phone numbers. I'm fairly certain that it is one of the officers' phone number. Almost any system can have glitches.

One of my colleagues has a "home office" phone that rings both at home and in the office. He monitors it, but the office staff can check it, too. That way, he doesn't have congregants tying up his home number. I suspect that he put that in when his kids were still home, in the era before everyone had a cell phone, but it seems to work well.

If you don't want to give out your own cell phone number, consider a google voice number it can forward to other phones, or leave a voicemail that goes to your email.

BOB: That was my preferred after-hours solution. A FREE GoogleVoice number which is forwarded to my cell phone. It has a "do not disturb" option that will send ALL calls to that number to voicemail – recorded AND/OR to a text message or email. Frankly, some of the transcription, done by algorithms, leaves much to be desired, but you can always listen to the recorded message. It also has a most useful feature: it asks the caller for a name, then rings your cell and says: "Call from _____. To accept, press 1, to send to voicemail, press 2." It then also informs you that you can MONITOR the call going to voicemail and interrupt and take the call at any point still in progress if you choose. Believe me. Better than a secretary or volunteer. All for FREE.

Of course, my secretary had my cell number and would call me, rather than give it out, should the call seem urgent. Our president's number was on the "in case of emergency" recorded office phone announcement, and she could always reach me on my GOOGLE VOICE NUMBER.

BOB: Let me raise a very controversial issue that all of us will be dealing with in one way or another. It's become a very hot topic on the campuses of major universities, and I think we need to take a stand.

The Board of a prominent Hillel organization of an important university decided they could not follow Hillel International's restrictive guidelines about what programs and speakers Hillel can be involved with on issues related to Israel, and now Hillel International wants to suspend their membership in International Hillel. I'd like to hear some of your views.

DON: As you will see, I have very strong views on this matter. Would any of our pulpit rabbis allow members to use the synagogue photocopy machine to reproduce material urging people to eat pork or to work on Shabbat? Probably not. Do people have a right to use synagogue facilities to, say, promote apostasy to another religion? Of course not.

A few points about terms that are being misused:

- Freedom of speech. This isn't a matter of free speech. Students have free speech. They can say what they want. They simply cannot use the facilities of Hillel to promote or allow others to promote anti-Israel positions.
- Academic freedom. Just to clarify. I have been told by a friend, who is an expert on the subject of academic freedom, that although students are part of the community of scholars, they do not, in point of fact, have academic freedom. Academic freedom is for faculty. What is or is not acceptable for students to write or present in a classroom is under the control of faculty. They can speak or publish, of course, but that isn't "academic freedom." That is free speech. They have that.

The move to "support" a particular Hillel will hurt it and all of Hillel, perhaps badly. Why so? Think. Why do donors support Hillel? Largely, to prevent assimilation and to support Israel in the "campus wars." The donors do not want their dollars to be used to promote anti-Israel activity, and will stop donating if that happens. This is donor driven.

No doubt some of you will respond to the effect that it is somehow illegitimate to put money above principle. This is seriously misguided. There really is no principle. This is not a free speech issue.

Hillel is not a mini AIPAC. Views are regularly expressed by students that are to the right and left of the Jewish establishment on Israel. It is a very big tent. Leftist critiques of Israel happen all the time, but the theme is "wherever we stand, we stand with Israel." As a private and privately funded organization, Hillel has a right to define the limits of the tent. It is a Zionist group. Perhaps, at times, non-Zionist or even Post-Zionist positions may be presented, but most certainly it is not anti-Zionist. Critics opine about the freedom of students. What about the freedom of the organization to define itself and how its facilities may be used? Is that not also a matter of freedom? Would you have the Newman Society allow abortion advocacy?

Students do not have a "right" to determine how Hillel money is spent.

A Hillel rabbi, a friend of mine, once found a student using the

Hillel photocopy facilities to reproduce very anti-Israel material. She immediately stopped it. That was a misuse of Hillel facilities and a misuse of the director's considerable efforts to keep the Hillel afloat. The staff has a right to determine its agenda.

SAM: But the students have a say in which speakers they can invite to speak to them.

DON: Sam, would you limit who might be invited to speak from your pulpit? What criteria? May I use your photocopy machine to promote eating pork? Don't you believe in pluralism?

Should the Newman Society on campus allow abortion advocacy? Why not? Lots of Catholics believe in reproductive choice. Are you afraid that they may drift away from the church? Shouldn't the Newman Society be pluralist?

What about the Muslim Students Association? Shouldn't it be expected to allow advocates for same-sex marriage? Isn't that pluralism?

Shouldn't the College Democrats be allowed to use the photocopy account of the College Republicans? Don't you believe in pluralism? Is this not censorship?

Leftists speak all the time in Hillel: Peace Now, NIF, Btselem, J Street etc. In point of fact they're more likely to be found at your local Hillel than at your local synagogue.

What we are talking about is barring anti-Israel spokespeople, both from the left and the right – or even the center. No one's free speech is being infringed in any sense, so let's please not follow the lead of the media in seeking to sensationalize events.

Hillel has a right to establish guidelines as the organization sees fit. Any individual Jewish organization on campus also has a right to establish guidelines as it so desires – just not in the name of Hillel. If any college group rejects Hillel's regulations then it has a choice: Either comply or leave the organization. There is no free speech issue here because free speech is not being suppressed – just the right to exercise free speech under the auspices of Hillel.

As someone who has spent many years working with students ages five through college, I welcome any student who challenges the status quo; who is willing to independently stand up and question the policies of Israel in particular or the standards of Jewish practice in general. However, I am still concerned that the zealous commitment of our college students to present a "balanced" view of contemporary Israel only supports the ideologies of those anti-Israel organizations on campus who will never present a balanced view of the Middle East under any circumstances.

Again, we cannot deny Jewish college students their right to exercise free speech. But if they want to ignore the standards established by Hillel, then they need to sever their ties and act independently.

SUSAN: Excuse me, guys, I see that there's an emergency coming in on my cell phone. Let me take this call from my office, be back in a minute.

[10 minute pause].

SUSAN: Oh my God! This afternoon one of our beautiful teenage girls committed suicide. Eighteen years old. I will be meeting with the family after *minyan* tomorrow. This is so very terrible for her family and our synagogue community. The parents are very active at our *shul*. Oh my God, I'm so shaken up. What do I do, what do I say?

I would appreciate any appropriate readings and-or material that might be helpful for my preparation for the funeral.

I am sick and stunned over this and very sad.

SAM: Oh Susan, I am so sorry for the family, for your, and for the community's loss.

In tragic situations such as these, I offer a simple message both to the family and at the funeral. Something along the lines of, "There are no words right now. There is no consolation. We are angry. We are confused. We are at a loss. We want answers and explanations. But, Judaism is not a religion that asks, 'Why?' There is time for that question later. Judaism is a religion that asks, 'What now?' And, so, today, we are here to bury . . ."

Something like that. I have found that, any time that I have used that line, I have met with head nods and tears of approval. So I have also been told afterward.

My hearts and thoughts are with you all, Susan!

BOB: This is the worst stuff – burying a teenager. I remember vividly every teen I buried and all the circumstances surrounding the death, burial and *shivah*. I don't usually say much. I go there. I hug them. I tell them that in Jewish tradition there is a response to every moment in life. We either say a *berakhah* or some set formula. But when a parent loses a child the only response is that of Aaron's silence. There are no words we can say that makes any sense when confronted with such a senseless loss.

When it's suicide I add one thing. There are many cruel diseases in the world and we've all known or watched people die from them. But the cruelest of all is depression which robs us of our desire to even live. I emphasize that she died of a cruel disease that is almost always undetected and even when detected often can't be healed.

DON: I have used this poem at times, and although it is very stark, it seems to provide an outlet. I have it here in my briefcase, I'll get it out. . . . It is called "Dirge Without Music" by Edna St. Vincent Millay.

Dirge Without Music

*I am not resigned to the shutting away of loving hearts in the
    hard ground.*
So it is, and so it will be, for so it has been, time out of mind:
*Into the darkness they go, the wise and the lovely. Crowned
    With lilies and with laurel they go; but I am not resigned.*
Lovers and thinkers, into the earth with you.
Be one with the dull, the indiscriminate dust.
A fragment of what you felt, of what you knew,
A formula, a phrase remains, but the best is lost.
*The answers quick and keen, the honest look, the laughter,
    the love –*

*They are gone. They are gone to feed the roses. Elegant and
    curled*
*Is the blossom. Fragrant is the blossom. I know. But I do not
    approve.*
*More precious was the light in your eyes than all the roses in
    the world.*
Down, down, down into the darkness of the grave
Gently they go, the beautiful, the tender, the kind;
Quietly they go, the intelligent, the witty, the brave.
I know. But I do not approve. And I am not resigned.

I wish you strength, Susan, to help this ailing family and community.

SAM: Let me scan through my laptop for a minute. . . . I think
I have something that would be appropriate. . . . . . Here it is: It's
something I used in a similar situation which I wrote for my
cousin when she lost a teenage daughter:

"The outpouring of love, affection and concern for Sarah and
her family is one that will be remembered long after the wounds
of pain begin to heal. Every single one of us is here today with
many more questions than answers, knowing that the answers
will remain forever elusive. Yet we are gathered as a community
that has chosen to stick together, cry together and support one
another."

Susan, if I can be of help in the weeks and months to come,
then please don't hesitate.

BOB: Here is a text I have used:

אמר רבי יוחנן: קשה לפני הקדש ברוך הוא בשעה שבניהם של צדיקים
מסתלקים בחיים דאביהם.
*Rabbi Yohanan taught: It is even difficult for the Blessed
Holy One when a good person's child dies during the life of a
parent.* Vayikra Rabbah 20:10.

Thus did our sages try to extend to parents who suffer the
loss of a child by saying so deep is the sorrow, so great is the

loss, so tragic the occurrence, that even God Himself weeps for them and with them.

We are all mourners here today. We share the deep pain of _____.

God too is a mourner. God grieves with you as we grieve with you.

SUSAN: Thank you all so much for all these beautiful thoughts. I'm very grateful. I think I'll go back to the office and get my thoughts together. I hope you'll excuse me.

DON: I think we might all take a break now, and meet again next week. It's hard to chit-chat when something like this just happened. See you all next time.

Week 10

SAM: Let's start off today with one of the most unusual requests I've ever had in all my years in the rabbinate. From the strange but true file.

A man has come to see me a few times, randomly popping in. He is a cousin of a congregant. He is homeless and seems to have schizophrenia, but neither I nor his family have been able to convince him to seek treatment. He keeps asking me to perform an exorcism on him or to point him to a rabbi who does exorcisms. I know that it will not solve his problem, but out of curiosity, does anyone know a rabbi who does such things?

BOB: Honestly! A rabbi performing exorcisms! Wouldn't doing so be irresponsible – rabbinic malpractice? Perhaps if it was under the supervision and guidance of a psychiatrist – and even then, it would be, to put it mildly, bizarre.

SAM: OK, let's forget that one. I don't think anyone has a good response for that issue. Who else has an issue to bring up?

DON: *Hevreh*, I have found myself so busy with a gezillion things lately that I can hardly breathe. I think I need a course in time management. Maybe you have some of the same issues, and can make some suggstions.

We all try as best we can to return calls from all sorts of people, but there are times when one's patience can be tested.

What do you do when you get calls or e-mails from people trying to solicit your synagogue for businesses, such as *sofrim*, insurance agents, architects, real estate agents, tour operators, and others? Everybody is looking for business and I understand that. But I seem to be getting more such calls over time. Obviously if the person is a congregant or a colleague, I do my best to get back to them in a timely way, but I'm conflicted whether I should even be returning unsolicited phone calls from others. What do you do?

Like many of you, I get lots of phone calls from people who tell me they want to convert. I could spend many hours every week setting up appointments with such people. Years ago, after lots of "no shows," I established the following guidelines. I tell them, "Come to our Shabbat services for a few weeks – usually Shabbat morning. Introduce yourself to me. Once you've come two or three times, we'll make an appointment." This way I think I'm able to figure out who is serious.

There are also several colleges in the area and I get SCORES of calls every year from students who are assigned to attend a service AND interview a clergyman of a religion not their own. I have no problem with inviting anyone to a weekday or Shabbat service, but these interviews can be very time consuming. How do you handle such requests?

A rabbi's time can be very precious, especially when the rabbi likes to golf, and see the family once in a while.

As always, I look forward to your sage advice.

BOB: I think all of us have many similar problems. Just keep doing what you're doing. I think you're on the right track.

SUSAN: I have a new topic that I could use some help with. Has anyone done a burial of *Shaimot* [books, scrolls, etc. with God's name in Hebrew]? Does CJLS have anything on this? There are some that cast their net quite wide for what constitutes names. How do you define it? Do we include pages with God's name in English? I think the Law Committee said this is not necessary.

We have a plot, and we want to make a program out of it. We have a *pasul* [unfit for ritual ruse] *Sefer Torah* that could be buried as well.

I could use any guidance your experience would provide.

DON: When I was at a previous congregation some twenty years ago we were moving buildings, and also celebrating being in existence eighty years, as part of that celebration, and because we had mounds of stuff ready for the *genizah* we decided to not only do a synagogue wide program one Sunday morning, but also to build on the idea of things coming to the end of their usefulness in the teaching in the Sunday School. We used ideas and texts for younger children including Earl Grollman's book on explaining death to children. We used a book I think called "The Day Grandma Died." We worked with the kids around pets dying, and also told the story of the Cairo *genizah*.

For teenagers we had the people from the *Hevra Kadishah* come in and speak and there was some discussion about visiting the funeral parlour.

There was a service created; we used a grave at the edge of the cemetery to deal with the issue of *Kohanim.* To be honest one of the most powerful memories for me is some of the very young children sitting at the side of the double-grave – that's how much stuff we had – and a few of them dangling their feet over the edge. Some adults had problems with it. Nobody fell in, and it was a positive program for all.

It was written up and published. I do have a copy of both the program and the article for those interested.

SUSAN: That sounds like just what I'm looking for. Please send me a copy.

DON: Be glad to.

Friends, I want to share with you a fascinating, well-written piece composed by our talented colleague, Rabbi Menachem Creditor. Very appropriate for the coming season of holidays – Christmas and Hanukkah:

A Rabbi's Christmas Thought
(for Jewish Parents and Others)

Rabbi Menachem Creditor

As a Yeshivah high school student, I was told to not enjoy Christmas lights, "tainted" as they were by non-Jewish "*cooties.*"

And, since I lived in a particularly lawn-obsessed neighborhood on Long Island, that meant ducking for cover every third house. The homes abutting my childhood *shul* were particularly hard to miss, with people driving from far away to witness a million-bulb spectacle, the carbon-footprint of which has yet to be determined.

When I got to college, though, something changed. First of all, the white lights adorning Columbia University's college walk didn't in the least resemble the garish ones I remembered. Secondly, I was done heeding the Jewish-insularists of my Yeshivah days. Most of all, I was a college student whose heart swelled with the romance in the college air – what could be more romantic than mystic lights on a cold winter night?

Which leads me to this thought. We, American Jewish parents, guardians of the faith, have a choice. Do we try to diminish the magic of the lights our children see? We don't stand a chance. And, furthermore, do we really not see the magic ourselves? Are we afraid of Christmas voodoo? Or, are we secretly, deep down, happy to see the lights on these dark nights?

So, if we are not going to pretend to not enjoy Christmas lights, let's really talk about what's going on. It's beautiful. Human beings ache for a magic that illuminates the darkness; that shines goodness into a sometimes cruel world. We don't need, as Jews, to be afraid of beauty. In fact, the more we try to look away, the stronger the magnetic pull of Christmas becomes. In America, it's everywhere. Sometimes garish, sometimes classy, sometimes commercial, sometimes spiritual. It's just there. Everywhere. We live in it. And it can be very, very hard.

So here's the thought: It was a blessing this year that Thanksgiving and Hanukkah coincided, a reminder to not confuse Hanukkah's modest lights with Christmas' spectacle-of-the-trees. If you are concerned that you and your children are becoming seduced by the lights, consider this: *magic is desperately needed in this world.*

Every Friday night and Saturday night Jews are called to banish the darkness with fire, bringing primal creative force into the world. Have you ever looked at someone else's eyes looking into the Shabbat candles' flames? *Shabbat is our magic.* Its cheer is waiting to pervade your home and your heart every week. The world needs more light, more spirit, and more goodness.

So love illumination when you encounter it, and let your precious Jewish light shine!

SUSAN: Thanks, Bob, for sharing this. If you can send it to me on computer, I may use it in my forthcoming *shul* bulletin.

Now let me raise a *kashrut* question, to exercise your brains a bit.

Our Social Action committee prepares meals regularly for patients at a local hospital with patients from all over. I just recently found out that the members who cook food in their homes and then come and serve the food are cooking meat and chicken dishes which are not kosher. I said I was not comfortable with this, but have received pushback. I am curious to hear if any of you have similar efforts. Do you require that the standards be consistent with our usual policy: dairy, vegetarian or fish, or are some a bit more lenient since it is not in the *shul* or even for members?

DON: We don't have such an active Social Action committee, but it seems to me that if the food is being fed to non-Jews, it has no need to be kosher. On the other hand, if it is going to Jewish patients, and it is done as a synagogue project, then it should be kosher.

BOB: We periodically cook meals at a soup kitchen in town. My assumption is that the overwhelming majority of patrons are not Jewish, so we buy non-kosher food. Our standard dish is chili. I have some concern about *basar v'halav* [mixing meat and dairy], but it is arguable that the way in which our people put the cheese and the meat chili together does not qualify as cooking. I feel uncomfortable about Jews, acting in the name of the synagogue, providing non-kosher food for other Jews, but I haven't gotten anywhere with that issue, so I have dropped it. The situation was one in which the synagogue matched up hosts and guests for holidays. Obviously, if certain guests keep kosher, then we match them up with kosher homes. I was hoping that, even if neither the hosts nor the guests regularly keep kosher, the hosts would buy kosher food for a quasi-synagogue event. However, people simply didn't understand what I was talking about. *Amcha* [the majority of Jews] here sees *kashrut* completely a matter of personal choice. I don't feel comfortable about buying non-kosher food for anyone, so, when I buy food for our food pantry donation barrel, I buy only kosher – not necessarily *hekhshered* – items.

My short answer to Susan's question is that, in the case which she describes, I wouldn't worry about *kashrut*.

SAM: We serve an annual Christmas dinner for the local Soup Kitchen. For years I tried to get them to make it kosher for two reasons. First, I felt it was an important symbol, even though we served non-Jews. Jews should serve kosher food! Second, inevitably there would be people from the *shul* snacking on leftovers. It was not a battle I was able to win, though I still think it important.

Anyway, it's time for a humor break. My senior colleague, Murray Stadtmauer, sent this bit of remembrance on our listserv:

In the summer of 1965, as the Vietnam conflict began to escalate, I was recalled to active duty for a three-month stint at Fort Dix, NJ. The officers in our BOQ (Bachelor Officers Quarters) became a close-knit group, watching TV together in our lounge.

A dental officer, Captain Farha, who was of Lebanese Christian descent, became known by a nickname after a comedian in our group dubbed him "Distant Laughter" (Far-Ha)!

Shortly thereafter, another officer asked me what my name, Stadtmauer, meant in German. I replied, "City Wall." Apparently, he didn't hear right, and exclaimed, "What? Sitting Bull!"

And so it was, for the rest of that summer, that the two of us were called by our new monikers, "Distant Laughter" and "Sitting Bull."

It was the kind of humor GI's often needed just to get by. Reservists, like me, went home at the end of that ominous summer. But many of the Regulars knew they'd soon be going to Vietnam. I sure hope they all got home safely.

SUSAN: You know, we haven't chatted about Israel much. Here's a great article written by Rabbi Reuven Hammer, a Conservative rabbi who made *aliyah* decades ago, and is active in lots of Israeli issues:

Haredi Army Service

Reuven Hammer

I find it difficult to understand why *Ha-aretz* has taken an editorial position opposed to having the *Haredim* "share the burden" and considering it a "credit to Israeli democracy" that the *Haredim* are not going to be drafted (*Failed Policies of Repression*). It is hardly undemocratic for a state that faces constant threats to its very existence to require its citizens to come to the defense of the nation and perform military service. On the contrary, not to do so would constitute a dereliction of duty and be in violation of common sense and the will to live. How wonderful it would be if Israel were not in that position and could do away with compulsory military service, but unfortunately that seems a far off dream. Under these circumstances true democracy demands that such a burden be shared equally by those capable of doing so.

Nor is this a matter of conscience. Nothing in Judaism justifies conscientious objection (C.O.). On the contrary, Judaism demands that when confronted with evil we oppose it and that when faced with an enemy who threatens to kill us or others, we defend ourselves. What the *Haredi* community contends is not that Israelis should not defend themselves, but that others should do so because their study of Torah takes precedence. That is errant nonsense with absolutely no basis in fact or in Jewish law. Jewish law – the Torah itself – makes it very clear that all are equally required to serve. There may be certain exemptions consisting of those who are facing conditions that should be completed and those who are afraid and would cause others to fear, but study of Torah is not a cause for not serving when lives are at stake (Deuteronomy 20:5-8). Rabbinic Judasim went further and said that all must serve when there is danger, even the bride and groom (Sotah 8:7)! Torah scholars should be the first to know this and to fulfill it.

The facts are quite simple. *Haredi* youth are encouraged to stay enrolled in yeshivot in order to avoid the draft because they are still living in a diaspora mentality that says that serving in any army is a disaster. For many of them Israel is not a legitimate state and they feel no obligation to it. Many – if not most – of these yeshiva students are hardly serious students. Furthermore the Israeli *Haredi* community has invented something new that never existed in Europe and does not now exist in America or elsewhere – the idea that all its men must devote themselves exclusively to study and never do anything else, be it army duty or work. Such a society cannot exist unless it depends on the support of the government and on others to keep society alive. Yet that is what they are attempting to do here. Is this fair and proper? The hypocrisy of this is seen in another article that appeared in the same issue. It stated that MK Yaakov Litzman (United Torah Judaism) was sponsoring a bill that would block negotiations regarding the future of Jerusalem with Palestinians unless 80 MKs approve it. But if this would pass and undermine any possibility of peace in the future, will Litzman's voters serve in the army that will have to fight the wars in the future? Not on your life. They will be busy saving the nation through studying Torah!

Israel cannot allow the current situation to continue. It must find a way to bring these young men into service of their country and into the productive work force. As their number

increases, as it does year by year, the current situation presents a threat to the existence of Israel as a viable state. Steps
must be taken immediately to stop the subsidization of yeshiva students and *kollel* students which alone permits them
to live this kind of life. They must be faced with the situation in
which they are called upon to provide for themselves. Should
they refuse to serve the nation, they should be deprived of all
financial help from the State. The army should provide appropriate framework in which they can serve and should then
have the right to decide who should be in a military framework and who is not appropriate and can do civilian service
instead. Only in this way can Israel survive.

SUSAN: What are your thoughts?

DON: I see red when I think about how *haredi* Jews evade their
military burden, as well as financial and social burdens. The fact
that the *haredi* population has perverted various *kulot* permitted by Ben Gurion and continued by future Israeli leaders is both
a violation of *halakhah* and democratic values. In my humble
opinion *Ha'aretz's* position is ludicrous and indefensible.

Thank you to Reuven for once again articulating our position
so clearly and forcefully. I have an Israeli colleague and friend,
who fumes while his twenty-year-old daughter is working in
harm's way up north as a paramedic, taking care of our soldiers
and wounded from the Syrian civil war.

SAM: I agree with Reuven's perspective on *haredi* army service,
but this claim does not seem to be correct:
    "Nothing in Judaism justifies conscientious objection."
Clearly the Torah supports the equivalent of C.O. status when
it allows army-age men to opt out of fighting, according to rabbinic understanding, whether they are afraid of being killed, or
afraid to kill. The latter is the equivalent of conscientious objection.

DON: I would suggest that there is a difference between a fear
of killing and being killed, and having a moral objection to doing

so. The rabbinic understanding seems to support the former and not the latter, therefore it does not undercut Reuven's claim in any sense.

In support of Reuven's understanding, I would note that the classical rabbinic understanding of the exemption is not that the fearful person is exempted because of his subjective feeling, but rather because of the effect that his fear may have upon the morale of other soldiers.

I would add that all soldiers presumably fear killing or being killed, speaking from personal experience. That point was recently made by Major General Elazar Stern MK [Member of Knesset/Parliament] in recounting a a discussion with cadets at the Israeli officers' school. The cadets were discussing how to deal with their soldiers' fear of combat. One cadet suggested that the best course would be for the commanding officer to share his own fear with his soldiers. Stern replied that while we are all afraid of killing and of being killed, an officer must not share that fear with his soldiers, as that might further demoralize them rather than assuage their fear. The officer must overcome his natural fear and encourage his soldiers by his show of courage. As Patton famously said: "Courage is fear hanging on a minute longer."

SAM: There are religious reasons for *hareidim* to request conscientious objector status other than fear of being killed or fear of killing. Of course, this would not accord with the general understanding of what C.O. status means, nor would these reasons be popular with the general public.

They might maintain:

1. That the culture of the military is not conducive to life as a *hareidi ben torah* [studious person]. It is inherently corrupting regardless of what attempts might be made to accommodate religious needs by the IDF. It starts with being asked to wear drab green instead of black, a beret instead of a *kippah*, and goes downhill from there.

2. There are supernatural/providential reasons why it benefits the Jewish nation to have a cadre of people studying Torah which is more important to the Jewish nation than serving in

the military. Military activities may or may not be important, but study of Torah is more important than anything. The *Shomer Yisrael* will protect us.

3. Serving in the military is dangerous and a *ben-Torah* ought not to be exposed to danger when somebody of a lesser status can do so. The Torah elite must be protected. Let the drawers of wood and carriers of water draw wood and carry water, but let the *b'nai-Torah* study Torah.

4. In some cases it might be asserted that the State of Israel has no religious legitimacy and therefore a *ben-Torah* ought not be participating in its defense, saluting its flag, obeying its officers or wearing its uniform. That is for Zionists.

5. A *ben-Torah*, having lived a life of study, does not have the skill set necessary to succeed as a soldier.

You and I may angrily reject this mindset, but it is a mindset articulated by many. Regrettably.

When I was in college, our congregational rabbi was David Slovak, to whom I will be forever grateful for introductory lessons in *Humash* and *Rashi*. He made it clear that he was prepared to support C.O. on *halakhic* grounds.

DON: Nothing in Judaism justifies conscientious objection.

Clearly the Torah supports the equivalent of C.O. status when it allows army-age men to opt out of fighting, according to rabbinic understanding, whether they are afraid of being killed, or afraid to kill. The latter is the equivalent of conscientious objection.

Maybe? I considered myself a conscientious objector when I registered for the draft after college. I said I thought I could not kill anyone. My draft status was made a "1AO" and I was drafted and served as a medic. I did not carry a gun into the field though I served in the field as a combat medic. I did carry extra ammunition for the combat forces that were protecting me.

Why can't the *haredim*, who enjoy the protection by the IDF, submit to the Israeli draft and volunteer to serve in a non-combat manner, such as medic, engineer, communication, etc.? I hardly think anyone would object to this criterion of service.

As my home rabbi did for me, I would be happy to compose a

letter to the IDF requesting non-combat status for anyone who enjoys the security of a peaceful Israel and still feels obligations to his fellow Jew.

Furthermore, I consulted an Israeli legal expert some time ago, and I have his email on my phone. Here's what he says:

Certain points should be made in this context:

1. Generally speaking, from a legal standpoint, "conscientious objection" must express a "blanket" or "general" objection, and cannot be "selective," namely, one cannot "conscientiously" object to a specific war or to service in a specific army. Inasmuch as the normative *halakhic* view is that ALL must serve in a *milhemet mitzvah*, with the exception of certain *hareidi* poskim who rule otherwise, and a dispute as to whether women must serve in general, or only in support areas in a *milhemet mitzvah*, *halakhah* does not support, and cannot be employed, to defend "conscientious objection" per se. That is not to say that one cannot or should not object to serving for moral or political reasons in certain circumstances. Indeed, arguably, international law may require such objection in some cases. However, such a moral or political objection would not be "conscientious objection," but rather civil disobedience, and would not afford a legal justification, except, perhaps, post facto.

2. *Hareidim* are not required to serve in combat units. Indeed, most IDF combat units are voluntary and are over subscribed. Moreover, a *hareidi* man wishing to serve in a combat unit would be limited to volunteering for service in one of the *Nahal Hareidi* battalions, or perhaps, a *bnei yeshivot* unit in the armoured corps, as other field units are simply unable to provide glatt meals.

3. Not only does a *hareidi* man have the option of serving in a non-combat unit, as does every other inductee, but he also has the option of volunteering for alternative national service, which can be performed within the *hareidi* community.

4. The IDF has set up special tracks for *hareidim*. These tracks are for service in technical units in the Air Force, computer services, and other technical units, such as electronic maintenance.

5. *Hareidim* are entitled to a two-year deferment allowing them to begin service at the age of twenty rather than eighteen in

order to address their fear that earlier induction would disrupt the process of becoming part of *hareidi* society. Moreover, if at that time they are already married, they are entitled to extra pay.

Bearing all of the above in mind, one may, I think, reasonably conclude that the *hareidi* objections to military service are ideological, and are founded upon a rejection of the State of Israel as a state. I do not qualify that with the word "Jewish" as the objection is not to serving in what they view as an illegitimate Jewish State. It isn't a theocracy and the Messiah hasn't come, etc., but rather it expresses an unwillingness to recognize the State of Israel as a state even in the secular sense. If that were not the case, they would be bound by the principle of *dina demalkhuta dina* [we must obey the law of the local country]. In that regard, it is further telling that the *hareidi* leadership terms IDF service as a *gezeira* in the sense of a catastrophe comparable to the destruction of the Temple, the Hadrianic persecutions, etc.

BOB: First let me suggest that there are three pracical lessons that Jews should learn from the Holocaust:

1. When evil people say that their intention is to kill Jews, believe them!

2. No Jew should voluntarily subject his or her body to cremation after Auschwitz.

3. No Jew should embrace pacifism in the face of evil. Such pacifism is in and of itself dangerous and partners with evil.

When I was a Reserve Navy Chaplain, I was assigned to the Navy Education and Training Center and was tasked with working on some educational materials. Among other things I was asked to review several Jewish books that were sent to the NETC, among them *Call to Consience – Jews, Judaism, and Conscientious Objection* by Rabbi Albert S. Axelrad, long time Hillel rabbi at Brandeis. I decided NOT to review this book.

I read this book almost with a sense of horror when I saw how the author, knowing full well that conscientious objection, as understood by U.S. law is based on someone claiming that status to object to ALL wars, not just a particular military action, was misrepresenting Judaism throughout the book. The fact that there is a *milhemet hovah* is enough proof that pacifism is

NOT a Jewish value, although some Jews are avowed pacifists. From the dedication page where he quotes "Thou shalt not kill," vs. the real translation which is "Thou shalt not MURDER," I knew that in my humble opinion this was going to be an unpleasant and misleading book, and so it was. While the draft was no longer in place at the time of publication (1986), Axelrad was coaching any Jew seeking C.O. status what to say, true or not, in order to achieve that status. The tone was such that the reader knew that these were not the beliefs of Judaism, but rather the lies that had to be uttered in order to excuse one from military service.

The book has no footnotes, but he quoted the following from the Rabbinical Assembly:

"We recognize the right of the Conscientious Objector to claim exemption from military service in any war in which he cannot give his moral assent, and we pledge ourselves to support him in his determination to refrain from any participation in it."

If the R.A. actually passed such a resolution, this would clearly contradict American law which defines C.O. status by someone who is morally opposed to participating in any war. We Jews, who have long been the victims of the sword, the bullet and the gas chambers, do not have the luxury of masking cowardice with C.O. status. The stakes are too high.

Some of you may have seen the young Pakistani girl, Malala Yousafzai, who was nearly killed by the Taliban for daring to pursue an education as a female. She was also nominated, and later received the Nobel Peace Prize. Malala appeared on the Daily Show with Jon Stewart and said the following:

"I started thinking about that, and I used to think that the Talib would come, and he would just kill me. But then I said, 'If he comes, what would you do Malala?' then I would reply to myself, 'Malala, just take a shoe and hit him.' But then I said, 'If you hit a Talib with your shoe, then there would be no difference between you and the Talib. You must not treat others with cruelty and that much harshly, you must fight others but through peace and through dialogue and through education.' Then I said I will tell him how important education is and that

'I even want education for your children as well.' And I will tell him, 'That's what I want to tell you, now do what you want.'"

Read more: http://www.businessinsider.com/malala-yousafzai -left-jon-stewart-speechless-2013-10#ixzz2p4VHWaCp. I recommend watching the video if you have a few moments.

Malala is a TRUE C.O., but I ask everyone here, honestly, if you tried to talk to an Islamo-fascist with a gun pointed to your head, and started telling him about the importance of education, how long do you think you'd live? She's a remarkable girl, but her philosophy of life, while pure and idealistic is nothing short of suicidal when facing unadulterated evil. And it surely is not a Jewish teaching.

I once had a congregant, many years ago – a professor – who questioned why I took such a strong position against Palestinian terrorism. "After all, shouldn't we all be friends?" He asked. And I kid you not, "Rabbi, doesn't the Torah teach us to turn the other cheek? And to love your enemy?" I gently reminded him that it wasn't OUR Torah that teaches us that.

There may be Jewish pacifists, but it is a stretch to maintain that normative Judaism is pacifist. Of course one might make some sort of pulpul to justify just about anything, but I think honesty is also a Jewish value.

A test for C.O.s: If somebody tried to kill your mother, would you sit on your hands and quote Gandhi? Perhaps you don't believe in the military, but do you believe in police?

SAM: When I was a student at university I wrote a paper on pacifism in the Reform Rabbinate during and immediately after World War II. It was a long time ago, so some of my recollections may be slightly off, but I believe they are substantively correct.

C.O. status means opposition to participation in war. It does not mean renunciation of violence in all forms and at all times. One could still maintain a willingness to personally defend their life or that of their family with force, even lethal force, and still be a C.O.

Up until the very late twenieth century one had to be a member of a religious pacifist group in order to qualify for C.O. status.

The Jewish Peace Fellowship was founded in 1941 specifically to provide that type of affiliation for Jews claiming C.O. status. Among the founding board members of JPF was Rabbi Arthur Lelyveld. Conservative rabbis who have served on the JPF board include both Herschel Matt and Max Ticktin.

While I think it would be ridiculous to say that Judaism is pacifist, it seems to me that there is room for pacifism – certainly as understood by the Selective Service System – within Judaism. This of course brings up a larger question as to what are the limits of being within the tent of Judaism. It seems to me that the very nature of Conservative Judaism, as I understand it as an outsider, means that there are positions we can profoundly disagree with without therefore saying that such a position is "not Jewish."

If I understand pacifism correctly – and maybe I don't – then I just don't see any room for it within the Jewish construct. There is an absolute obligation to protect oneself and one's country if attacked. Now it doesn't always mean having to kill the other person, but if that is what is necessary to stop the attack against your country, or to save your own life, then it is a religious obligation to do so. My understanding of pacifism is that you 'die' rather than kill your attacker.

On a personal note, pacifism is for me the ultimate evil in the world. Why? Because when good people stand by and let evil triumph they are worse than the evil itself. Because as my mother would always say, they know better! Evil is sometimes the result of severe mental illness. No, I'm not feeding you the liberal excuse for evil doers – it just is true that sometimes it is mental illness, as we have seen in some recent mass murders – and we regretfully have to kill the attacker to stop him or her. But what excuse could goodness possibly have to let evil triumph?

The definition of partnership with God is combating evil while building this world. Pacifism is for me the same as a conscious philosophical decision not to procreate. It is denial of partnership with God, and just like a philosophical decision not to procreate – adopting and raising is the same as procreation for me – is the ultimate act of selfishness. So too, in my humble opinion, is pacifism. It's a wonderful philosophy with only one problem.

It has no basis in an unredeemed world, and it gets good and innocent people killed. It violates the biblical injunction, "Do not stand idly by the blood of your neighbor."

DON: I must chime in, for what my uninformed personal reflections might be worth, or not. The conflict with the Palestinians did not begin with the Six Day War, nor will it likely end with any kind of bifurcation of Israel into two states.

Longstanding deep-seated emotional hostility towards Israel's very existence as a Western cultural and predominantly Jewish state made up largely of immigrants and refugees from elsewhere has existed ever since the rise of political Zionism, and its goal of creating a secular and religious Return (*Yishuv*) to a biblically-promised land from which we were long exiled.

We were seen as unwelcome "invaders," a threat to a mostly Arab world tainted with more than merely a touch of antipathy towards Jews that the rest of "civilization" termed antisemitism.

As Israel grew and prospered, so did the antipathy. The vastly unequal standards of living on either side of the armistice "green line" simply fueled the resentment of the poorest Palestinians, by which I mean Arabs living in British Mandatory Palestine, both before and after *Milhemet Ha-Shihrur* [Israel's War of Independence].

Following the crushing Israeli victory in the Six Day War, the Palestinians' fate, or at least their perception of it, became far worse. Humiliated, exiled, separated from families and lands long believed to be "theirs," that resentment festered and flared into burning hatred, further fanned and incited by Palestinian politicians who stubbornly refused to recognize and accept the new reality. That rejectionist attitude and its concomitant hostility, often horrific and brutal, became the "new norm."

Israel never sought to dominate, control, occupy or persecute the Palestinian population. Every war that Israel was forced to fight further aggravated the situation as hopelessness and helplessness overcame the rank and file Palestinians, while inflaming the radical elements promising them revenge and return for acts of martyrdom.

Mutual suspicion, wariness and security concerns have, to a large extent, colored the "conversation" ever since.

Understandable but unforgivable retaliatory brutality against Palestinians by "settlers" and the IDF for Palestinian slaughter of innocent civilians, children, whole families, and other "occupiers" has only raised the intensity of hostility.

Israel should never, in my opinion, compromise its right to exist in safety and security. Nor should it have to ride roughshod, as it occasionally may have done in the opinion of some over Palestinian rights, to live in safety and security. Retaliation leads to escalation, and a vicious cycle ensues.

To break the cycle will take time, trust, and the careful and systematic diffusing of active and passively simmering hostility and official governmentally-sanctioned incitement.

Small steps can lead to larger, more confident strides. A culture of suspicion and antipathy must gradually give way to a culture of compromise and compassion.

As to the question of C.O., nobody I know wants war. War is a tragedy and a *hillul HaShem*. There is ALWAYS collateral damage, ALWAYS a victor and a victim and ALWAYS death and destruction.

Our Jewish tradition teaches that we must be *Rodfei Tzedek* [Seekers of Justice] and *Rodfei Shalom* [Seekers of Peace], two ideals or qualities that are perhaps the most desired but the most elusive. That's why they must constantly be pursued. Without getting "mushy," let me simply say that the Torah's admonition "*tzedek, tzedek tirdof*," ["justice, justice, shall you pursue"] is addressed in the singular, to each and every person, and to me connotes the pursuit of righteousness by means that are just and righteous and lead to peace, not war. The statement in *Pirke Avot*, "Be disciples of Aaron, LOVING peace and PURSUING peace," means BY BEING LOVING AND THEREBY BRINGING PEOPLE CLOSER TOGETHER THROUGH TORAH, namely, teaching of the principles of Godly living. That is to say, justice, righteousness, and love – hesed, human kindness – lead to peace via patient education and loving commitment to a culture of mutuality that will always necessitate compromise, the sacrifice of some seemingly desirable goals by both sides, in order to attain a higher, workable, good.

SUSAN: I want to share the contents of an Israeli colleague who sent me an email recently: Here's what he wrote:

> "I share my son's response to my question of how he, as a sensitive Jew, felt about saying "the Lord is a man of war" every day, and I pointed out that even the Nazis (*l'havdil elef havdalot*) ["of course a thousand distinctions"] had a statement of God being with them on their belt buckles. He shared in response what he once told his soldiers. The verse, he noted, uses the Tetragrammaton, not "God" and he further noted the long standing tradition that the former reflects mercy, the latter, judgment. The verse then states, he said, that if, and only so long as, we are merciful, even in war, will God be with us.
>
> "It was one of those times that I thanked God again for bringing me to Israel and for the (many) officers in the IDF who maintain this merciful strain."

I thought it was an interesting wrinkle on this discussion.

BOB: This has been a fascinating discussion. I'm sure we've all learned a lot, and have given each other much to chew on. Now let me turn to another question that is more psychological than philosophical.

A young man died in my community, leaving an eight-year-old son. Am I correct in thinking that the boy, in third grade, has no real obligations during *shivah*, or in *avelut* in general? He can certainly say *Kaddish* with his mother, attend the funeral, perhaps even do *kri'ah* along with her, but as a minor. Anything beyond that? The mother would like to send him to school during the *shivah*, attempting to give him some semblance of normalcy, peer and teacher support, etc. Very sad situation. Any thoughts?

DON: What's good for the goose is good for the gander. His life isn't normal and attempting to make it seem normal could be psychologically devastating. Let him spend the week home with his mom.

SUSAN: Bob, sending him to school is only if children grieve the same way as adults do. They do not.

There are ample data in support of returning directly to "routine," although even those who advocate for routine are aware that there is no routine. Usually the adults are grappling with the same. And probably suffering while trying to get back to work "ASAP." There are those who say that the child should be allowed to stay home for a few days and then school, in conjunction with which parents should arrange for friends to come – one or two at a time – to help. Everything else in between has also received statistical support.

What this means basically, is that there is not a general recommendation, rather each case, that is, each child with his or her parent-adult family members/clergy, needs to work out what seems best.

What is clear across the boards is that kids don't like to cry in school. It is also clear that telling someone, kid or adult, "don't cry it'll be all right" is bad practice and counterproductive.

Finally, it is appropriate NOT to turn to psychologists in the first month of mourning. They try to "make it better" rather than "letting it get better" whatever that may mean.

SAM: I agree with Don, but for a different reason . . .

When you send a child right back to school after a death in the family, the child gets the erroneous, but valid, feeling that she or he "is being left out" of a family "something," which she or he then may carry on to other family event feelings, namely "they don't want me, I'm not really part of this family because I'm just a kid," and more.

It's just like not allowing a child to attend a funeral. They get that "I'm not part of the family" feeling, and it doesn't go away easily.

BOB: This has been very helpful. Thanks to all of you.

DON: A very interesting piece came to me across the internet the other day by the distinguished scholar and rabbi, Richard L. Rubenstein. Let me read it to you, and get your reactions:

As the Secretary of State, whose Jewish grandparents changed their name from Kohn to Kerry and their religion from Jewish to Catholic, arrives once again in Israel in his protracted attempt to force a suicidal "peace" on Israel, perhaps the real question is whether genuine peace is possible between Islam and the non-Islamic world. In reality, only someone ignorant of Islamic law – Shariah – as are the overwhelming majority of western politicians, diplomats, and all too many Israelis, would believe that peace is possible with Islam. Islam is in a permanent state of war with the non-Islamic world. When convenient, it is willing to accept a "*hudna,*" or truce, until a more opportune moment arrives for "*reqonqista,*" a Spanish word that applies equally to Islam.

Shortly before 9/11, I participated in an international, interfaith conference in Cordoba, Spain, site of the medieval Caliphate of Cordoba. On one of our sight-seeing trips, we visited *el mesquita*, the great Cathedral/Mosque of Cordoba. Originally built as one of Islam's largest and most important mosques, it was converted to a cathedral as a result of the *reqonqista*. I remember seeing a member of our group, an American convert to Islam, who appeared distressed immediately after our visit. I asked him, "Is anything wrong?" He replied, "You can't imagine how sick this place makes me. It was originally a mosque and was desecrated by the Christians." In reality, by converting the mosque into a cathedral, Christians were doing exactly what the Muslims did when they converted Hagia Sophia, for centuries the greatest cathedral in Christendom, into a mosque, when Constantinople was conquered in 1483. The Muslims regarded the conversion of Hagia Sophia as a legitimate reclaiming of a building that belonged to Allah, whereas they regarded the conversion of *el Mesqita* as the illegitimate seizure of that which originally belonged to Allah. Since the early 2000s, Muslims living in Spain have petitioned the Catholic Church for permission to pray in the cathedral. Both the Spanish Catholic Church and the Vatican have rejected the request on numerous occasions. They understand that conceding any territory to Muslims is only the first step.

Unfortunately, this well-known fact about Islam is all too often ignored, out of either malevolence or incompetence, by non-Muslim authorities. Let's hope that the Israelis remember it when they negotiate with Secretary of State Kohn-Kerry. Let's also hope that, in spite of his family's desire to escape from Judaism, the secretary can be more impartial than have been some earlier former Jews of similar background.

I can name many more former Jews who brought death, destruction, or at least political havoc to their former people. Such as Don Pablo de Santa Maria (a.k.a. Paul of Burgo), Archbishop of Burgo and years before that Rabbi Solomon Halevi, chief rabbi of Burgos. Check him out on Wikipedia. Also, Caspar Weinberger, Secretary of Defense under President Reagan. He was a convert, or his parents were, and he was also one of the most hostile U.S. officials toward Israel, and the American official who insisted on the harshest possible sentence for Jonathan Pollard. I can't look into the heart of Arthur H. Sulzberger, Jr, publisher of the New York Times. He is a direct descendant of Rabbi Isaac Mayer Wise, and is now an Episcopalian, because of his non-Jewish mother. The owners of the New York Times have always been afraid of being labeled as a "Jewish" paper.

BOB: While I certainly appreciate the point that I think Professor Rubenstein is trying to make, as far as I am aware, no one is attempting to negotiate a peace with Islam, any more than one could negotiate with Judaism. Who would be representative? The Israeli Rabbinate? Hasidic Courts? Neturei Karta? Whether or not there are problematic principals in the religion of Islam that some Muslims adhere to is not entirely germane to the reality of negotiating with Muslims of any nationality. While Abbas may not have an actual mandate from anyone, he's also not a particularly fundamentalist Muslim and more of a political opportunist. Religions are ideals, but they are practiced by people who are real. While I believe, for example, that my practice of Judaism is one hundredd percent valid and authentic, not all Jews feel the same way, and some – even to my face – would say I am not "really" Jewish.

SAM: Since Don brought something from the internet, let me also read something interesting which I found the other day on the internet, another piece by the distinguished scholar, Rabbi Reuven Hammer of Jerusalem:

Ben Dahan Must Go

Reuven Hammer

Imagine for a moment that the Minister of Religions in some democratic country – England or Swizerland for example – were to make a public statement that "the souls of all Christians are superior to the souls of Jews." Would Israel not make a fuss? Would not the ADL and the Weisenthal Center cry out in protest? Would not Jews in that country demand the immediate resignation of such an official? But in Israel the man who fills such a slot – Deputy Religious Services Minister Rabbi Eli Ben Dahan recently said just that about Christians. He is quoted as saying in an interview which he knew would be published, that the souls of all Jews are higher than those of Christians or Moslems or anybody else, yet his job is secure.

Nearly a week has passed since his outrageous statements were printed in *Ma'ariv* and, to the best of my knowledge, nary has a peep of protest been heard from any member of the government, from the President and the Prime Minister on down, nor from our esteemed Chief Rabbis, who should know that silence is equivalent to acquiescence. I have waited to hear the head of Ben Dahan's party, *Habayit Hayehudi*, Naftali Bennett, who supposedly represents enlightened Orthodoxy, say "it isn't true, all humans are equal," but that hasn't happened. Nor has Yair Lapid, whose *Yesh Atid* favors progressive religion and who is responsible more than anyone else for Ben Dahan having his position, denounced this teaching. A government that had an

ounce of integrity or shame would have insisted on the resignation of a person in charge of religions who dared to make such a
statement. How can he represent Israel to leaders of other religions or be allowed to represent Judaism to Jews?

Unfortunately Ben Dahan's view of the inherent superiority of
Jews over Gentiles is not his alone. He represents a well-known
teaching prevalent in certain circles, including many Hasidic
texts such as those of Chabad. These concepts, that view the
Gentile as somehow inferior to the Jew, are diametrically opposed to the teachings of Judaism's basic texts – the Torah and
the prophets, as well as to those of many great rabbinic Sages.

The most fundamental teaching of the Torah is that human
beings – all human beings – men and women – Jews and non-
Jews – are created in the image of God. "And God created man
in His image, in the image of God He created him; male and
female He created them" (Genesis 1:27). It was on that basis
that murder was forbidden. "Whoever sheds the blood of man,
by man shall his blood be shed, for in His image did God made
man" (Genesis 9:6). When the prophet Amos said, "To Me, O
Israelites, you are just like the Kushites – declares the Lord"
(Amos (9:7), he was expressing the concept that although Israel
has a covenantal relationship with God, there is no inherent
superiority in the people of Israel. All peoples are God's equal
creation.

The Sages taught the same lesson. "Why was only one human
being – Adam – created? So that no one should say to his fellow,
'My father was greater than your father'" (Sanhedrin 4:5). Ben
Azzai said that the greatest principle of the Torah was expressed
in the verse, "This is the record of Adam's line – When God created man, He made him in the likeness of God . . ." (Genesis 5:1)
(Gen. R. 24), stressing again that God created all human beings
in His likeness. Rabbi Akiva based his theology on the idea that
"Beloved is man for he was created in the Image; greater still was
the love in that it was made known to him that he was created
in the Image of God, as it is written, 'For in the image of God
made he man' (Gen. 9:6)." (Avot 3:15). As the midrash says, "I
call heaven and earth as witnesses: The spirit of holiness rests
upon each person according to the deed that each does, whether

that person be non-Jew or Jew, man or woman, manservant or maidservant" (*Seder Eliyahu Rabba* 9).

The pernicious doctrine that Jewish souls are higher than other souls is a perversion of these Jewish teachings and should be denounced as a dangerous heresy. It is dangerous because any such teaching of superiority of one group over another leads to actions in which humans can be treated as inferior, as less than human and eventually can be disposed of as well. We have suffered from this ourselves, and teaching it to our children will only lead to Jews treating others badly, as indeed has already happened.

It may be that others who held prominent positions in our governments have held the same view as Ben Dahan, but at least they never uttered it in public. By doing so, Ben Dahan has rendered himself persona non-grata and should have the good grace to resign his position. If not, he should be told to leave. We are constantly asking others to condemn those who speak disparagingly of Jews or Judaism. We have asked more than one Pope to change the liturgy so as not to show Jews in a bad light. Should not we ask the same thing of ourselves and denounce any Jewish teaching that demeans non-Jews? Israel must not be in a position in which others can point to us and say, "Look what your government is teaching about non-Jews before you complain about what others are saying about you." As Hillel said, all of Judaism can be encapsulated in the idea that we are not to do to others what is hateful to us (Shabbat 31a). Ben Dahan has violated that rule.

SUSAN: Then, too, Orthodoxy must change the wording of their traditional morning *berakhot* – *shelo asani Goy/ishah*, etc. [. . . for not making me a gentile/for not making me a woman]. Don, you may disagree, but this is how I feel.

There is more precedent in traditional Judaism than we are comfortable acknowledging for statements presuming superiority and inferiority among humans.

Perhaps they don't upset us as much any more since the Conservative movement's prayerbooks have expunged them, but they are still recited and studied daily by vast numbers of Jews.

The attitude of Jewish superiority over Gentiles is likewise reflected in statements such as, when Israel is worthy, their work – labor – is done for them by "others." Classifying women together with idiots, mutes and deaf people and minors with no understanding, is anything but acknowledging the equality and dignity of every human being created *b'Tzelem Elohim. Habad's* beloved and revered *Tanya* allegedly teaches that "*goyim* have no souls." Clearly, though, they do, as evidenced by their constant concern that their souls go to Heaven!

It's time that ALL Jews cleaned up their prejudices against ALL groups, religions and nationalities, and thereby "burn out the evil from our innermost beings."

DON: I think it's time to lighten the converstion a bit. Here's a question for y'all:

Who is the Israeli Prime Minister who responded to another foreign leader: "I am the Prime Minister of a nation of Prime ministers." What is the exact quote?

SAM: Actually, the source is attributed to a conversation when Chaim Weitzmann visited Harry Truman here in the U.S. Weitzmann said: "Mr. President, I envy your position." To which Truman responded, "Why, I am president of 180 million people, and you are president of two million people." Weitzmann replied:"You are president of a hundred and eighty million people, but I am president of two million presidents!"

BOB: I am puzzled. I never heard the Chaim Weitzman-Harry Truman story until now. However, I did hear this one when it happened:

Mayor John Lindsay of New York said to Mayor Teddy Kollek of Jerusalem, "I am Mayor of more Jews than you are." Kollek responded, "Yes. But I am Mayor of one million mayors."

Can someone track down a source?

SUSAN: I just googled this issue, and the earliest references I have seen to this story are from 1950:

Ruth Gruber, *Israel Without Tears*, 1950, p. 14:

According to Chaim Weizmann, one of the juiciest storytellers I have ever met, President Truman, congratulating him on the establishment of the new state, said: "I am the President of a country of 140,000,000 people. And you, Dr. Weizmann, have become the President of a country of a million people."

Dr. Weizmann shook his head. "Ah, you are wrong, sir. I have become the President of a million presidents."

Israel Laughs: A Collection of Humor from the Jewish State, by Paul Steiner, 1950, pp. 86–87.

In Israel today the people have a great sense of freedom and independence. Many business enterprises are owned cooperatively and office help, mechanics, drivers all own a share in the firm. This type of business is being encouraged by the Israel Government, which is striving to raise the dignity of labor to a new level. On the streets of Tel Aviv, the other day, a taxi driver summarized this feeling by saying: "Everybody's a boss in Israel." So we have this apocryphal story about a meeting of Chaim Weizmann with Joseph Stalin and Harry S. Truman. The three heads of state were discussing the complexities of their respective jobs. Stalin said: "There are 200 million people in the USSR, but only two million are Communist party members. My job is not an easy one." Truman said: "There are 150 million people in the United States and I'm responsible to every one of them."

"Your job is easy compared to mine," smiled Chaim Weizmann. "Do you know what it means to be president of one million presidents?"

DON: Susan, thanks. However, since there are two entirely different versions of the setting and I do not recall any meeting that Chaim Weitzmann had with Stalin and Truman when he was President of Israel. My suspicion is not allayed that all the versions of this story are apocryphal.

BOB: OK, let me pose another ritual question. This one is probably fairly common in this modern age of technology. A congregant asked me if it is permissible to use my cell phone on Shabbat, and to bring it to *shul*?

Here's my answer: I carry an iPhone at ALL times and places, almost ALWAYS set by its geofencing reminder capability to remind me to tun off the ringer in the area of any *shul* I attend, whether on weekday or Shabbat. How do I justify carrying this ultimate intrusion of *hol* on Shabbat? *Pikuah nefesh doheh et haShabbat* [Saving lives trumps observing Shabbat].

When my beloved mother, *aleha hashalom*, was alive, and I was the responsible son, I needed to be reachable in case of emergency. If and when you or I, God forbid, have sick children, relatives or even dangerously ill congregants, we need to be reachable, for notifications, even if we judge or choose, after knowing the circumstances, to wait until after Shabbat or Yom Tov to respond. Is it an intrusion on Shabbat? Certainly. When my pocket vibrates, however, I steal a quick glance at the notification. What about the petty annoying notifications we all get on our phones unsolicited? Apple, at least, has an answer. You can go to Settings and enable "Do Not Disturb." That means that nothing comes through EXCEPT from people or numbers you designate. In addition, if someone not designated calls repeatedly within a two-minute timeframe, the application will allow it to go through to your phone, under the assumption that it is urgent. While not perfect, this is a vast improvement. You can set it up by hours, days, or flip it on any time you choose in between your set times.

Do we always need to be "reachable," even on Shabbat? As long as the *malakh hamavet* does his work without regard to Shabbat rest, I feel the answer is yes.

SAM: For better or worse, people in my community relate to their cellphones the way that they relate to their wedding rings. Yes, I can also, and have, preached about and against that. They feel naked without them. Yes, if asked, they'll remove their wedding rings for *netilat yadayim*, but that's just for a few moments. Any longer than that would be intolerable.

Every bar or bat mitzvah child who comes to services carries a cell phone with them. They obviously don't drive, so they can't leave their phones in their cars. And they know not to leave them in the unattended cloak room. I have my own "cell phone in *shul*" story.

A few years ago, on a quiet summer Shabbes, just after services had come to an end and everyone was heading to *Kiddush*, I and a few stragglers were leaving the chapel. We discovered that one of our members, a man in his nineties, was unresponsive.

We happen to have an intensive care unit nurse in our community, and he was there that day. He went over to the man, began to examine him, and called out, "Call 911."

My *shul* president said, "I'll take care of it." She had previously turned off her cell phone lest it ring aloud in *shul*, and so she then pushed the on/off button, and waited, at first patiently, but then increasingly impatiently, as it booted up. As the seconds ticked by, she realized that this was inexplicably taking longer than anticipated, so she ran to the *shul* office to make the call from our land line. She picked up the receiver and found that the line was dead. The phone people were working on the lines. She ran back to the chapel. Her phone had still not booted up. "Does anyone else have a cell phone?" she cried out. There were only three or four of us there. Everyone else had gone off to *Kiddush*, unaware of the incident. No one else did. Finally, her cell phone booted up and she made the call. It took longer than expected, because when one calls 911 from a cell phone, the call is routed to the state police, rather than the local police. Eventually, she got the information across, and, about five minutes later the police arrived, and revived the gentleman. He's still fine, now in his mid-nineties.

There's no obvious lesson from this story, but I can tell you this: my president now keeps her cell phone on at all times. On mute, to be sure, but she keeps the phone on her person, and keeps it on, even on Shabbat, and even in *shul*.

SUSAN: Staying on ritual matters, here's another one on the same line: A problem I never thought I would encounter has just arisen:

A few years ago a small number of our members and members of a neighboring Reform congregation joined together to form a Jewish community choir. The cantor from the Reform synagogue directed it and they sang at a couple of local events, but not at any services in either congregation. The cantor who works part-time in the congregation but has other jobs, decided it was too time consuming for her and disbanded the group. Recently a few of the women who'd been involved, decided that they'd like to try to form a group through our congregation. I received an e-mail about it recently asking for an opportunity to meet with me and discuss the matter. This morning, there was a flurry of e-mails originating with one woman who happens to belong to both the Reform congregation and ours, excitedly reporting to the rest that she'd run into the "perfect person" to lead their choir. As she described her, I knew exactly who the man was, a very talented member of the community. The problem: the person is not Jewish. His wife is very active in the local – liberal – Baptist church. I'm very friendly with their pastor, and for many years, he has conducted various church choirs in the area.

My question for you: What's the status of a choir leader? Would you allow such a person to be hired if he was leading a choir that would not be participating in services? In my experience here we've never used a choir at services, and we only have a guest *hazzan* on the *Yamim Noraim*. Any input you're willing to share would be appreciated.

BOB: Some years ago, we considered the possibility of hiring a non-Jew to direct our High Holiday choir. In the end, we hired a Jew. Here is what I wrote at the time. The short answer to Susan's question is that, if the choir doesn't sing at services, there should be no problem with a non-Jewish director. Once you have him directing the choir, there might be a desire to have the choir sing at services, and, then, the situation might become awkward. However, I held then that it would be alright to have a non-Jewish choir director even at services. This is what I wrote to my congregation:

MAY A NON-JEW SERVE AS DIRECTOR OF THE SYNAGOGUE CHOIR?

The Committee on Jewish Law and Standards of the Rabbinical Assembly, at its meeting of August 31, 1954, instructed its chairman to respond to an inquiry that "it is the unanimous opinion of the Committee that the practice of having non-Jews in synagogue choirs is not in keeping with Jewish standards." Rabbi Phillip Sigal, in his capacity as Secretary of the Committee, wrote on June 3, 1958 that "choirs are regarded as extensions of the Cantor's voice, and it is deemed therefore, incorrect to use non-Jewish singers. By the same token, gentile choir leaders at services, are deemed contrary to the spirit of Jewish tradition and practice although there would be no objection to using them in training a choir."

I would point out that neither statement of the Committee makes any references to *halakhic* sources. The statements are simply the opinion of the Committee, although Rabbi Sigal's letter gives those opinions a rationale which relies, ultimately, on *halakhic* considerations. The *shaliah tzibbur*, in the strictest construction of his functioning, fulfills the obligation of prayer on behalf of the congregation as a whole, and it is a *halakhic* principle that one who is not obligated to perform a commandment may not perform it on behalf of one who is obligated. See tractate *Berakhot* 20b and elsewhere. Thus, a cantor certainly must be Jewish, and, to the extent that a choir is an extension of the cantor's voice, then choir members must be Jews.

However, that last assertion is open to question. If the *shaliah tzibbur* recites all the obligatory words of the prayers, then the choir, while esthetically significant, may be regarded as liturgically nugatory. In such a case, the requirement that choir members be Jewish, while plausible, would seem to be a matter of judgment rather than of strict *halakhah*. The same argument would apply a *fortiori* to a choir director who, we may assume, does not sing. The fact that the Committee found no objection to having a non-Jew train a choir supports this line of reasoning.

I concur with the Committee that choir members must all be Jews. With regard to a non-singing choir director, however, I would decide otherwise. It is certainly preferable that a choir director be Jewish, in order to do justice to the idea that the choir is an extension of the cantor's voice, and that the choir director is part of the choir, and in order to avoid the importation of "churchy" esthetics into the synagogue service. However, I would regard this to be a matter of preference rather than of requirement.

It is interesting to note in this connection that Salamone di Rossi, in the seventeeth century, wrote synagogue music in which there was no sharp division between cantor and choir, and that different voices shared the singing of the prayer text.

SAM: I was kind of happy to see the question. I don't really have an answer since in my community most synagogues for the most part don't even care if the choir members are Jewish let alone the choir director! And I'm not talking about choirs that just "perform." I'm talking High Holiday services! Being Jewish in a choir here doesn't seem to be even a consideration. The best singer wins.

With your permission, friends, I'd like to raise another question, which we've probably discussed before – maybe more than once – but it's come up again recently. So here goes.

We have a family with plots in our cemetery – a section within a larger cemetery that hosts both Jewish and non-Jewish sites – and I just learned that a congregant currently in hospice is planning to be cremated. He and his family would like his remains to go into the plot. They are questioning the cemetery as to the possibility of this practice. Does anyone permit this? I would love guidance from anyone who has faced this issue previously.

SUSAN: There is a reference in one of the popular manuals citing a position taken a long time ago by the London Beit Din allowing it, provided it was buried in a full coffin. I have once officiated at such an interment in a Jewish cemetery – once, in several years in the rabbinate. Some Jewish cemeteries now have in-ground plots, or above-ground niches to accommodate the "new" post-mausoleum craze among assimilated Jews. There were no such ridiculous demands made as requiring the burying of the urn in a full casket. I suspect that the cemetery or funeral director, or both, are insisting on this so they can charge the family for a casket, and/or to make it appear as if they are not burying ashes, since that might give others the idea that it's OK to do so or, equally likely, out of fear that their cemetery will be declared *treif* by the *haredim* if it looks like they're burying anything but bodies in caskets. In short, it seems that there are ways to do it, without too much publicity.

SAM: Thanks. So let me raise a related question. I noticed on my recent trip to Israel, that at least at the Har Herzl cemetery, the *matzevot* [monuments] read *ploni ben ema v'abba* [x son of Y and Z], not how we would have it in the States with the father's name first – or as was often the case, only the father. First, is this true everywhere in Israel, and what is the explanation?

BOB: I have seen references to a difference in Ashkenazi and Sephardi *minhagim* for names on the *matzevah*. Ashkenazim use the father's name and Sephardim use the mother's name.

In this case, I believe that what you are seeing is the trend to include the formerly omitted parent following the traditionally included parent. Nowadays we have a tendency to be more egalitarian and use both names, mother and father.

BOB: Friends, I have a very serious concern that I would like your thoughts about. Yesterday I just had an unexpectedly unnerving experience in my classroom. I suppose, after many years of teaching, I shouldn't be so naive, but this caught me off guard.

I had invited three of the graduates to our high school program to talk with some of our juniors and seniors about college life and, specifically, Jewish life on campus. The college and high schooler students present were not your average Jewish kids. The ninety-minute conversation was entirely in Hebrew. Two of the three guest speakers had been weekly participants in our *shul's* Shabbat services, Ramah veterans and products of deeply committed Jewish homes. The third, from a Reform congregation, had much the same background within his own movement and is majoring in Jewish studies in college. The high school students in class were easily able to engage in ninety minutes of give-and-take in good Hebrew. They are active in Jewish life, come from good Jewish homes and are involved in a wide range of serious Jewish commitments in their daily lives.

The three college students were from three very different colleges. Two are keeping kosher on campus. Only the Jewish studies major is taking Jewish or Hebrew courses. They occasionally go to a Friday night service at Hillel or Chabad but find them meaningless. They have no other Jewish involvements, except for the Jewish studies major, who is teaching Sunday school in a local Reform synagogue. None of them seemed particularly perturbed by the sudden absence of any significant Jewish experiences in their lives. One of them even argued that college is, for her, a kind of hiatus from Judaism. This from a young woman who insisted on laying *tefillin* at Ramah, even when almost no other girls did so! None are involved in anything to do with Israel. None are reading Jewish books or periodicals.

I cannot predict what kind of Jews these students will be after four to ten years of college studies. One is pre-med. I know that they will grow and change immeasurably in every way, and that their world will support those changes: intellectually, emotionally, socially, philosophically, politically, etc. But there is no support for their Jewish growth.

Orthodox Jews know exactly what to do on college campuses. They make sure there is a place to *daven*, eat kosher food, make Shabbos arrangements, have a *beit midrash*, etc. Indifferent Jews and minimalist Jews also know "what to do." For the Jews who are serious but not Orthodox, that is, for our best Jews, there are no options on most of our campuses. Do we teach our families how to choose a college and what to do when they get to college?

The old joke goes that, for Jews, three things are inevitable: death, taxes and college. When are all of these young Jews leaving? I don't know, but I'm guessing a very large percent of them break away when they go to college. I live in a very small world, teaching kids much of the time, but from here, it looks like college years might be the best place to start, institutionally, to re-grow mature committed Jews, and to save a lot of potentially great kids from Jewish oblivion.

SUSAN: In my personal experience, I have often heard of kids from an intense Judaic background becoming less religiously observant and connected while in college, as they encounter more and more of the "real," vs. "ideal," world and prepare for a career. College campus life is not usually very conducive to maintaining observance as we know and love it in community, as there are comparatively few who take that lifestyle seriously. The Orthodox have little problem, as do the Reform. My Conservative kids may be attracted to Hillel, but rarely find their kind of community there. They may try Chabad, but are often put off by what they find there, too.

While it is probably true that we "lose" a number of kids to the increased openness and secularity of college campus life, others really do take a hiatus until they establish themselves with a career and family, and then come back. You are absolutely correct in asserting that we need to seek to provide these committed kids with some sort of caring committed community of their peers during their college years, but the question remains, as always, how.

BOB: I would like to take comfort in your words, Susan, but I've been around too long. I have been teaching for a long time, and I have watched too many of my best kids leave Judaism in both Pewish senses of the word: the Jewish religion and all Jewish connection, over their college years. I have also seen deeply committed kids become incidental Jews, in droves, and remain that way even when they marry and start families. I'm talking about supplementary-school kids who could read and understand *Humash* with *Rashi* and carry on extended conversations in Modern Hebrew, who could lead Shabbat and weekday *davening* and understand some of Heschel and Buber. We have a very serious supplementary school program here, along with a great *shul* where many, even most, of our kids continue to be engaged after *b'nai-mitzvah*. And then they go to college.

DON: Some years ago I taught history on the west side of Chicago, in the inner city. I remember being overwhelmed by the task. They might really like my class. They might really like me. I even helped some of them to a higher reading level. Perhaps I gave some a glimpse of a different world. But I couldn't change their home lives. I couldn't change their neighborhood. I couldn't change their lives. Now I have been a rabbi for many years. I don't feel a lot different than I did at that inner city High School. I was then a very small part of a change that was happening in black America – I had also been a civil rights worker.

If there was a vision to serious Judaism it was supplied by Mordecai M. Kaplan and Abraham J. Heschel. On a mass level, those visions are crumbling. But we have been a part of creating a different kind of Jewish community, one whose shape is only now beginning to come into view. The synagogue centers of Kaplan are dying. Heschel succeeded in giving inspiration and rekindling for a few of us. We have to take comfort in the small contributions we have each made in the lives of our students and congregants. Some of us have children and-or students who continue the struggle to create holy Jewish communities. That is what I take comfort in. That, and the love and understanding and forgiveness of our Creator, the God of Israel.

BOB: Don, I understand what you are saying, but I think you are answering a much bigger question than I am asking. I am asking a very tiny question: I have wonderful students who love being Jewish, speaking Hebrew, going to *shul*, going to Ramah, learning Torah. Thank God, I am very blessed in what I do.

These students go to college and want to continue to enrich their Jewish lives. But they can't, because there is no opportunity for them to do so. They do not want to be Orthodox Jews. Some would not be recognized as Jews in the Orthodox community, and others want to *daven* without a *mehitzah*, to ask challenging questions, to observe more liberally, to engage in the Jewish arts, politics, Israel issues, social action, spirituality, theology: options that the Orthodox campus communities do not provide. So they go to their wonderful universities and find least-common-denominator Judaism, vapid Hillels, a Jewish world void of the richness and seriousness that they enjoyed in high school. For four years they grow intellectually, emotionally, socially, physically – in every way but Jewishly. In four years they are twenty-two-year-old adults and high-school Jews. Their Judaism has become puerile and irrelevant.

That's because we failed them. We led them to the Promised Land of college, where they discovered that Judaism is utterly incompatible with, and inferior to, the real thing, the maturity and excellence and seriousness and value of the real-lifeness of a college education and beyond.

For this, we don't need a new vision of Judaism. We need to take the riches of Judaism and bring them to the campuses. We need to let our best Jewish students know of those campuses where they can continue to grow as Jews. We need to help them, and their parents, understand that this is both possible and necessary. My tiny question: we know what to do, but why don't we do it? Why are we letting the millennials, by the thousands, slip through our fingers?

SAM: Do we know which campuses have been successful lately at getting Jewish kids like your students to be involved in some aspect of Jewish life?

SUSAN: I have been trying to follow the thread of this conversation, because it is a very serious structural problem for American Jews that we Jews have created for ourselves – we have made secular education at the highest levels an aspiration, an aspiration that is very much tied to our Jewish legacy. But in doing so we have placed achievement in secular academics and scholastics as the ultimate goal, and relegated quality of Jewish life and intellect to an insignificant place in our people's collective psyche. It is not naiveté nor willful ignorance when members of the *haredi* community tell me that college is dangerous and should be avoided other than for professional degrees which one acquires part time while learning in yeshivah or Kollel.

BUT, I am lost about what exactly is Bob's point.

On the one hand, Bob describes what sounds like simply the most wonderful supplemental Jewish educational program I could imagine. I can't tell you how jealous I am that I don't have a job in your *shul* to send my kids to your program, AND STILL these three highly educated and motivated Jews go to college and 1) don't take Jewish or Hebrew classes 2) only go occasionally to Friday night services 3) find those services meaningless 4) have no significant Jewish involvements 5) are not even troubled by this drop off of meaningful Jewish life 6) have nothing to do with Israel, and 7) do not read anything associated with Jewish religion , cultural life or spirituality. Moreover, they are not even embarrassed to come back to their school where they loved *Yiddishkeit* and were highly involved in Jewish education and tell their younger contemporaries how little they are involved or interested in Jewish life on campus.

This is enough to make one join ranks with the *hareidim* and discourage our best and our brightest from going to college. I will never forget a Dennis Prager rant where he interviewed some young Jewish college student who was leading an anti-Israel organization on her campus and discovered to his chagrin that she grew up in an active Jewish and pro-Israel home, only to learn the "truth" when she got to her liberal arts university.

On the other hand, Bob is criticizing Hillel as vapid, local rabbis as not committed enough in doing outreach, home *shul* rabbis for not doing enough to stay in touch, basically the entire Jewish institutional community for turning their backs on our university age demographic and allowing them to turn away from meaningful Jewish life forever.

So is it an existential dilemma or quality control issue? Because a lousy Hillel is not at fault when a formerly motivated Jewish kid decides she is taking a hiatus from Judaism during her college years. Local rabbis in college towns can't compel eighteen- and nineteen-year-olds to take Jewish classes or volunteer on behalf of Jewish communal issues. Home *shul* rabbis should absolutely stay in touch with their college youth – let's assume that they have some relationship with them in the first place – but that contact will not bring college students looking to explore new vistas to the Hillel house. Every year I make at least one visit to a college campus and bring dinner to the Hillel. It is my way of keeping connected to the kids but I also do it that way because it is usually the only time these kids stop in at Hillel. I would like them to at least know the address. But it does not guarantee return trips.

Hillels can do a much better job, of course. One of my kids is at a great university, and it kills me that of the 4500 Jews, yes, ten percent of the campus, with an excellent Jewish studies department, they can't organize one Shabbat morning *minyan*, but even Chabad and Aish HaTorah don't succeed. And yes, local rabbis, if they can, should reach out to Jewish college kids, and home *shul* rabbis should stay in touch when the kids come home. But it is so much more comfortable to criticize known institutions for not doing enough than to admit that maybe it is a structural dilemma whose solutions are unthinkable. If committed serious liberal Jews go to college and are unabashed in sharing their drop off in enthusiasm for Jewish life during college years, is the problem Hillel or the American college scene and the core values – scholastic achievement, professional success, prestige, humanism with disdain for particularity – with which our young people are raised.

I think Bob has touched upon a very serious issue and a disturbing reality. I have no doubt why he was unnerved to listen to his former students.

BOB: Susan, you are right about Brandeis. A fourth graduate, who could not attend that evening, goes to Brandeis. He and I went for coffee before he returned to college, and he's enjoying the riches that Brandeis Jewish life provides.

Let me try to be clearer. I don't think the problem I'm describing is existential. There are plenty of those. Nor am I suggesting that there is some way we can compel or even persuade Jewish college students to engage in Jewish life on campus. I believe there are many Jewish students who would get involved in Jewish life if it were available and worth their while. These include, among others, some of the "best" of our kids. But they go to the wrong colleges, or they go to colleges where there should be a plethora of excellent Jewish opportunities, only to find stuff that has no value. My "hiatus" student would have eagerly gotten involved in a program that combined serious Torah learning with social action, but she found neither. On the other hand, the campus was rich with wonderful non-Jewish options, so she made the same decision I would have made when I was eighteen: put Judaism on hiatus and go for the good stuff.

When I was an undergrad in Madison, Max Ticktin *z"l*, and, later, Richard Winograd *z"l*, were the Hillel directors. We had a class in Jeremiah, we had interesting Shabbat services with challenging *divre Torah* and serious discussions afterwards. I learned *Humash* and *Rashi* with Max and a bit a *Gemara* with Richard. There were exciting guest speakers, lively Jewish arts programs, political and Israel-centered activities, wonderful holiday celebrations, social action programs in the Madison community: real substance.

Yes, I know that's paleo-Judaism. But all of those values can be updated and made available, with the help of the students. Along with bowling parties and luaus with sushi.

I've spoken to some of my students who attended Chabad or local Orthodox *shuls* during their undergraduate years, even though they felt very out of place, because there was nothing else for them on campus. Unfortunately, too many of my students just give up. One student told me, after trying to work with a Hillel director, that he just stopped "doing Jewish stuff." He is now living in the East with his non-Jewish girlfriend and refuses to attend a synagogue, even when he comes back for a visit. This kid used to join his friends every Shabbat afternoon at my home, 3:30–5:30, where we learned *Humash* with *Rashi*, after going to *shul* every Shabbat morning. He was fairly fluent in Hebrew. And he's not unique. I believe this is our fault.

SAM: College is broadening. No doubt about it. It makes our best and brightest question their assumptions and beliefs and often shuck these entirely to fit in with the "college culture" which is disdainful of "what was and is" in these kids' lives and unabashedly libertarian and, dare I say, counter-our-insular-culture. The kids are away, out of their comfortable and familiar environment and in contact with new and interesting ideas and people. Their ties to family and community back home may be fond, but the bonds definitely loosen in favor of their contemporaries and the new culture in which their professors and their peers take the place of their parents and closest lifelong friends. It is little wonder to me that they wander and seek and explore their new world, its inhabitants and culture and want to "fit in."

Even our most committed often break loose and throw off their bonds and loyalties to embrace those of their new culture and new friends. I see no way that Hillel, for one, weak and inclusive as it is, with a reputation on many campuses of isolation in "our world that was," could hold, let alone attract these kids. They are like children let loose in a candy store who want to experience campus life in all its secular-liberal-decadence. What's Shabbat and kashrut got do do with "real life?" Unfortunately, we don't teach them that in a way that makes sense when they are tempted and challenged to view these "tribal" rituals and practices in the glare of the light of new thinking.

The miracle is, absent a nearly *haredi* background, that ANY of them stick and come back home to roost in the Faith of their Fathers after a liberating and self-questioning period of on-their-ownness.

We need to reach and teach them during their high school years, but teach them as if they are already the adults they are starting to become.

I don't think we have sought to create a Protestant Judaism. Reform attempted to do that in its early years. Nor do I think Christianity "is a civilization, built on the presumption of 99% illiteracy." Illiteracy is likely to be highest among Catholics because of the centrality of the sacraments. In the case of Protestants, it depends on which branch. My cook, for example, spends every possible minute studying Scripture and she is not unique. Protestantism was built on the idea of *Sola gratia, sola fide, sola Scriptura.* [Salvation comes by grace alone, by faith alone, by Scripture alone]. According to both Lutheranism and Calvinism, the Church and the sacraments are powerless to save us. We are saved by faith in what is revealed in Scripture. This means that the study of Scripture has a preeminent role in Protestantism, and I would guess that there are many Protestants who study Scripture very diligently. We may not agree with their interpretation of Scripture, but these Protestants are hardly illiterate.

I repeat: socio-cultural background had a great deal to do with the success of CONSERVATIVE JUDAISM in, for example, the Finkelstein era, and it has diminished success today. Although I have no contact with Conservative schools, I would guess that they are attempts to provide both the cultural and social background necessary to maintain a vital CONSERVATIVE JUDAISM. In any event, a philosophy or theology of CONSERVATIVE JUDAISM alone cannot change the situation.

DON: There IS a gap that needs to be seriously filled in places that do not have a meaningful, serious, vibrant and effective Hebrew High School or youth group culture in place.

Clearly, as kids mature towards college age, they need to be treated as the adults they are becoming, especially when it comes to serious study and decision making. They need to have their "peer" group at home and the collective experience that helps lead them towards individual feelings of competence in decision-making. They cannot leave for college as sheep, nor as lost souls, isolated from the stream of college life, its joys, sorrows, lessons and challenges. They need to be able to confidently articulate who they are as Jews, and why that is important to them and to the Jewish people.

BOB: High school is not enough. I've been teaching high school students for decades, and I know enough to say how inadequate it is. College years are when we make the two most significant decisions that will shape our Jewish lives: our personal philosophy of life, and the kind of life partner we will choose. If you add to that the kind of community we will join, you have the makings of a future Jew. Or not.

Without an active, interactive, dynamic Jewish presence available, the best of our best kids are going to make those decisions in a universe-ity that's Judenrein. We can expect a large number of them will leave the fold and never return. I'm talking specifically about the students who complain that the quality of Jewish life on campus is inadequate, not those who say that they aren't interested. One of my best grads told me, Hillel is interested only in basketball, movie night, bagel brunch, etc. These are the kids who wait for their summers in Ramah, or similar movement camps, to rekindle their Jewish spark. And often that's not enough.

Why can't the movements take them seriously and provide for them the other forty weeks a year?

SUSAN: A very useful dialog on a very important topic. I'm glad I didn't miss today's discussion. Hope to see you all next week!

Week 11

ళ

SAM: Hi Folks! Here's a question for Don. I have a member of my congregation whose son-in-law is studying for conversion with an Orthodox rabbi. One of the rabbi's criteria for conversion is that the person who is converting must move within walking distance of the Orthodox synagogue. Is this a common standard for Orthodox conversion? How do Orthodox colleagues in other communities address this issue when doing conversions? Inquiring minds want to get a sense if this is common or unusual.

DON: RCA [Rabbinical Council of America – the Orthodox Association of Rabbis] conversion standards can be found on this web site, http://www.judaismconversion.org/, and clearly indicate the requirement regarding walking distance to an Orthodox *shul*.

SAM: Wow, I never knew that. I suppose it's logical. It sure is a major commitment.

DON: We think it's crucial.

SAM: OK, here's a question for my Orthodox and Conservative colleagues: I was asked if I would allow the donation of a dining experience/meal for a member of the synagogue who owns a restaurant. No meat is served, it's dairy/vegeterian, and the restaurant food is ingredient-kosher, for a synagogue fundraiser. For business reasons which I perfectly understand, it did not make sense for the restaurant owner to go through the local popular – though very strict and extraordinarily expensive

– kashering agency here. Note that the restaurant is open on Shabbat and it was proposed that the gift certificate would only be eligible to be used Sunday-Thursday.

Thank you in advance for your help and advice.

SUSAN: My policy rubric on this one is, essentially, "I try to maintain synagogue *kashrut* standards at all synagogue-sponsored, or synagogue-connected events, unless there is a compelling reason to do so." For me, this community-building fundraiser would certainly qualify as a compelling reason to veer from the policy rubric. So my answer is, no problem.

DON: I'll leave it to the rest of you to guess what my answer would be. [Smiles]. I want to raise a different issue. I'm curious whether colleagues have written policies regarding speakers at their *shuls*.

SAM: I would never ban any legitimate Jewish group that's "within the spectrum" from speaking at my *shul*. If they are interesting and have a real point of view, it will bring people into the *shul*, which is always a good thing. That certainly includes AIPAC and J-Street. We have a major speaker on Israel almost yearly, and I think it absolutely adds to the view that the synagogue is a marketplace for ideas. We have sponsored AIPAC and AJC programs and have had speakers such as Peter Beinart, Yossi Klein Ha-Levi, Michael Oren, pre-ambassadorship, and will have Ari Shavit soon. We do not have a problem with civil discourse. I usually handle the Q and A and precede it with a stern warning that people must ask questions and not make statements of their own, as we are here to listen to the speaker's response and not them. I say it a lot more elegantly. I also refuse to charge for these talks. It just feels low class to ask for $15 or $25 to hear some interesting person who has a point of view that provokes some thought, which can be a challenge considering how much some of these speakers charge. It basically works.

BOB: Sounds reasonable. Our policy is somewhat similar,

though many of our colleagues would not permit any J-Street speaker in their *shul*, for obvious reasons.

Permit me to raise another important question, which will probably be raised in your synagogues, if it hasn't already. I am helping a bar mitzvah student research how we fulfill Leviticus 19:19 – not sowing with two kinds of seed – in light of GMO [genetically modified organisms] and so many of our seeds being a combination of multiple influences. I am looking for some contemporary rabbinic insights on this topic and appreciate any suggestions.

SUSAN: Let me recommend that you consult – and selectively share with your student – Hans Jonas's book *The Ethic of Responsibility*. Jonas's message, to the best of my memory, is that in recent times the expansion of our technological capacity to change the planet's environment, for better and for worse, imposes on us new kinds of responsibility that go beyond the responsibilities we had at an earlier stage of human history. It's quite a complicated issue, but I'm sure you'll find some direction in Jonas's work.

BOB: Thanks, Susan, I'll take a look at it, and let you all know my thoughts after I read it.

Right now, though, I have to share a horrendous experience I had last night.

We all have interesting experiences as rabbis, but some days are more interesting than others. Today I had an unusual encounter at a local hospital.

A colleague from another community e-mailed me yesterday, saying that he had a faithful congregant who had suffered a stroke, and asked if I could make some time for a visit. The first thing that we did was figure out where the patient was. I left to go to the hospital after evening *minyan*.

So I called the hospital, about fifteen miles away. There's no highway along this route, so it takes about forty minutes to get there when it's not rush hour. I ask to speak to the nurses' station in ICU to see if any family is there, and she responds "Ain't nobody here." I told her that I'm a rabbi, and that I'm on my way to visit. Click.

I had the wife's phone numbers, and left her a message on her cell phone, and reached her at the home number en route. She explained that her husband's condition was grave, so I asked if I could offer *Vidui*, explaining that even when someone is near death, we still pray for their recovery in this "final confession." She thought that it was a good idea.

I park a little bit away from the hospital, get to the ICU at about 7:10 p.m., ring to get in, and I'm told that it's time for the rotation of staff and that I should return at 8 p.m. Not happy, I ask to speak to the head nurse, who also insists that they are busy right now, and that I should return at 8. I'm hungry and grumpy, not a great combination.

Someone else walks into the ICU with an electronic key. I follow her in and find the room. As I approach, "Nurse Ratchet" asks me who I am and what I'm doing. I tell her that I am here to offer the final prayers at the request of the family. She digs her heels in and says I must return at 8 p.m. I notice that nobody is working with this patient. There are just a few people sitting around the nurses' station. I tell her that I would just be a few moments. She said that they are discussing patients, and nobody is allowed to hear them because of privacy concerns. I offered to close the door to the patient's room, but she insisted that I leave.

Then, just as the Hulk emerges from Bruce Banner when he is upset, the angry New Yorker in me emerged, uncontrolled. I smile at "Nurse Ratchet" and say "I'll tell you what. I'm going in to offer this man final prayers as per his wife's instructions. You call security, and I'll bet you that before they arrive I'll be gone." I entered the room, a nurse closed the door behind me, I spoke to this unresponsive man kindly for a few minutes, and then recited *Vidui*. I also offered a *Mi Sheberakh* at the wife's request.

I know that there are times when the clergy needs to stay out of a patient's room, during a procedure or a consult, but I've never been denied admission during the "changing of the guard." I was a bit hard-nosed, but don't feel too guilty about it. After this brief and unpleasant encounter, I treated myself to sushi on my way home. So ends my fish tale.

Thank you for letting me vent. I feel better now.

DON: That's a great advertisement for sushi. *Kol hakavod!* You deserved a suitably adjusted "Love Boat" at the sushi place in view of how you maintained the balance between *Hesed* [compassion] and *Din* [strictness]. As a Jew I realize that being paranoid is normal. If you were a priest dressed like one, would it be different? You deserve a *Yasher koach*. It wasn't your angry New Yorker persona, but the rabbi on a very special critical situation who couldn't submit to bureaucracy. *Kol Hakavod.*

SUSAN: We all have days like this from time to time. It comes with the territory. It has, on occasion, made me question whether or not my decision to become a rabbi rather than a physician was a wise one. Once, physicians were hard working and greatly envied for their lucrative remuneration; except for the in-demand specialists with mostly non-Medicare patients and surgeons doing highly specialized and sought-after voluntary surgeries. But that just ain't so no more. When I see my father's Medicare statements and see how pitifully and poorly the excellent physicians get paid for their attentiveness and professionalism compared to what my salary is, I smile heavenward and give thanks to the *Ribbono Shel Olam* who guided me in the right path at a crucial fork in the road of life.

SAM: Let's hope we all can maintain our cool as Bob did in difficult situations.

SUSAN: Here's a quick question: Does anyone know the old limerick about God that concludes with "His ways are inscrutable?"

DON: Our God, some contend, is immutable,
And their faith is, indeed, irrefutable,
When He does what he should,
It's because He is good,
When He doesn't His ways are inscrutable.

SUSAN: Hey, Don, you're a whiz. Thanks! Now I have another

question. Let's see if you can answer this one as quickly. At the World Wide Wrap recently, one of the members of my Men's Club referred to the assertion that the pressure exerted by *tefillin* on our arm and head corresponds to the points used in acupuncture to increase spirituality. I didn't say anything, but, inwardly, I scoffed. As I thought further, however, I wondered. Certainly, the mental and physical realms are linked. If meditation, which affects breathing, heartbeat, etc., can have a spiritual effect, why not *tefillin*? In fact, of course, I believe that physical acts such as laying *tefillin* do have spiritual significance. However, I see *kavvanah* as the bridge over the physical-mental divide. If it is a matter of pressure points, then the spiritual effect would seem to be automatic, and that certainly is not the case. On the other hand, I don't know anything about acupuncture. Perhaps it is a mistake to judge it by the standard of causation recognized in western science. What do you think?

DON: Much has been written about *tefillin* and accupressure. Take a look at this web site: http://www.koshertorah.com/PDF/tefilin.pdf.

SUSAN: Wow! You are truly a whiz! Two in a row, *yasher koah*!

DON: No problem. Keep firing away!

BOB: Let me turn to an issue that all of you either faced in the past, or surely will some day in the future. I have a congregant wanting to know what to do if his mother passes away just before his daughter is called to the Torah as a bat mitzvah this month. It is very likely that this will happen. I'm inclined to say to call his daughter to the Torah, but that he would avoid any parts of the reception that have festive music, etc. However, I would like feedback from colleagues before I have this painful conversation with the poor fellow.

Any advice would be very much appreciated.

SAM: Let me share a personal experience in reply to your question. My mother passed away just before my son's bar mitzvah.

She put up a valiant fight to stay alive so as not to destroy the *simcha*. My sister smartly told her that her that heroics would cause one of us not to attend the bar mitzvah since we were not going to leave her alone in hospice in Columbus. I made her the promise that I would not cancel the bar mitzvah if she promised to give up her heroism, requesting medicines to prolong death from happening at great pain to her. She passed away the next day on the Friday, a week before the bar mitzvah. The funeral was Sunday morning, just after one of the worst snow storms in the Northeast and my sister and I got up from *shivah* Friday morning in time for the bar mitzvah. I arranged to serve as a waiter for one of the courses and therefore I was there as *halakhah* allows as a "*shushbeen*" [formal attendant]. As I promised my Mom, I danced one *hora* just to keep my promise to her and then spent the rest of the time talking to people. My Dad died under the same circumstance for a cousin's bat mitzvah. Once again I became the waiter for one course to my table. I did not dance. My parents were in each picture, as the photographers told me, since I was unshaven. Every time I look at the pictures I am reminded of that fact and realize that I kept my promise to my Mom.

Many years ago I had two situations at my congregation with regard to weddings. In one, the grandmother passed away on Thursday and the wedding was Saturday night. We did the wedding on Saturday night and the funeral on Sunday. Everyone danced and celebrated since there were no mourners sitting *shivah*, since *shivah* did not start until the next day. I found this permissible in *Kol Bo Shel Avelut*. In a second situation the groom's mother died on the Sunday prior to his wedding, and since he was still in *shivah* we rescheduled the wedding.

I hope that my experiences can help you in helping your congregant.

BOB: Thanks so much, Sam. This is extremely helpful!

Can I now raise a question regarding that sticky, pesky issue of the "*Agunah*," a woman whose husband refuses to give her a divorce? Actually, this question is a wrinkle which is perhaps a corollary of the "*Agunah*" issue.

Over the weekend I heard that an Orthodox colleague recently presided over a marriage where the groom had received a *get* using one hundred rabbis from three countries. I am not sure if the *kallah* had been married before.

Does anyone know of how acceptable this process is in the Orthodox world?

DON: It sounds like you're talking about a "*Heter Meah Rabbanim*," which is a possible avenue for permitting, on a single-case basis, a relaxation of the *herem* [ban] of Rabbeinu Gershom against a man taking more than one wife. Obviously, we Ashkenazim have frowned, for more than a thousand years, on the possibility of a man being married to more than one woman – even if only technically, Jewishly – at a time.

It would require very special circumstances for self-respecting rabbis to sign on to such an undertaking. Perhaps a civil divorce has already taken place, and there is no chance that the couple will reconcile, but there is some technical barrier to the execution of the *get*, such as if the wife is in a vegetative state, but could live for many years, or is mentally incapacitated.

The procedure of *Heter Meah Rabbanim* is *halakhically* respectable in the Orthodox world, by which I mean that I have not heard that anyone in the Orthodox world has ceased to respect it.

Needless to say, a successful *Heter Meah Rabbanim* could allow a husband to get married, but it would not be an effective way to gain legitimacy for a wife to get married. In that sense, although it does not seek to be anti-egalitarian, it is not equally helpful for a man and a woman. Many might say that solving one person's predicament might be better than solving no person's predicament.

BOB: *Heter Meah Rabbanim* is in regular use in the Israel Chief Rabbinate. According to Hebrew wiki, it's used on average eleven times a year. I presume it's only talking about in Israel.

I don't know how often it's used, so I'll assume the eleven times in an average year is accurate. I do know of two cases where it was applied, one seemed to me to be reasonable, the other – perhaps, but it depends upon accepting certain values.

In the first case a woman in her late twenties was in a car accident and was in a persistent vegetative state for an extended period. Her husband, same age, wanted to remarry. There was at least one or two kids involved. He promised to provide for her continued care, including all medical issues and caretakers as needed. He was given the *heter* and remarried.

The other case was a couple who could not conceive. After ten years the man said that he did not want to divorce his wife, and she wanted to stay married as well. He also, with her consent, got a *heter* and remarried. They still live in one house, two "moms" with six kids. People who know them say that the barren woman is not the happiest person in the world, but many assume that she would not have been able to remarry, so they rationalize that this is better.

The first seems humane, the second I attempt not to judge. Are there cases where this is abused? I assume so. But that's the case for many bureaucratic solutions, no?

DON: One of my professors was married to a woman with mental illness, and he re-married, using the *Heter Meah Rabbanim*. When a hundred rabbis agree on something – anything – that is a miracle.

More than seventy years ago, my father had a distant cousin, an Orthodox rabbi, whose wife was institutionalized for insanity. He wanted to remarry, but, obviously, could not give her a *get*, since she would not have been of sound mind and could not understand what she was getting. He managed to get a hundred rabbis to sign a *Heter Meah Rabbanim* to allow him to marry a second wife without incurring the *herem* of Rabbaynu Gershom on having more than one wife. He married another cousin of his and had two children with her. Interestingly, having once achieved the goal of getting a hundred rabbis to sign his *heter*, he was able to help other individuals with the same problem by keeping in touch with this coterie of rabbis and providing those in such need with the desired *heter*. He became the "go to" rabbi for those seeking such a *heter*.

I heard that it was used by husbands who traveled, in case they were kidnapped or killed without witnesses and hence leaving their wives as *agunot*. A religious friend of mine who traveled a few weeks every month was advised to have such a document created.

There was a story about 9/11, about some of those in the twin towers calling their rabbis instructing that a *get* be written so that the wife would not be an *agunah* – whether it was a *get* or a conditional *get* was never clear.

By the wy, IDF General Staff Order 34.0402 provides for the giving of a conditional *get* by IDF soldiers.

Here is another source of information about war, *agunot*, and conditional and non-conditional *gittin*: http://koltorah.org/ravj/Wartime_Gittin_1.html

The author, Rabbi Howard Chaim Jachter, "serves as chairperson of the *Agunah* Prevention and Resolution Committee of the Rabbinical Council of America, where he champions the use of prenuptial agreements to avoid the issues created if the husband refuses to give or receive a *Get*." (http://en.wikipedia.org/wiki/Howard_Jachter):

SUSAN: Friends, I have a related, and interesting question which I think deserves our collective attention. I understand about giving a conditional *Get* when someone is going off to war or on a dangerous trip. My question is about a situation where, for example, a man is diagnosed with early Alzheimer's but still mentally competent and wants his wife to be able to remarry once his dementia became so severe he could not recognize her but to continue living with her in the meantime.

Does anyone know whether this has been discussed or written about in a *halakhic* context?

Rabbi Josh Yuter discusses "Solutions to the *Agunah* Problem" in a podcast with a pdf of sources here: http://www.joshyuter.com/2012/03/25/podcasts/current-jewish-questions/ep-63-current-jewish-questions-10-solutions-to-the-agunah-problem/. He refers to three types of *Agunot*: (1) Recalcitrant Husband (2) Missing husband / Location unknown: e.g. MIA, 9/11, lost at sea/ Willing but unavailable and (3) Diminished faculties: deaf mute, dementia, loses *halakhic* capacity to voluntarily give wife a *Get*.

Rabbi Dov Linzer has a study guide: "*Study Guide for Sources on "Proposed Solutions to the Agunah Crisis"* http://tinyurl.com/mjets7l

I can print this out on the restaurant's printer. He gave me permission a few weeks ago to use their printer whenever I want.

In the section dealing with the conventional *Get*, Rabbi Jachter wrote:

A Conventional *Get* – Rabbeinu Tam and Rabbeinu Yechiel of Paris

Rav Yosef Eliyahu Henkin (*Teshuvot Ivra* number 80) and Rav Yosef Zevin (*LeOr HaHalacha*, p. 67) note that the preferred method to avoid wartime *Agunot* is for a married soldier to divorce his wife with a conventional *Get* before he leaves for war. The advantage of solving the problem in this manner is that it is a straightforward and (unfortunately) common procedure and is free from *Halachic* pitfalls. Indeed, Rabbeinu Yechiel of Paris (cited in the *Mordechai Gittin* 423) instituted that if a *Get* is administered when a childless husband is deathly ill in order for the wife to avoid *Chalitzah* (*Get Shechiv Mera*; see the article on this topic available at www.koltorah.org), the *Get* should not be conducted on condition that the husband not recover, so that the couple will remain married if he recovers. Instead, the partners should conduct a standard *Get* and solemnly promise that they will remarry should the husband recover.

The Rama (*Even HaEzer*: 155:9) rules in accordance with *Rabbeinu* Yechiel of Paris. The *Aruch HaShulchan* (E.H. *Seder HaGet HaTemidi* 1) likewise notes that we do not administer conditional *Gittin* in our times and that a Rav should refuse to administer the *Get* if the husband insists on issuing a condition. In fact, while observing the Jerusalem Rabbinical Court in 1993 in the course of training to become a *Get* administrator, I saw a husband (who happened to be a rabbi) stubbornly insist that the *Get* between himself and his wife be

conducted conditionally. He argued that the Talmud was re-
plete with discussions of *Gittin* conducted conditionally. One
of the *Dayanim*, the great Rav Zalman Nechemia Goldberg,
said to the man, "You are a *Talmid Chacham* (Torah scholar).
You have heard of Rabbeinu Yechiel of Paris, yes?" The husband replied that he had. Rav Goldberg continued, "*Rabbeinu*
Yechiel of Paris decreed that we do not conduct conditional
Gittin," which ended that discussion.

Rabbeinu Yechiel's primary concern was the many *Halachic* complications in properly executing a conditional *Get*.
An error could easily creep into the process, resulting in an
invalid *Get*. Unconditional *Gittin* avoid many of these complexities and therefore result much less frequently in disastrous mistakes. Indeed, the Maharsha (end of his commentary
to tractate *Gittin*) cites the aforementioned view of *Rabbeinu*
Tam that wartime *Gittin* are conducted unconditionally in
support of *Rabbeinu* Yechiel. For this reason, this remains the
preferred *Halachic* option for conducting wartime *Gittin*. In
fact, I recall a case in 1994 where a husband was undergoing
very risky surgery and wished to give his wife a *Get* so that she
would not remain an *Agunah* if the surgery rendered him incapacitated and incompetent. Rav Peretz Steinberg, a noted
Dayan from Queens, New York, conducted a conventional
Get, and the couple remarried after the surgery was successful.

There are some obvious disadvantages to conducting *Gittin*
in such a manner. First, many couples may find it too discom-
forting. Moreover, there is no guarantee of remarriage, since
violation of the solemn promise to remarry does not invalidate
the *Get* according to most authorities (see *Aruch HaShulchan*
E.H. 145:30). Furthermore, it might demoralize soldiers at a
time when courage is needed most. Finally, and perhaps most
importantly, this approach is unsuitable for a *Kohen*, since a
Kohen is forbidden to marry a divorcee, even his former wife.
Thus, conditional *Gittin* were often conducted in wartime.

Despite the concerns regarding improper delivery of a conditional *Get* that are referred to in the section above, Rabbi Jachter
provides information about support for conditional *Gittin* in his

next section: Conditional *Gittin* – *Teshuvot Divrei Malkiel* and Rav Chaim Ozer Grodzinsky.

In the third section, Rabbi Jachter describes a proposal by Rav David Singer of Pilzno:

> In the fall of 1914, as World War One commenced and Jewish young men were being drafted into the army, Rav David Singer of Pilzno, Galicia suggested an alternative to soldiers giving their wives a conditional *Get*. He wrote that soldiers could appear before a competent rabbinic court and appoint a scribe to write a *Get*, witnesses to sign a *Get*, and an agent to deliver a *Get*. The *Beit Din* would record this event and write and deliver a *Get* only if the husband did not return from war and his death could not be ascertained. The wife is then permitted to remarry since either the husband is dead, obviating the need for a *Get*, or he is alive, and the *Get* is valid.
>
> The advantage of conducting a *Get* in this manner, explains Rav Singer in a poster circulated to soldiers leaving for service during World War One, is that it is simpler to execute than a conditional *Get*. It is easier on the couple, as it avoids the discomfort of the husband handing a *Get* to his beloved wife. This, in turn, motivates soldiers, who might otherwise not do so, to give wartime *Gittin* to their wives in order to avoid a potential *Agunah* situation. Moreover, it facilitates conducting large numbers of wartime *Gittin* for the thousands of soldiers who are being rushed to battle. Appointments of scribe, witnesses, and agent take a fraction of the time that it takes to execute a full *Get*. Furthermore, it eases the toll on morale, as there is a more remote connection between the soldier and the *Get*, which would otherwise be performed in contemplation of the disturbing possibility of becoming missing in action. Finally, this method is in harmony with Rabbeinu Yechiel of Paris's edict to avoid conditional *Gittin* as much as possible. Note that the husband does not stipulate any conditions with regard to the *Get*. It is simply understood that the *Beit Din* would not allow the scribe, witnesses, or agent to execute the *Get* until it is appropriate to do so. (This is not considered to be a conditional *Get*; see *Baeir Heitev* E.H. 156:1.)

Rav Singer's proposal was endorsed by two renowned *poskim* of the time, Rav Meir Arik and Rav Yosef Engel, as recorded by the Munkaczer Rav (*Teshuvot Minchat Elazar* 3:68). (Rav David Singer is my great uncle, and his son, Rav Yosef Singer, gave me a copy of the poster that Rav David produced to publicize the need to conduct such *Gittin*. The poster hangs in my office as inspiration for my work as a *Get* administrator.)

This proposal, however, is not without its disadvantages. It does not address the problem of *Chalitzah*. In case the husband dies without children, the wife is not permitted to remarry until she receives *Chalitzah* from her husband's brother. Accordingly, if the husband dies or goes missing, the *Get* appointments would not avoid the *Chalitzah* requirement. Unlike the first two options that we outlined, this solution does not take effect immediately, but rather only after the husband is no longer assumed to be alive (i.e. he has no *Chezkat Chaim*), at which point the *Get* does not avert the need for *Chalitzah* (see *Pitchei Teshuvah* E.H. 141:70).

In addition, since it does not operate retroactively, it is not effective in case of the husband losing his mental faculties in war. A *Get* cannot be executed in such a situation since *Halacha* requires that the husband be of sound mind both at the time of appointing the scribe, witnesses, and agent and at the time of the delivery of the *Get* (*Shulchan Aruch* E.H. Chapter 121). The *Minchat Elazar* (ad. loc.) addresses the question of how we can write a *Get* on behalf of the husband and not be concerned with the possibility that he became mentally incompetent and unable to have a *Get* executed on his behalf.

Finally, Rav Singer does not address the possibility of the scribe, witnesses, or agent moving overseas or dying. Subsequent variations of Rav Singer's proposal, such as that of Rav Herzog (*Teshuvot Heichal Yitzchak* E.H. 2:41), offer the option of appointing alternate scribes, witnesses, and agents in case any of the people appointed to execute the *Get* are unavailable to do so.

I hope this is helpful. It's a lot to digest, but I think the study of this and other *teshuvot* will bear rich fruit.

SUSAN: Yes, extremely helpful. Thanks for all this. I'll study it more thoroughly at home.

SAM: *Haverim*, let me raise another issue. I have been asked to perform a wedding between a Rabbinite groom and a Karaite bride. How do modern *poskim* [decisors] rule on such a possible marriage? I am aware that Rabbi Ovadiah Yosef ruled that Karaites are considered Jewish in Israel. I need a little guidance in navigating if anyone has practical experience with this type of marriage.

BOB: A British colleague of ours wrote a thesis with Rabbi Louis Jacobs at the London Hebrew College, titled "The personal status of the Karaites in Rabbanite *Halakhah*."

As you can imagine, it's a very complex subject. But the bottom line, the way I remember this thesis – though I read it many years ago – is that you are permitted to perform the marriage.

Here is the problem, as I recall the details. Karaite *Gitten* are radically different from ours. If a Karaite woman remarried in the strength of a Karaite *Get*, there is a question that she would still be married to the first husband. We do not know who, among the Karaites, might have been descended from such unions. The result, according to the Remah [Rabbi Moshe Isserles] and others, is that, as a result, the entire Karaite community would be possible *mamzerim*.

The Radbaz [Rabbi David ibn Zimra, sixteenth century], whose opinion has been accepted by many, holds that this isn't a problem insofar as the original *Kiddushin* was likewise invalid.

And there are other issues. Some Karaite authorities maintain that rabbanite Jews, which we are, are possible *mamzerim* in their view, because we marry relatives whom they might regard as within the prohibited degrees of forbidden marriages.

Further, there is the issue on both sides that each regards the other form of Judaism as heretical. This objection becomes moot if there is a *teshuvah* – in other words, that a rabbinite became a Karaite or vice versa. But, of course, these days, according to some authorities, many or most Jews are heretical even within their own stream.

Based on the Radbaz we can intermarry with them. But this presumes *teshuvah;* that the Karaite becomes a Rabbanite Jew.

SAM: Thanks so much, Bob, this is extremely enlightening. So now I can tell the couple, that I can perform their wedding. They will be very relieved and happy.

DON: Here's a homiletical querie for you preachers. I'd love to know your favorite text – ancient, medieval, or modern – regarding *Moshe* breaking the two tablets of the Law on Mount Sinai when he saw the people dancing around the Golden Calf.

SUSAN: I like the saying attributed to the Kotzker:
Why did Moses break the tablets of the law when he came down from Mt. Sinai and saw the people worshipping the golden calf? Not because he lost his temper, but because he realized that, if people would make an idol of something as foolish as a golden calf, they would certainly make an idol of the Torah, which is of great value, but which is still not God.
In other words, don't go to the extreme of making the words of the Torah an idol. They too are not God!

BOB: I don't remember the source, but I recall someone mentioning that Moses, being eighty years of age, needed a bit of assistance carrying those heavy stone tablets down the mountain. The Almighty held onto the top and Moses supported them on the bottom. However, once the people started worshiping the Golden Calf, the Blessed Holy One let go and Moses had no choice but to allow the tablets to smash on the ground. Just a thought. As the Talmud says *"Yasher koach she-shibarta!"* "It's good that you smashed them!"

DON: Here's a beautiful midrash: הלוחות ושברי הלוחות מונחים

בארון. (Talmud Bavli, *Bava Batra* 14b) – "The Tablets and the broken Tablets were both kept in the Ark."

This quotation has also been used to teach the value of a human being: a scholar who has forgotten his learning is to be accorded honor, for what he was and who he still is.

As it is written: The tablets and the broken tablets both rest in the Holy Ark.

שנאמר: הלוחות ושברי הלוחות מונחים בארון.

DON: Thanks, folks, these are really beautiful. I appreciate your help.

SAM: OK, guys, here's a question about naming. I'm really curious to hear your thoughts. A couple has just had their second child. They would like to name the child for the same person after whom they named the first child. The first child was given the person's first name; they'd like to give the second child the person's middle name.

They spoke with the *mohel*, who told them that this is highly unusual – probably true – and that it is as frowned upon as naming an Ashkenazi child after a living relative. My sense is that it's all *minhag*, and makes no difference, and besides, it's two different kids getting two different names. Anyone have a different opinion?

BOB: Your opinion jives with my thoughts. But once at a park in Los Angeles I met two brothers both named Herman after their respective fathers. I'm not creative enough to make that up.

ALL: (Huge laughter).

SAM: Oh, c'mon, can't be.

BOB: I swear.

SAM: OK, who has a real answer for me?

DON: Sam's answer raises an interesting question that I hope others will weigh in on: how much weight or preference should be given to Ashkenaz vs. Sefardic *minhag* in naming and other customs? To what extent does it really "matter"? Perhaps this question is most practically applicable to those of us in "mixed" marriages. In my own case, having been married to a pure Moroccan, when we had our first daughter, my wife wanted to name her Avivah, after her mother who was still living. I wanted to find a way to honor my Ashkenazic mother, named Avigayil, by giving my daughter a name that would be a reflection of my mother. Knowing that Mom would be offended if she knew her granddaughter were named after her, as she was still living, we settled on Avivah Avital, because it "incorporated" the first two letters, *alef* and *bet*, without sounding quite like it – and in an irony, when she turned sixteen, Aviva didn't ask anyone, but went on her own and legally changed her name to Avital Aviva because "Avital" was modern while "Aviva" was old-fashioned. Another example of "*Mann tracht und Gott lacht . . .*" [We worry, God laughs].

In a tangential but somewhat related vein, my first clash of *minhagim* came in my first year of marriage over the issue of our eating rice on *Pesach*. I never had, she had never been without. When I mentioned to her that according to *halakhah* the wife is supposed to follow the *minhag* of the husband, her reply was short, sweet, simple and definitive. "OK, then YOU do the cooking for *Pesach*."

Let me tell all you folks, rice on *Pesach* is GOOD – MIGHTY good – I mean REALLY GOOD !

Sic transit gloria minhag [Latin-Hebrew for "Thus passes the glory of Jewish custom"].

SUSAN: Just met a *Hayim Yosef* whose three-year-old younger brother is *Yosef Hayim*. Thank goodness these were only for the Hebrew names! Their English names were different.

BOB: Here's a serious question, though not too important, just out of curiosity. At a wedding in Israel is the *ketubah* text generally in Aramaic or Hebrew?

DON: The standard Israeli *ketubah* is in Aramaic. Though at different times I've seen three *ketubot*: Aramaic, fairly traditional, Hebrew version of the Aramaic, and Hebrew egalitarian.

BOB: Typical for Jews, right? Four Jews and five different options.

SUSAN: Well, on that heavy note, maybe it's time to take a break. See you all next week, God willing.

Week 12

BOB: Hi everybody. I so look forward to these weekly meetings. For social reasons, as well as getting new perspectives on the issues we face. I never walk away from our luncheon meetings without a warm feeling in my heart.

I have an interesting question to start us off. I'd like some advice. In the past year I have been approached by a number of couples where one of the parties was a Patrilineal Jew, namely, that the father was Jewish, but not the mother. Sam, I know the Reform movement now accepts such "Patrilineal" Jews as fully Jewish, with some privisos. I'm thinking of ways that Conservative, and maybe even Orthodox rabbis can accept such people as full Jews, with some conditions, of course.

I can only surmise that my experience isn't different than what many of you, perhaps most of you have experienced. In all instances, I insisted on *mikvah* and thankfully, only *hatafat dam brit* [a pin-prick to draw a tiny drop of blood from the penis], for males, but the experience raised a number of questions.

Obviously this phenomenon is not going to disappear. Coincidentally, my attitude has changed in the past several years, from considering them "not Jewish" to, they are Jewish but simply require some additional stuff to complete the process. As one of our colleagues calls it a "completion ceremony."

But the larger question, if we wish to increase the number of Jews in the world, remains. How do we more aggressively attract and integrate this population? Should we be reaching out to unchurched patrilineals? Should we be using our youth groups, as one of our colleagues suggested, to attract patrilineal young adults so that eventually they can be brought to *mikveh*? Should we develop a common language that all of us could use to provide some consistency in our various Movements?

SUSAN: Thank you, Bob, for bringing this up. I'm "completing" someone just next week, in fact, a college student whom I know well. She was raised in a Jewish home and attended a Reform synagogue in New York. Since we do lots of community wide youth programming, she knows me better than the new rabbi at her place.

So when she was on Birthright recently she heard about this, that other Movements don't accept Patrilineal Jews, for the first time, and was thrown into a major identity crisis.

We need to address this in a sensitive way. I don't think "complete" quite satisfies that. It sounds too much like the approach of missionaries – to become a "completed Jew." Plus it implies that they were somehow incomplete before. In her mind, there was nothing half-baked about her one hundred percent Jewish upbringing.

I'm just calling this a technicality. But there needs to be a better way of saying it. At least *mikveh* is all she needs.

DON: I find it somewhat disgruntling that so many colleagues feel that the status of conversion – opposed to "completion" – is something negative, a matter to be apologized for and requiring euphemism. Yes, we could say, "Don't worry, you are not really a convert except in some unfortunate technical sense," but we could also say, "You should be so lucky to be counted among those who seek to accept Judaism in its terms, rather than through your own self-definition." It is to our credit that we are so open to converts, not so much to our credit that we feel the need to apologize for the status of the convert.

SAM: It's not an either-or kind of thing. Someone who was, for instance, raised as a Jew in a patrilineal home IS taking care of some technicalities when he or she goes through the *halakhic* steps of formal conversion. Someone who was NOT raised as a Jew in a patrilineal home, but who wants to embrace Judaism would obviously need to engage in a course of study to make an informed decision. And then, like any other Jew by choice, is taking care of the technicalities of going through the *halakhic* steps of conversion.

Calling them "technicalities" should not and need not diminish the significant personal and spiritual significance of the process and the rituals. As long as we view the process and the rituals as a burden, there's no reason to expect that a person from a patrilineal home will view it as such. How we present it is as important, and, often, much more important, than the person's opinion. Again and again, I've seen indecision, defensiveness, and even outright resentment about the process melt away with the right presentation.

I will often hear, "As far as I'M concerned, I'm already a Jew." To which I will often reply, "As far as I'M concerned, you are, too. So all that's left to do is the formalities and the paperwork. It's sort of like buying a car, except a lot more meaningful."

I would also caution against the use of the phrase "completed Jew." For those of us of a certain age, and life experience, "completed Jews" were Jews by birth who accepted Jesus as their personal Lord and Savior. Ironic, eh?

SUSAN: I would question the requirement of *hatafat dam*. Clearly the circumcision was initially done as a *bris*, and also, an uncircumcised convert is still a convert – they are just an uncircumcised Jew with an obligation to be circumcised, no different than any other Jew whose parents decide not to do a *bris*.

DON: Actually, Susan, if the circumcision was done *l'shem mitzvah*, then it's ok. But there is no such thing as an uncircumcised convert. Such a person has not converted according to *halakhic* standards.

It's troubling indeed, especially to the unhappy Patrilineal Jew who blanches when told by us that he's not "really" or "fully" Jewish. It's like a slap in their face. What we really mean is this: we are less accepting and less welcoming than the more liberal movements. They certainly ARE Jewish if raised, educated and living as Jews, JUST NOT BY OUR STANDARDS.

No wonder they flee. We shatter their whole world and expect them to thank us for it! What hutzpah!

Here's what's REALLY going on, as if you didn't already know: The Reform movement goes back to a biblical standard of Jewish identity and acceptance IN ADDITION to the Matrilineal standard created in Roman Times and modeled after Pagan, hated Roman Law.

We scream NO! You can't do that and we swear eternal enmity towards these hapless fully-Jewish – by Biblical tradition, if not later politically-inspired Rabbinic Law. Does not Torah Law trump Rabbinic Law? It should, in cases of personal status and Jewish identity. For purely practical reasons, the Reform movement recognized the importance of holding onto and reclaiming those who would otherwise be lost

The fact is, we are a biological and adoptive people. Religion and Law are certainly central to our approach and teachings, until now.

Movements that did not meet the needs of Jews either became sects or vanished entirely over time. We can, as others have occasionally pointed out, assume that a person who has ever gone into the ocean, or swam in a body of water like a fresh water lake, has had *mikveh b'di'avad* [after the fact]. Even were we to balk at considering Patrilineally Jewish males as needing *bris milah*, if they already had the *milah* without the *b'ris*, give them an *aliyah* to the Torah. If their fathers were Jewish, chances are good they DID have *milah*, whether on the eighth day or not, or *l'shem b'ris* or not. So what?

We are hemorrhaging Jews in this country like never before. Some of our Conservative colleagues say that it's time to put aside our grumpiness and resentment of the Reform Movement and looking over their shoulder to see whether the Orthodox would accept them and simply accept these Jews as they are, Jewish sons and daughters of Jewish fathers.

It is forbidden to embarrass anyone. That's only part of what we're doing here. In this view it's high time we stopped. I find myself saying things that I wouldn't normally say, but I want to share some thoughts that the rest of you might be thinking.

BOB: I don't agree with the whole matter of "completing one's Jewishnss," because over and over again it has not worked for me. Perhaps because my excellent Reform colleague in a nearby town is available for weddings and b'nai-mitzvah for Patrilineal Jews, and because in this part of the country, unlike other places colleagues serve, the language doesn't resonate as positively as I state it nor as meaningfully as I intend it.

Honestly, I have a track record of about three in ten. Of the ten people who have come to me as Patrilineal Jews, I have succeeded in "convincing" three of them to go through the *mikveh* and complete their entrance requirements into Judaism.

Are you folks having similar percentages of "success" and "failure?"

I'm asking myself when I meet with individuals who have been raised to be Jewish, have gone through BBYO or NFTY as Jews, who are active on Campus in Hillel, who are professionally identified by Federations as Jews and who volunteer their time and give as generously as they can because to them it is tzedakah, are we at a moment in time when the sense of the concept of Peoplehood needs to be redefined in light of the diverse Jewish communities in Israel, the Americas, Canada, Europe, Africa and Asia? Can we afford to count anyone "out" who sincerely wants to be in, and is in according to many in our larger, multi-denominational and secular community?

SUSAN: It is abundantly clear to me that the rabbinical decision to change the determinant of Jewish citizenship from the biblical patrilineal to the matrilineal system which was how a Roman Law defined citizenship, was an accommodation made as a political decision. I would be surprised if in the several centuries of transition, both or either lineage was acceptable as a determinant of Jewish citizenship. Even today, tribal heritage among *Kohanim* and *Leviim* are determined by patrilineal descent, and, until the present era, Hebrew names of both male and female children still include the patronymic only.

Seeing how rabbinic law was designed to consolidate power in the hands of the leaders of the powerless, and to assert some higher authority above that of the state, while still assuring Jewish survival by not contravening benign *dina demalkhuta* ["the law of the local country must be obeyed"] and aggravating the ruling conquerors.

Although the rabbis pretended that their "interpretations" of biblical laws were based on oral and written precedents, they still needed a basis from Torah to ultimately back up that their assertions were related to, if not directly, derived from the biblical text.

Therefore, biblical law, being more authentic prior to being over-interpreted by the rabbis for their own "good" reasons, simply overrides such textual manipulation and clever reasoning that distorts or obliterates the source text which it purports to explain.

Which is more important? A rabbinic ordinance – *mi d'rabbanan* – or a Torah Law – *mi d'oraita*?

I don't, of course, mean laws relating to sacrifice or the Ordeal of Jealousy and the like, but rather real, practical stuff.

SAM: Facing facts: Reading Torah through the eyes of the rabbis who created Jewish Law in Roman times and under Roman occupation, who wore glasses made of Roman glass, may have been suitable for them, then, but not necessarily for us, now.

I do not mean to imply that everyone should ape the Reform movement in all or even any ways. I simply mean that those practicing Jews who were raised and educated exclusively Jewishly and have and do participate actively in Jewish family and communal life, and happen to only have a Jewish father ought to be automatically accepted as Jews. I'm not at all advocating extending this courtesy to those who do not care to share a Jewish future. I feel that even as "evolved rabbinic Jews" we dare not be so discriminatory when we have a clear prior biblical precedent to be accepting of those life-long Jews who are of only Patrilineal Jewish descent. Obviously I'm not advocating stoning or capital punishment for Shabbat violations or other ritual infractions. Nor am I advocating returning to a Temple-oriented animal-sacrificing form of worship. I'm simply saying that there's no good cogent reason for embarrassing and excluding Patrilineal Jews from acceptance in our communities without further "proof of purchase," or ritual requirements. Why should we treat converts from other faiths better than our own Jews by birth? Or, put another way, why should we require of Jews by birth the same ritual admission price as converts from outside?

BOB: I am reminded by what you say of some of the people in my *shul* who want to copy what our Reform neighbors have done. Namely, once a week Hebrew school, fully accepting Patrilineal Jews, giving non-Jews *aliyot*, etc. And then I point out to them, why would we want to replicate a model of an institution that has lost half of their members? While that may not be true nation wide, that is certainly true in many Reform synagogues. If you look at the retention rate of Reform nationally, it is abysmal. Yes, they are getting some of our Conservative Jews "on the way out." Many, many Reform synagogues have fifty percent intermarried populations today. The vast majority of their children intermarry, and do not choose to raise their children as Jews. I predict that over the next ten years, as the incredible number of intermarried families in Reform synagogues that have almost zero commitment leave, the floor will fall out from under them. We need to decide what our standards are and hold firm to them. Just because an idea comes from the Reform movement doesn't make it *treif*, but neither does it mean it is kosher. We are foolhardy if we choose to copy them, and it will lead to an even quicker demise of the Conservative movement.

Finally, we see Judaism as a religion that keeps developing. The Torah is our base. It is the first word, but it is certainly not the last, and we always read Torah through the eyes of the rabbis. If we want to go back to Torah standards, should we give up equality of women, put to death one who breaks Shabbat, or revert to calling homosexuality an abomination? Of course not! It's a long marathon and we need to have faith in who we are. That is, in my view, the only way the Conservative Movement will have a future.

DON: I have appreciated the conversation, especially the attention being paid to the nature of *halakhic* authority and the difficulty of balancing a desire to respond to another's need with the sources as they have been understood thus far. I hope that we can extend the benefit of any doubts on each other's strong opinions about the topic, and not look for ways to take each other to task personally.

That said, I am not sure I understand the either/or that is being posited here between political motivation and sacred authority. I accept that much of the Talmud and other layers of what we call the Oral Law can be explained from the point of view of politics in a broad sense. But so can the sources that make up what we call the Written Law. Why should we dismiss Hillel's attempts at asserting authority, but not the Deuteronomist's reshaping of earlier material, accept P's [the Priestly author, according to the documentary hypothesis] take on purity, but not Rabbi Akiva's, and let both J and E [according to the Documentary Hypothesis, J is Jehovist, or Yahwist, and E is Elohist] be the word of the living God, but be suspicious of Rabbi Joshua vs. Rabbi Eliezer?

All of the pieces that make up the puzzle of Jewish traditions are easy to dismiss on grounds of being situated in their time, place and social circumstance. However, while in some quarters there might be fear of such scholarship, as far as I understand it, the Conservative movement has embraced it precisely because they see both the holiness and the authority of these sources as unmitigated by the circumstances in which they are produced. With respect to that holiness and authority, however, I believe we can avail ourselves of the same audacity of interpretation and reapplication that the ancient rabbis and later sources demonstrated as *halakhah* have developed and changed throughout the history of different Jewish communities.

I can imagine patrilineality finding expression in some movements, but not without grounding it in a framework that deals with the sources.

No one who meets whatever criteria are agreed upon by the majority should be discouraged or disparaged from joining the Jewish Family. I wasn't suggesting that anyone was being dismissive in any way.

We need to be more welcoming, which means more accepting, if we want to remain relevant as a people. There are many out there who just might jump at the chance to formally "convert" and join the Jewish People, if we made the process seem a little less daunting and dogmatic. As to those who want in to our gang but were converted by the others, or who have monolineal Jewish parentage, if they seek us out, let's let them in.

Thanks to everyone for their passion on the topic.

SAM: Many years after leaving my first civilian rabbinic post I encountered one of the former teenagers of the Youth Congregation that I had led on Sabbath and Sunday mornings.

"I remember you," he gushed excitedly. "And I remember how you concluded every Sunday morning service. I still do it that way myself."

Puzzled for a moment, I replied, "What did I do?"

"Oh, at the end of the Psalm for Sunday, you said the line, *mi hoo zeh melekh ha-khavod, Adonoi Tzeva'ot* **hoo** *melekh ha-khavod* ["Who is the King of Glory, *Adonai Tzeva'ot* HE is the King of Glory"], and you always stressed the word '*hoo*' [HE]. And I still do that!"

I marveled at how he remembered such a small detail, and how great an impact it made upon him.

You can never tell, in Jewish religious life, what little thing you do may be remembered forever by an impressionable youngster. And how even that little thing may help make a better Jew of him!

BOB: We live in an age of "now." I want it NOW, I want to know about it NOW, I want to make money NOW.

Contrast this with a teacher, or rav, who imparts of himself today but most often is never around for the "payoff." Did he really have an influence on those of his "flock" with whose lives he interacted? To me this was always the most frustrating part of the rabbinate. We all seek validation that what we are doing is "good," and in the rabbinate what could bring more validation than to see the seeds we planted, eventually germinate and blossom into the kinds of Jews upon whose lives we were hoping to make an impact? Most often we have moved on, either to another congregation or even to another, non-rabbinic, form of work, so we're just not around to witness the "payoff." I often wonder whether most of us are fortunate enough to experience the kind of event that Sam is talking about.

I can only recall one instance where something similar happened to me, but I will remember it until the day I close my eyes to the world. Many years ago I had a congregation in the South, at the time the only Conservative synagogue in town, and the largest *shul* in town. I left some years later. More recently, I happened to find myself back in the same town on Rosh Hashanah. By then the city had grown tremendously, there were other Conservative *shuls* in town, and I happened to find myself in another one which was closer to where I was staying.

After the services for the first day concluded, a young woman with two small children walked up to me and asked me if I was Rabbi Bob Goldberg. I said "Yes," and then she introduced herself. It turned out that her family had been members of my *shul*. Her mother had been on the board and her father, a lawyer, had served as a *mohel* in the community. She had been one of a group of post *b'nai-mitzvah* students I had taught on a regular basis. She told me that what she remembered most was a talk I had given about the concept of *met mitzvah* – one of the subjects my Seminary professor talked about many times in the two years I was fortunate enough to study Talmud with him. But he also homileticized the term to mean any mitzvah which was "dead," namely, not being practiced by you, and his approach was to take one such mitzvah and start to do it, then keep adding. Apparently in that class I had adopted the professor's approach and urged my students to do the same. And this young woman told me that she found keeping Shabbat and *kashrut*, neither of which her parents had observed with any degree of regularity, were the two things that grounded her life, gave her stability and direction, and that she had built an entire home, family and life by starting with these two.

And I remember, standing in front of her and after hearing her tell me this, just breaking down into tears and hugging her and saying, "What a lucky guy I am. . . ."

Those of my colleagues who have had this kind of experience will "get it" in their *kishkes*. Those who have not experienced it yet – I hope you, too, will "get lucky."

SAM: Very touching, Bob. I hope I do have such experiences.

SUSAN: I have a special request, stemming from some things that happened in my congregation recently. Does anyone have a prayer for victims of sexual abuse to share that I can refer to or use?

BOB: I have one on my laptop. Let me take a peek. OK, here it is:

Avinu ShehBashamayim

Our Parent Who Dwells on High:

Grant perfect and full healing, we pray, to those among us whose lives have been deeply affected by the hateful behavior of those in whom they once put their trust.

Used and abused, their souls are tormented by the cruelty experienced by their bodies, created בצלם אלהים, in Your Divine Image.

Calm their terror and anguish, we pray, that they may, one day, as a result of Your compassion and Your boundless love, find peace once again.

Heal them, God our Healer and Redeemer, that they may lie down in peace and in safety each night, assured by Your loving protection, that no more pain and evil shall afflict them.

Amen

SUSAN: Thanks so much, Bob, that's perfect!

BOB: Let me change the conversation a bit. In Torah class this week, we were talking about the feminization of our society, and I took a negative view, although understanding the realities of our time and supporting egalitarian hopes and dreams of women, saying that today's "real man" looks and sounds more like a woman than like the macho man of old. And that in addition, women take roles of leadership in our *shuls* today way more than men do. By the way, a Seminary professor of mine predicted this would happen in a conversation I had with him many years ago.

Here's the question: One of my female students asked the following:

If a man is "in charge" of the home while the wife goes out to work, wouldn't he therefore be exempt from *davening* with a *minyan*, for example, since he's taking care of the kids?

Talk about role reversal . . .

I admit, I never thought of exempting someone because of "the role," rather I assumed, as we all did, and as *halakhah* did, that men went to work, so they need to *daven* with a *minyan*, while women stayed home, so they couldn't be counted on, and therefore counted in, a *minyan*.

Today that ain't necessarily so.

SUSAN: I seem to remember a lecture which I heard some years ago, when the scholar spoke about the past two thousand years of *halakhic* evolution moving along according to the second chapter of Genesis – the patriachal vision of woman formed from man's rib, woman being subservient, etc. – and his suggestion was that the coming few decades should evolve according to the first chapter, where male and female are created at the same moment, absolutely equally in God's image – that is to say, egalitarian.

If you or I had actually embraced that suggestion to its logical conclusion, as opposed to simply voting to support what eventually became the JTS decision to ordain women, your student's *halakhic* question would have truly been a *kashya*, namely, a difficult question.

But, we didn't. And, yes, it would make perfect sense if male and female rabbis relieved the obligation of community prayer for men who are house husbands for the length of their tenure as such. What a wonderful world this would be. And I would call it the egalitarianizing of our society, and not the feminization of our society.

SAM: This is a principle that I have been working from personally but have not worked on any possible *halakhic* approach.

Since my kids came into the world, I have had the blessing of bringing them with me to *minyan*. As they grew and progressed from lumps in a blanket to toddlers, my participation in the *minyan* changed. I rarely lead the *davening* because I am often needed to deal with or care for one of my children.

But it goes further. What happens when I am in the middle of the *Amidah* and one of my children comes to me and says "I have to go to the potty"? Do I say, just wait a few minutes and I can take you? No, with a three year old that would be ludicrous. It is at those moments that I see my obligation go out the window. While I may finish up the *Amidah*, I don't wait for *kedushah*, but rather remove my *tallit* and take her to the bathroom. I always felt that at those moments my obligation for *mitzvat aseh she-haz'man grama* ["a time-bound mitzvah"] melted away.

As I said, I have never worked through this thinking *halakh-ically*, as I don't think there would be support for it, but I am comfortable with it personally.

Thanks for bringing it up and letting me bring my personal practices into the public.

DON: I am not convinced that the traditional exemption for women has anything to do with child rearing. The Talmud does not make that point and, in fact, the *hiyyuv* [obligation] of teaching a child falls more explicitly on a father. The three categories of those exempted from certain *mitzvot* in the mishnah, namely, minors, slaves and women, have the opposite in common: not someone they are obligated to raise, but someone to whom, at least potentially, their time is obligated to. From that perspective, being egalitarian, or more accurately equal-obligation, is a more fundamental transformation of the category of women as fully responsible directly to God, and therefore obligated in a way children and slaves would not be.

With that approach no situation of raising children for men or women would affect the status of being *hayyav*. That is not to say that a person of either sex or any gender could not make an argument that the immediate need of a child supersedes the need of the moment as an *osek b'mitzva patur mi'mitzvah* ["one performing a certain mitzvah is exempt from another mitzvah"].

I do have to say that couching the conversation in terms of the feminization of society and identifying men as acting like women really strikes me as counterproductive. Dinosaur or no dinosaur I see the *halakhah* as timeless and precisely there to inspire us to see beyond the assumptions of our own times. I am a fan of Rachel Adler's *Engendering Judaism* in which the idea is not about empowering one set of people at the expense of others but, rather finding a fuller expression of our whole people and our connection to God.

SUSAN: In the discussion around the Conservative movement's *teshuvah* announcing full *hiyuv* [*halakhic* obligation] for women discussed at a recent meeting on the law committee, the issue came up. But what about child care responsibility which might make a parent unable to do *tefillah bizmanah* [prayer recitation at its proper hour], and the most elegant solution, to my mind, is to understand that child and husband care were seen to be the whole of a woman's identity in the past, therefore she was *p'turah mi'mitzvat aseh she-hazman grama* [exempt from a mitzvah tied to a certain time of the day]. But that we no longer see women that way, and so should understand, and state, that the *p'tur* [exemption] applies only as a working out of the concept of "*haosek b'mitzvah patur mi'mitzvah*," which applies selectively, and equally, to men and to women.

DON: I believe that a more in-depth examination of the sources on time-bound mitzvot and other so-called "exemptions" for women shows that it is not the "role" of women that grounded the exemption, but rather their relative place in the societal and family hierarchy. In other words, it was an issue of a "woman's place" and her subservience to her husband. A woman was exempt not because she stayed home, but because she had to stay home, and her comings and goings were subject to the approval of her husband, who expected dinner on the table, *Minhah-Ma'ariv* notwithstanding. This, of course, was not unique to Jewish society, and its equivalent can be found in Anglo-American law until the early twentieth century. Therefore, in an egalitarian society, the logical conclusion should not be that a stay-home dad is exempt, but rather that women and men are equally obligated. I'm speaking in a totally theoretical way, of course, since I don't think my Orthodox colleagues would accept this line of thinking.

In this regard, I am reminded of the case of an IDF reservist I heard about, who once asked for a lift to base. As they drove, she said that when she was up for promotion to the rank of lieutenant colonel, she was informed that she was going to be passed over because promotion would have required that she attend meetings at night. She asked to meet with the Chief of Staff, and informed him that being a woman and mother had never caused her to miss a meeting during the day, and the night presented less of a problem, since her husband would babysit. The result? When asked how one would recognize her at the bus stop, she replied: "I will be the only woman at the bus stop with the rank of colonel." She continued to serve in reserves after her retirement from regular service, because she felt that as the first woman to break the glass ceiling by insisting upon equality in promotion, she was morally obligated to accept equality in regard to reserve duty, even though the law exempted women of her age.

SAM: With the exception of rabbis who clearly take the *hiyyuv* of *T'fillah B'tzibbur* [the obligation of public prayer] seriously, the challenge with our congregants is much different.

Rather than asking "Can Mister Mom be exempt from a daily minyan?" the more apt question might be "Can we impose a *hiyyuv* on anyone?" There is an ever diminishing number of people who are committed to supporting a daily *minyan*. When I first came to my congregation some years ago, we had a *minyan* a vast majority of the time. There was a core of eight to ten regulars, morning and night, and few others with *yahrzeit* who would show up. Over time, several of the *minyanaires* died or became too ill to come, so the core is now three or four, except for Thursday morning which has a breakfast club after *minyan*. We still manage to eke out a *minyan* on many days, and we have enlisted a few new regulars, but those who commit to come generally tend to be older and are not easily replaced. I keep trying to plug *minyan* attendance, but the only "hook" which resonates with some is "Please come to help others say *Kaddish*." The plea

"Please come to fulfill your *hiyyuv* of *T'fillah B'Tzibbur*" seems to fall on deaf ears.

While the original question was a fair one – Can Mister Mom be exempt from daily minyan? – in many ways it is moot. Outside the Orthodox world, American Jewish laypeople are not impressed with words like, "obligation" and "responsibility;" yet they are obsessed with "rights" and "choice."

DON: Here's an interesting question. Jerusalem has a *mikveh* which accommodates women who are wheelchair bound and even quadriplegic.

How is *tevilah* usually done in areas where no handicapped accessibility exists?

BOB: You would probably need people to go into the water with the person and hold him or her – women for women, men for men. The *mikveh* in Chicago, at a Reform Temple and certified by both Orthodox and Conservative *halakhic* experts, is also handicapped accessible. Anyone contemplating a new *mikveh* can contact the colleagues there.

SAM: Another question. Over the months and years, our *Mi Sheberakh* [prayers for healing] list has become WAY too long. On any given Shabbat I may read sixty plus names. I do it quickly, but I find that it is really a *Tirha D'Tzibura* [burden on the community].

It's not that we have a disproportionate number of sick people. Many are relatives and friends, some local, some not. Some Jewish and some non-Jews. Some names we read both in Hebrew and English. Others, just English.

The problem, as I see it, is that there is an increasing number of people who call and ask to have names added PERMANENTLY – people who have been on the list for years. In general, I think of the *Mi Sheberakh* list – which we refer lovingly as the "Mish List" – as something that we should be saying for acute illnesses, surgeries, and the like. But we've been getting people who simply say "I'm not a well person," or "I want my

cousin on the list until they've been in remission for five years
and considered cured." There are people who are just aging and
have aches and pains. And there's one woman I can think of in
her thirties who, ten years after a terrible car accident, lives on
painkillers.

So, while I would happily keep people on the Mish List for a
matter of weeks or months, I'd like to make the list more manageable. I'm thinking that after each of the *Shalosh Regalim*
maybe we should press the "reset" button and tell people that if
they want to "renew" that they should call the synagogue office
to keep the names on the list.

If any of you have experienced a similar challenge and resolved it satisfactorily, I'd like to know how you managed it. Any
suggestions would be welcome. In particular, I'd like to know if
you have any useful ideas regarding *Mi Sheberakhs* for acutely
sick people versus chronically sick people.

SUSAN: These can get out of hand.

Perhaps say a *Mi Sheberakh* and pause for a moment for
people to quietly say names to themselves . . . or reference "our
prayer list" without reading it.

Also, although this isn't a HIPAA issue, it is a privacy issue
insofar as not everybody wants their name mentioned but may
want prayer, nevertheless. And even if they have no problem
with having the name read, most of us don't know that *Yankel
ben Shoshana* is Oscar Goldberg the CPA even if we know him
well.

Yes, I had "chronic" long term people on my list, which is
quite one thing, but in one case, I learned much later that one
had been deceased for quite a while and nobody thought to ask
that the name be removed.

The *Mi Sheberakh*, of course, is an old prayer but it became
the center of focus during the "Jewish Healing Movement" of the
90s and was buoyed by the popularity of the Debbie Friedman
song. In "the old days" of the nineties it was usually said, but
only by request, and usually for a specific person. It can become
unwieldy.

BOB: I just ask people to say their sick person's name out loud, no muss no fuss. We also print names in our Shabbas handout. After three weeks, your name is deleted. Unless you are deleted first. Sorry, couldn't resist. Then we sing Debbie's melody. By the way, I do this after the seventh *aliyah*, before the *Kaddish*. Then I'm done.

Theologically I have a real problem with this prayer. Are we saying that God actually heals the sick? What if they die – and please don't start with "sometimes death is a healing." So what IS the point of the *Mi Sheberakh*?

My answer: when a loved one is sick, so are you, and we pray for YOUR healing as much as theirs. They have doctors to care for them, you have your *shul* community to care for you.

DON: What's my brilliant *hiddush*?

I go around the room asking for names from the persons standing. I do NOT repeat the proffered names, I simply say either, "May it be God's will" or *Ken y'hi Ratson*, and go on to the next person. Those present get recognized that they ache for their sick, and I don't have to get the proffered names correctly. It goes quicker.

I also remind people to use only a last initial if they are giving an English name, unless they KNOW that the ill person consents to the public mention of their name. The people who take the time to submit names in writing are few. Phone calls for this purpose are not usually accepted. Thus most prayers are by attendees.

I think it is important for people who have ill relatives and friends to feel that their prayers are heard by those present. Silent prayers, or speed reading prayers, or mumbled prayers don't pass muster in that regard.

I hear about this issue from other colleagues. They tell me that they used to have long lines for Shabbat. Now they have the *Mi Sheberakh* text pasted inside each *Humash*. Between the sixth and seventh *aliyot*, the congregation reads aloud the *Mi Sheberakh*, pausing to allow time for people to quietly add appropriate names.

SAM: OK, time for a bit of humor, and let's let go of these serious discussions.

I want to thank everyone who took time to discuss how to best prune my interminable *Mi Sheberakh* list. For me, this was our rabbinic luncheon group at its finest.

As an expression of my gratitude, I threw together this list of the Top Ten Ways to Shorten the *Mi Sheberakh* List: (#4–9 were inspired by the Affordable Care Act).

1. Establish an online payment program and charge $18 for each name on the list, to be read for a month. Watch your list disappear in a week.

2. Insist on the proper Hebrew names. Examples: "*Shayne Punim*" and "*Yoodl Doodl*" do not qualify.

3. In the case of death, insist that names come off the list before the unveiling.

4. If the *holeh* doesn't sign up for synagogue membership by March 31st, fine them up to 10% of their salary or social security (union members exempt).

5. If she or he is over eighty years old, put them on the *Vidui* (Confessional) list instead.

6. Modify Debbie Friedman's *Mi Sheberakh* to pray to God that you can keep your doctor and your healthcare plan (For more information, refer to *T'filallat Shav* – Prayers in Vain).

7. Pray only for those working thirty hours or more.

8. No "young invincible" allowed on the list. They can't afford to be sick.

9. Have your synagogue website redesigned to allow people to register the names of those who are ill, and hire CGI to do the job for under $1 billion dollars. Contact Michelle O. at the White House for more information.

10. Pray only for recovery of congregational members. After all, you get an honorarium for non-member funerals.

BOB: Cute, Sam. Thanks. [Laughter].

I have an interesting question that I'd like some advice for. In a few weeks, a widower in my congregation will be marrying a divorcee. Both have kids who would like to participate in the service. Some of the kids would like, if possible, to read something in Hebrew. Some of the kids are under thirteen. Any suggestions for an appropriate reading or two?

DON: Years ago I created an extra prayer under the *huppah* for a mixed family. I take the cup and mix it with wine from the other two cups and have everyone in the mixed family share from the third cup.

Interesting you should ask this, Bob. I just faced the same issue earlier this year and came up with a solution that worked very well for us, though a little esoteric.

I had heard from some friends from my Yeshivah that there has been a rediscovery of the "eighthth *berakhah* of the *Sheva Berakhot*," namely, an addendum to *Sheva Berakhot* that is found in *Seder Rav Amram Gaon,* and has also long been part of the wedding liturgy for Jews of India. It has been rediscovered in Orthodox communities that are searching for something for women to say under the *huppah* if they are not comfortable assigning women to recite *Sheva Berakhot.* It concludes with a "quasi-*berakhah*" without *shem u-malkhut.* The words are beautiful.

At a wedding in my community earlier this year, the bride and groom wanted all their nieces and nephews to read something in Hebrew under the *huppah.* Those who were over bar or bat mitzvah age read *Sheva Berakhot,* and the one who was under bar mitzvah age read this, and it went over very well.

It goes like this:

The "Eighth *Berakhah*" of the *Sheva Berakhot*

(postscript to *Sheva Brakhot* as found in *Seder Rav Amram Gaon* and in the wedding liturgy of Jews of India)

כהיום הזה בירושלים – ירבו שמחות בישראל, וינוסו אנחות מישראל, ירבו בשורות טובות בישראל, ירבו ישועות בישראל, ירבו נחמות בישראל. תרבה אהבה בישראל, תרבה ברכה בישראל, תרבה גילה בישראל, תרבה דיצה בישראל, ירבה הוד בישראל, ירבה ועדת בישראל, ירבו זכויות בישראל, ירבה חתן בישראל, ירבו ימים טובים בישראל, תרבה כלה בישראל, יצליחו חתן וכלה, ישמחו שניהם זה עם זה ויעלצו

שינהם זה עם זה, ישמח חתן בכלה, תשמח כלה בחתן. ברוך אתה
משמח חתן בכלה וכלה בחתן!

May there be many days in Jerusalem like this one!
May celebrations increase in Israel, and may agony depart
from Israel.
May good tidings increase in Israel.
May salvation and consolation increase in Israel.
May love and blessing and joy increase in Israel.
May honor, cooperation and merit increase in Israel.
May bridegrooms and brides increase in Israel.
May festive days increase in Israel.
May this groom and bride find success.
May they gladden each other's hearts and exult with each
other.
May the groom take delight in the bride,
and may the bride take delight in the groom.
Blessed are You,
who brings together groom and bride, bride and groom, to
rejoice in each other!

From the wedding liturgy found in *Seder Rav Amram Gaon*

DON: OK, folks, I need to change the subject. For a sermon I'm
writing for this coming Shabbat, I need an opening joke about
minyan – getting a *minyan*, not getting a *minyan*, waiting for a
tenth to show up, and so on.

BOB: I have a few favorites.

Harry Golden, South Carolina comedian and journalist, of
blessed memory, asked his father, who was an atheist, why he
goes to *minyan* every morning, since he doesn't believe in God.
His father replied: people go to *minyan* for different reasons. My
friend Schwartz goes to *minyan* to talk to God. I go to *minyan* to
talk to Schwartz.

My last one. It's Jackie Gleason. I know he's a *goy*. He walks
into a bar and in a menacing tone asks several times whether any
one there is Jewish. The one Jew in the bar, terrified, finally ad-

mits to his creed. Gleason says "Well let's move it, you're needed for a *minyan!*"

DON: Wow, thanks, Bob. More than I need. That's great!

SUSAN: I have an interesting situation for which I could use your sage advice.

A woman in the community – not a member – is in a difficult situation. Her husband, who is not Jewish, is opposed to circumcision. She, on the other hand, although she shares her husband's queasiness about circumcision, has *sort of* decided that their son should be circumcised. I say "sort of" because she's really on the fence. She's uncomfortable with it, but she sort of realizes that it would be best to do it to help their son when he grows up as a Jew. They also have a five-year old daughter, who they're raising as a Jew. During our conversation, it was clear to me that she could go either way.

The husband is opposed to any kind of a public "*bris*" ceremony, but is willing to have the child circumcised in the hospital. The wife has told me that at this hospital none of the pediatricians who would perform circumcision are, in fact, *mohalim*. In fact, it wasn't clear whether any are Jewish. The wife is convinced that the only way that she could have her child circumcised is if it were to be done in the hospital. Going out of their way to do it in a public way would be problematic for her relationship with her husband.

I told her that, in order to be "effective," the *milah* should be accompanied by the *bris*. That is, the physician should say the proper blessings to communicate his intent, as an agent of the mother, to bring the child into the covenant, and should do the "*milah*" in order to carry out this goal.

"What if the doctor isn't Jewish?" she asked. Could her father, the child's maternal grandfather, authorize the doctor to do the circumcision for the sake of bringing the child into the Jewish people?

At that point, I wasn't sure what to say. I've never dealt with a situation like this.

Whenever I've dealt with hospital circumcisions, they've always been Jewish doctors who have known how to say the blessings.

I'm wondering: Why can't the doctor be a gentile? Is it because of the traditional concern about non-Jewish doctors? Probably not. Is it because, since he is not a member of the covenantal community, his act can't render someone else a member of the covenantal community?

But the child will already be, as we know, a Jew. The child will be the child of a Jewish mother, and will therefore be Jewish. Why indeed must the *mohel* be Jewish? Now, yes, of course, I know that in a case like this, we could always arrange for *hatafat dam brit*. That's the natural, usual way to handle this.

I, however, believe that this would not be easy for the mother to arrange. If necessary, I suppose that she could raise the possibility of *hatafat dam brit* with her husband, but the sense I got was that this might very well be a "deal breaker."

Hence, I would like to figure out a solution that wouldn't require a second procedure, notwithstanding how minimally invasive *hatafat dam brit* is. I'm curious: have colleagues ever faced a situation like this?

DON: The situation which you describe, Susan, of a Jewish newborn boy for whom the only circumcision that's going to happen, because of the family dynamic, will be a hospital circumcision by a non-Jewish physician, is essentially the same situation with which I have been presented in my occasional work with a nearby community, which is not my congregation, but for whom I serve as a kind of consultant.

Let me tell you what I was able to work out for circumcisions in this case. Immediately after the circumcision, a Jewish person – it could be another physician, or a nurse, or any adult Jew – would press a sterile gauze pad very lightly on the wound, until the most miniscule drop of blood visible to the eye appeared. That would constitute *hatafat dam b'rit*, and the appropriate *berakhot* would be said.

I never wound up making this happen for a newborn, but a version of this approach was used with a *ger* whose *milah* took place at a private hospital in a nearby town.

Of course, we risk undermining the practice of having a *mohel* perform every *milah* if we publicize this option, but in the situation that you describe, Susan, it seems to me to be a way, and maybe the best way, to have the child undergo a *halakhically* valid procedure now, at the end of his first week of life.

SUSAN: Interesting. Anyone else have any thoughts?

BOB: I have always avoided the scenario in which a doctor, frequently non-Jewish, does the actual circumcision, while a rabbi says the blessings. It is a distortion of the place of *berakhot* and of rabbis in Judaism, and I see it akin to the idea that rabbis make food kosher by blessing it. I have insisted, when we want a medical circumcision to count as *bris milah*, that a Jewish doctor say the *berakhot* and perform the procedure.

On the other hand, I believe that many of our colleagues go along with the doctor-plus-rabbi team. Also, *berakhot* are not *halakhically* required, so, if a Jewish doctor does a circumcision and acknowledges, in any terms, that what he is doing has religious as well as medical significance, it should be alright.

I consider the statement that none of the pediatricians are *mohalim* to be meaningless. What is a *mohel*? A Jewish person who does religious circumcisions. *Mohalim* should be certified for quality control, but they don't have to be "ordained' or anything like that.

Of course, the child will be Jewish no matter what, even if uncircumcised. The question is whether the mitzvah of *milah* will be performed, and that is no small matter. I don't see how someone who is not Jewish can perform a specifically Jewish mitzvah, but some colleagues see things differently.

I think a bigger issue is that the circumcision if performed in the hospital, at least under contemporary maternity procedures, would be well before the eighth day. So it does not really matter if the doctor is Jewish or not. Maybe better if he is not.

I'll never forget the conversation I had with my mother while I was in rabbinical school. My family belonged to Reform synagogues, and she mentioned how I was circumcised in the hospital. All of a sudden a shiver went down my back. I was circumcised before the eighth day? How embarrassing that I, a future Conservative rabbi, will need *hatafat dam*! "So I was circumcised before the eighth day by a doctor?" No, said my mother, you were C-section and they kept babies in the hospital for over a week. The rabbi came to the hospital."

I'm not sure, but in such a case, unless the family were willing to go back to the doctor on day eight or after for a *bris*, I might tell the mother to allow the kid to be circumcised in the hospital, and if he or she so chooses to have *hatafat dam* later in life. Because if he is not circumcised — besides the identification issue and health issue — it will be far more painful for him to correct it in later life.

SUSAN: Folks, I just see an email on my smart phone that the expectant mother with whom I spoke a week ago had her baby boy. Contrary to what she had planned to do, she and her non-Jewish husband decided not to circumcise their son. She writes, "When he grows up, we'll give him the choice to do what he wants." Sigh.

I'm wondering if anyone has had any experience, much less success, talking to a new mom under these circumstances. Are there any good guides for new parents making the pro *bris milah* arguments?

SAM: The very few times I have encountered this I just asked them some questions such as:

Are you going to let them grow up and decide if they want inoculations? Of course not. We have to take care of their health. Then I say: You are responsible for giving the child an identity. If you wait for them to grow up to choose an identity they will choose what you gave them — nothing. So if you are ok with them having no identity then your decision is ok. You know and I know that as a grown up they will not opt to circumcise unless it is medically necessary, or they meet a Jewish girl who just can't stand the thought of being married to an uncircumcised Jewish male. At which point they will curse you for not having done what was your obligation as a parent. You will not leave their health up to them, you will not leave their education up to them, you will not leave teaching right or wrong up to them, but you are willing to leave their identity as a Jewish man up to them. Admit it – and it's ok – you just don't care enough to put forth the effort and make a positive decision to give your child a Jewish identity. And if you do decide to do that later on by giving them a Jewish identity you will have created a problem for him that will make him feel like the outsider, and he will most likely choose to be the outsider. So in effect, my dear lady, you have made the choice. You have chosen to give him every reason not to seek to identify as a Jew. Inaction is as much a decision as action.

SUSAN: That's heavy medicine. I guess I could say that in more diplomatic terms. Thanks to all three of you for some interesting perspectives.

BOB: I have a related question. A mother has two boys, ages eight and five, who were circumcised in the hospital at birth. She has asked me about *hatafat dam brit* for them. She and her non-Jewish husband are fine with the idea, but concerned that the boys may "freak out" from such a strange-sounding procedure.

   I'd be grateful for suggestions on how to best sensitively approach the subject so that it is not a negative event for the boys.

SAM: Though I am not an expert in psychosexual development – others may wish to weigh in –it seems to me that this age in particular is not a good time to do such a procedure. I have had occasion to have *hatafat dam brit* done prior to bar mitzvah when it was learned that a child who had been adopted, for example, had not been properly converted or something like that. At that age, there was a bit of bravado associated with it and it seemed to give the young man "bragging rights" among his peers. Moreover at that age, it seemed much more like his decision, which had a very positive effect on him. It seems to me that in the case you describe, Bob, since it was the mother – since the father is not Jewish – who did not fulfill her obligation when he was a baby – I wouldn't word it to her that way, and the child himself does not become *halakhically* obligated until bar mitzvah age, that I would counsel waiting until then.

DON: I agree with Sam. I quite frankly would wait until they are older. Like six months or a year before the bar mitzvah. At least that's what I've done in a number of situations. Explaining it to them the year before the bar mitzvah is not all that difficult. They are a little bit more mature then. Since the mother is Jewish, they are Jewish whether they have this or not. So I would give it to them as an option and tell them they could wait until they're older if they want. It's not like a conversion situation where we need to get it done for them to be Jewish followed by *mikveh*. In this case the Jewish identity is not being brought into question so we don't need to pressure them to have it done. It becomes an educational opportunity and offering them an option they could fulfill now or someday in the future. That's how I view it, but I'm looking forward to seeing other opinions.

BOB: You both seem to make perfect sense. Thanks for the great advice.

SUSAN: Meanwhile, I have another question. I have been meeting with a family regarding a funeral. Since the deceased practiced both Judaism and Buddhism, the family would like to have a Buddhist chant a Buddhist prayer. I was somewhat taken aback.

Has anyone participated in such services allowing a Buddhist prayer to be recited? Any cautions? I do have the choice of saying: Sorry but I am not able to participate in such a service.

SAM: I have allowed such readings. And, it was absolutely beautiful and provided much comfort to the family – and their yogi friends. It was at a "pause" in the Jewish funeral service, where we also include different relatives and friends to give eulogies, and it worked just fine.

I've also had a Native American ceremony tucked into a few funerals. That was even wilder – with drums and incense and the whole thing. And the best part there was that a few *Hasidim* were there, friends of the deceased. One approached me after and asked "Is it always like this by you?" – Ha!

Good luck. I don't think that you'll regret it when you see the impact it has on the bereaved.

DON: I think this is more complicated than Sam believes. The line is difficult, and once crossed where do we stop? What if the person had a Christian spouse who wanted a priest or minister to say a prayer that included Jesus? That might also bring much comfort to the family. I would be inclined to do two things. First, I would find out the content of the prayer. Not all Buddhist prayers are compatible with Jewish theology. Second, I would do what we do for Masonic funerals, and have it recited prior to your beginning the service, maybe even before you enter the room.

SAM: Perhaps you should begin by finding out exactly what the words are that would be chanted. Not everything recited in other traditions conflicts with Jewish teachings. Many of us feel comfortable bringing various readings from other traditions during the course of weddings. For example, Rumi's *This Marriage* is very popular:

This Marriage

May these vows and this marriage be blessed.
May it be sweet milk,
this marriage, like wine and halvah.
May this marriage offer fruit and shade
like the date palm.
May this marriage be full of laughter,
our every day a day in paradise.
May this marriage be a sign of compassion,
a seal of happiness here and hereafter.
May this marriage have a fair face and a good name,
an omen as welcomes the moon in a clear blue sky.
I am out of words to describe
how spirit mingles in this marriage.

In thinking about the funeral, see the booklet *A Guide to a Proper Buddhist Funeral*, found on this web site: http://www .buddhanet.net/pdf_file/buddhist_funeral.pdf. On page fifteen there is a reading that I believe would cause very little concern for most of us:

Verses for Contemplation

Short, alas, is the life of man, limited and fleeting, full of pain and torment. One should wisely
understand this, do good deeds and lead a holy
life, for no mortals ever escape death.
Just as the dewdrop, at the point of the grass-
blade at sunrise, very soon vanishes and does
not remain for long: just so is the dew drop-like
life of men very short and fleeting.
Just as at the pouring down of a mighty rain,
the bubbles on the water very soon vanish and
do not remain for long: just so is the bubble-like
life of men very short and fleeting.
Just as a furrow drawn with a stick in the water
very soon vanishes and does not remain for
long: just so is the furrow-like life of men very
short and fleeting.
Just as the cattle for slaughter, whatever their
footing, stand on the brink of death: just so is
the life of men very short and fleeting.
One should wisely understand this, do good
deeds and lead a holy life, for no mortal ever
escapes death.

The Buddha, Anguttara Nikaya

There are translations of other Buddhist texts in the booklet. Reviewing the material may help you prepare to discuss the matter further with the family and with the person who would be the one to chant.

SUSAN: As always, you folks are extremely helpful in helping to resolve such conflicting issues.

BOB: OK guys, I think we've dealt with some very heavy stuff today. Let's pause till next week. Enjoy your week!

Week 13

Bob: Let me start with an issue that will most likely become more and more of a problem for all of our colleagues in the future.

A twenty-nine-year-old Jewish woman came to me this morning. She's in her eighth month. She and her Jewish boyfriend would like to have some sort of "committment" ceremony before the baby is due, or at the baby's *bris milah*. She doesn't want to get married in a civil ceremony because she is on some federally funded entitlement program, which pays for her medical care, and for her college tuition, and she says that being married in a civil ceremony would jeopardize that government support.

I told her that I couldn't marry them without a civil license, so I am looking for some Jewishly-flavored ceremony where they could express their commitment to each other, before the baby is born.

I thought about an expanded *tena'im* ceremony. Her mom lives in town, his parents will be here for the *bris milah*, but wondered if that would steal thunder from the *bris milah* ceremony.

Any ideas?

Don: I think this will become a more and more frequent situation. Should we develop a way to lend sanctity to relationships that are not *Kiddushin*? Is there anything written about it? I know there have been suggestions to revive a version of the *pilegesh* status, though we should call it something more acceptable. We really ought to be thinking of all the people who are living together without being married.

SUSAN: Here are three thoughts:

1. Perhaps the *brit ahuvim*, which some colleagues celebrate with same-sex couples, would be appropriate.

2. You could meet with the couple in a counseling mode, talk with them about their values, their hopes, etc., and then construct a ceremony from appropriate *p'sukim* and rabbinic sayings or stories.

3. You will want to be sure that whatever you do is far enough from being a wedding ceremony that you don't violate the letter or the spirit of the prohibition of *siddur Kiddushin* without a civil marriage license. You don't want to violate the law, and get yourself in big trouble.

The question shouldn't be "How can we accommodate this couple and facilitate their cheating the U.S government?" Rather, it should be "How can we possibly consider doing this commitment ceremony, which would not violate either Jewish or civil law?"

It sound's like we're adopting the motto of Burger King: "Have it your way!"

SAM: Question: now that same-sex marriage is the law of the land – at least for now – would you do *brit ahuvim* for a same-sex couple without a civil license?

I actually thought that *tena'im* was a neat idea, in that it is a kind of "down-payment" on a marriage at a later date, presuming that's what they actually plan to do.

SUSAN: Good question. I don't know. I have never officiated at a *brit ahuvim* for anyone. I was just trying to think of something that would give expression to the couple's feelings but would not be *Kiddushin*. You may note that my third point to Bob was that he should not violate the letter or the spirit of the prohibition of *Kiddushin* without a civil license. Some of our colleagues think that anything done in this situation would violate the spirit of the prohibition.

BOB: Thanks to all. I'll check out the wording of *brit ahuvim*, and discuss with the couple, and see if it meets their needs, de-sires and goals.

SAM: I want to raise the matter of all these new restrictions for Pesach. Seems like the *haredim* are getting more and more *frum* – more *frum* than the pope, as the expression goes.

I've said for years that no one should breathe on Pesach be-cause air is *chametz*. For that matter, don't breathe around non-kosher restaurants. It's the *treif*-sicles in the air that are the source of those fine aromas.

Both *humrot* [difficult restrictions] are waiting for the right *haredi* company to sell appropriate portable air tanks. Then they'll go viral. Another reason not to breathe.

SUSAN: No problem. I sell my breath to a *goy* along with my *chametz*.

DON: Hey, guys, let's not over-do it with sarcasm. Some of these *humrot* are important in order to keep us from *averot* [trans-gressions].

SUSAN: Sorry, Don, just trying to be playful a bit.

DON: I know, but you know what Freud said about humor.

Let's focus on another topic. I could use some ideas from the group. A few years ago I was approached by nine active guys in their sixties and seventies who wanted to meet periodically to discuss what life is all about. They asked me to be their spiri-tual guide and mentor. We meet twice a year at a nearby coastal resort for a few days. The first day is a "climate check" and ev-eryone opens up and shares what is going on in their lives. They are friends, but when in the group, they truly open up. There has been some amazing honesty, and advice is offered by all to each. Then I teach or share texts with them to evoke conversations about various issues. I have done the *midrashim* about the death of Moses; discussed the *Unetaneh Tokef* prayer; read *Kohelet*; taught *middot*; and other things. I am always looking for inter-esting ideas, and would like to know if anyone has any suggestions that would be helpful, or if anyone has any experience with this kind of group. Thanks in advance.

SAM: Just yesterday, during a hike in a nearby mountain range, a friend shared with me an idea. He said the Ten Commandments divide into the well-known groups of five *ben adam l'makom* [between person to God] and five *ben adam l'havero* [between person to person]. He thought of "adding" a third group of five, *ben adam l'atsmo* [between a person and him or herself]. I thought this is an intriguing idea.

He told me his list of five *dibrot ben adam l'atsmo*, but rather than list them *ab initio*, I thought I'd invite colleagues' suggestions and reactions. I believe there could be a great High Holiday sermon/exercise in here, or a basis for a discussion.

So I invite reactions and thoughts.

DON: Fabulous idea, Sam! Thanks.

SUSAN: I know that the High Holidays are a good way off, but I have a problem that occurs every year, and it's never too early to start accumulating solutions.

A constant issue is that it is difficult at times to find people for *aliyot* since the Torah service – at least in their minds – is too early. Do any of you face the same issue and, if so, what do you do? One person suggested: why not have the Torah service after *Musaf*!

BOB: What we do is nearly every *aliyah* is read by a different *Ba'al Koreh*, by a post *b'nai-mitzvah* student. They usually own their *aliyah* until they go off to college. It's hard for most to make it home for the High Holidays. They are all told to be in the sanctuary by X time – usually 15 minutes pre-Torah service – and their family is there to hear them read. Hence, more bodies in the seats at the earlier time.

DON: Adding English readings and cantorial renditions of previously skipped *Piyutim* in *Shaharit* would solve that problem. That way, those who come early, who tend to be the more traditional folks, will be happier with a more complete *Shaharit* and repetition. As to those who come later, they obviously would prefer that the Torah service be later, and probably won't stay until the entire service ends on Rosh Hashanah. And most will leave after the sermon, or after *Hineni*, or after *Kedushah*.

Problem solved!

SUSAN: Well, maybe. In any case, I have several ideas to work on. Thanks, guys!

DON: Here's a theological question about which I know we're going to have very different opinions. You all know my traditional views, but I am prepared – believe it or not – to share some "unorthodox" views, explaining that I personally do not accept them.

I sat down with a bar mitzvah student the other day to choose his essential question, and this was the question he came up with, "Who wrote the Torah?" I am working on some things to offer in response, but I was wondering if anyone has written a piece on this.

Clearly it needs to be in the language and on the level of early teens.

SAM: To be honest and fair, you should probably tell him that Jews have different beliefs about that. Orthodox Jews tend to emphasize *Torah MiSinai*, the most prevalent view throughout most of Jewish history. *Torah MiSinai* means that all of the five books of Moses, the *Humash*, were literally dictated by God, word for word, while Moses wrote the words down. In this view, God is the true "author" of the Torah, and Moses, the scribe. My view, and that of most modern, non-Orthodox, interpreters, is that the Torah was written from collected oral and written stories, laws, poetry and historical bits and edited much, much later by the Prophets or the Men of the Great Assembly – whatever that may have been. We believe that the writings comprising the Torah were "divinely inspired," *Torah Min HaShamayim*, but written down and preserved and edited by human beings into what we know today as the Torah. You could also get into a simple explanation of the "documentary hypothesis," namely sources J, P, D, E and R [Jehovist or Yahwist, Priestly, Deuteronomist, Elohist, and Redactor], and the notion of an "Oral Torah" tradition that was passed down through the generations to flesh out or explain and elaborate on the written text. This was necessary as language and meanings changed, and because the Torah text had become "sacred" – fixed and unchangeable. The Oral Torah traditions, including *halakhah* and *aggadah*, namely *Midrash, Mishnah,* and later *Gemara*, became the basis of today's rabbinic Judaism.

DON: I could probably say something similar, as long as I emphasize that my own view is the *Torah MiSinai* – the first view.

SAM: I agree. Sounds like something any of us could teach.

Let me bring up another interesting question. This may be a bit pedestrian, given the nature of recent discussions in our meetings, but what's the deal with wedding receptions?

Back in the old days in Dallas, the reception was typically dinner, followed by dancing, speeches, more dancing, etc.

The last decade or so – at least in New York and now in other places – this has morphed into a marathon. Receptions begin at 6:00 p.m., and dinner may not be served until after 8:00 p.m. Instead of feeding your guests first, it now seems like dinner is the proverbial carrot on a stick to make sure you stay for the speechifying, hora-dancing, chair-lifting, etc.

So, is this the way things go in your *shuls* too? In my place, it's spilled over into *b'nai-mitzvah* parties and even Jewish communal events.

SUSAN: There is ample precedent for this. Didn't the rabbis do the exact same thing with the *Seder* meal? At one time, the dinner preceded the *maggid*, and the questions were prompted by what differences were actually observed. When people then, as today, made the meal the main event, the rabbis moved it so that everyone would have to be there for the *maggid* if they wanted, ultimately, to eat.

We still sit through the *maggid* today, and if we wait to start the *Seder* after dark, may wind up eating dinner by 9:30 or 10.

I've basically switched it back. Nobody around my *shul* will wait until that late to eat Pesach dinner.

So I've made a small but important shift. The order is now such that dinner is earlier.

A slight change that makes all the difference. Now, if we could just change Daylight Savings Time back. . . .

SAM: I have another ritual question. While most of my members certainly want to be informed and observe the *yahrzeits* of all their loved ones, I have one woman who grew up in a particularly *frum* background who insists that a *yahrzeit* is only for parents. Is there any real basis to this that anyone knows of?

DON: The *yahrtzeit* custom is one of the Jewish rituals that is fairly recent – in the historical scope of things. I observe the *yahrtzeit* of my grandparents, since no one else is left to do so. You will never convince her to change her mind.

SAM: I'm not looking to change her mind. I just don't want to give her false information.

BOB: A good answer is that many Jews observe *yahrzeits* for relatives other than parents, and even for close friends. Some of us in the Jewish world also observe *yahrzeits* for great scholars or leaders, from Moshe Rabbenu on the seventh of Adar, to Abraham Joshua Heschel.

If you believe that *yahrzeits* should be observed only for your parents, you are free to observe those only. Others, who have differing traditions, are also free to observe *yahrzeits* for whomever they wish. If you are being notified of *yahrzeits* for other of your relatives and would prefer not to receive these notices, please inform the office and they will make proper notations and adjustments to honor your preferences.

SAM: Great answer. Thanks!

BOB: I have another practical question for which I'd like your views.

We will be discussing at my Ritual Committee soon the question of having a video camera trained on the *bimah* which would continually film what is going on, and then make it available for families if they want it.

In this regard, I am interested to know your thoughts on the difference between the following options:

a) Having a video running 24/7 like a security tape, which will include taping over Shabbat as well
b) Setting the video to a timer so that it would go on and off during Shabbat
c) Having a custodian turn it on and off during Shabbat as a part of their regular duties

The camera is built into the wall and does not require anyone to operate it. It is so unobtrusive that no one will actually know it is running.

SAM: I have some experience with these matters. Here are my thoughts:
a) Option "a" won't really be good, as security recorders tend to record at an interval frame rate making the video look like a choppy crude animation, even if sound records.
b) Option "b" is better, but set the timers carefully and make sure your recorder and camera are plugged into battery backups, so that the timers record at the proper times even if the power goes out overnight. This way, your settings should remain correct.
c) Use option "c" only when all else fails. The less one has to depend on human fallibility, the better.
    Also:
Use hard drives or flash memory cards to record, not tapes. Video tape is so twentieth century and can, and does, often tangle and fail. Digital recording, even using a solid state flash drive chip camera, or a really good out of service smart phone, is far more reliable and has no moving parts. The resulting recording resolution and fidelity is vastly superior to tape. Moreover, digital video can easily be edited on most computers, tablets and even smartphones; tape, not so easily.

If you don't mind, I'd like to change the subject. I want to just mention something that my personal physician shared with me, that I think you all will be interested in hearing about. No need to reply. I just want to share this very interesting data with you.

An article in the current issue of the *New England Journal of Medicine* discusses the positive health outcomes of same sex marriage. I'll read you an excerpt. If you are interested in reading the entire article, you can find it at http://www.nejm.org/doi/full/10.1056/NEJMp1400254?query=TOC.

> Public health research has suggested not only that discriminatory environments and bans on same-sex marriage are detrimental to health but also that legalizing same-sex marriage (among other policies expanding protections) contributes to better health for LGBT people. For example, data from Massachusetts and California respectively, indicate that same-sex marriage led to fewer mental health care visits and expenditures for gay men and that it reduced psychological distress among lesbian, gay, and bisexual adults in legally recognized same-sex relationships.

This in addition to increased access to health insurance for spouses and children.

Among the other reasons for supporting this development perhaps we need to include *pikuah nefesh* [the Jewish value of saving lives]. I don't expect you to react right now. Just give it some thought, and if you care to read the entire article, be my guest.

SUSAN: Thanks for that, Sam.

So, friends, enough for today. Let's continue next week.

Week 14

BOB: Hi folks! So now let me bring up something that just occurred this week. A congregant of mine will get married soon, God willing, in Los Angeles. He will go there on the Thursday before the wedding, which will be on a Sunday. The bride doesn't want to see him for a week before the wedding, and so they will not be able to get a license in California. Their plan is to have a religious wedding ceremony in L.A., and then, when they return here, have a civil ceremony. That is how I come into the picture. The groom asked me how to arrange that. This sounds nuts to me, not to mention illegal – having a wedding ceremony in L.A. with no license. I asked the groom what traditional people he knows would do, and he answered that people get their licenses farther in advance. It has occurred to me that it might be better for them to have the civil ceremony here first, and I could take care of that, but I don't want to push myself in here. I will attend the wedding in L.A., but will not be *m'sader kiddushin*.

DON: *Minhag shtut* [a foolish custom]. Who veils the bride before the ceremony if not the groom? They might as well play "Here Comes the Bride" as she walks down the aisle.

SUSAN: I think that your intervention in this case, pointing out the illegality, and offering a simple solution – obtaining the civil license beforehand at home – is a wonderful thing to do.

BOB: I agree. Thanks for affirming my position, Don and Susan.

SAM: In my Torah class this morning, a student asked why we cover our eyes when *v'ahavta* is recited, in addition to *Shema*? Most of us cover our eyes only for *Shema*, not for *v'ahavta*. I still have people who cover their eyes during *Shema* of the Torah service. What's the answer?

DON: As an aside, the Vilna Gaon, in addition to his *p'saq* not to kiss the *tzitzit*, also *pasqened* that one should NOT cover one's eyes when reciting the *Shema*. Saul Lieberman, of JTS − so I hear − in his later years, adopted the Vilna Gaon's *p'saq* and, needless to say, almost everyone in the Seminary synagogue followed suit.

BOB: I look at it as follows: When we say the line *Shema* during the Torah service it is being said as a proof text whereas when we say it with *v'ahavta* and blessings it is being said as a "prayer." We cover our eyes for the prayer but not the proof text. Unless you follow the G"ra and don't cover your eyes at all!

DON: The Mishnah Berurah mentions that all other recitations of *Shema* that are not the primary ones for morning and evening are not fulfilment of the mitzvah of *Kri'at Shema*, and therefore we do not cover our eyes. Presumably, in order to have proper *kavanah* for the mitzvah. The other *Shemas* are declarations of faith.

In addition, we cover our eyes while reciting the *Shema* for the following reasons:
a) To prove that we know at least those six words in Hebrew by heart, and
b) To prove that we can ONLY recite those six words by heart because we don't know how to read Hebrew.

Not rabbis, however. WE cover our eyes so as not to see those who can't EVEN recite those six words by heart, so they won't be embarrassed − nor will we!

BOB: There you go again, Don. You're in quite a mood today. Did you have a drink before you came?

DON: No, just feelin' a bit high – high on *HaShem* that is!

BOB: Oh, I see. Hmmm. . . .

SAM: This may be a bit early in the season, but I have a question about the size and shape of a sukkah. Who has expertise on the *halakhah* concerning the shape of a sukkah and could answer a question on it? The area we have available for our new sukkah at *shul* lends itself to an 'L' rather than a rectangle. But that creates more than four walls. We would end up with five walls and the sixth side open.

SUSAN: If you were to research the traditional sukkot of Eastern Europe, you would find that there were various practices in use.

My father grew up in a small town, Chelsea, Mass. just outside Boston, in the 1930s and 1940s and was part of a Jewish community practically transferred from Eastern Europe. Of the 40,000 population, 22,000 were Jews. There were almost twenty Orthodox *shuls* and no Reform or Conservative. There was a Carpenter's *Shul*, a Shneider's *Shul*, a Litveshe *Shul* and a Rushiche *Shul* etc. among others. The very large sukkah at the Orthodox Rushiche *Shul*, Dad once told me, was a beautiful permanent wooden separate structure, which had two "skylight" sections that could be opened to the sky by rope pulleys for a sukkah. Knowing the *halakhot* I was surprised by this, so I did the research into East European practices and discovered this was an accepted practice.

SAM: Hey, Susan, this is so helpful! Thanks! Now let me raise something that annoys me.

I just got a call from a member whose father passed away. They'd like me to co-officiate at his funeral, but they would like another rabbi, who has known them for thirty years, to deliver the eulogy. He's not a bonafide rabbi; but he served successfully at a local Reform Congregation for many years. He's now a flight attendant with SouthWest airlines, and I hear he's very good.

Since my primary goal is to serve the family of the deceased, I am inclined to go along, read a psalm or two and chant the *El*

Maleh Rahamim – which is what they'd like me to do. As far as the "rabboid" is concerned, I'm tempted to just bite the bullet – hold my nose – and co-officiate with him. Does anyone see any other viable options??

BOB: Yeah, I know what you mean. When I was faced with a similar situation, I did my requested part, for the sake of the family, sat down, and opened a newspaper. Remember those?

I would not introduce him, or simply say, "The eulogy today will be delivered by a long-time friend of the family who knew him well," at their request. Then go down and sit with the family, so as not to appear to be co-officiating. Then I'd come back up for the *El Maleh*.

DON: Here we are on the eve of Sukkot and denigrating people's work. Our dignity is not compromised by being present with another Jew at a time when we are asked to be comforters of mourners. Sam, you certainly have nothing to be insecure about in your rabbinate, and neither do any of us. This man is a family friend, served as a *hazzan* and rabbi of a congregation, and the fact that he is now a flight attendant means nothing. You don't need to admit him to the Rabbinical Assembly. We may not desire his presence on a *Bet Din*, but to officiate at a funeral where both of you matter to the family – seems like the right thing to do. Finally, the term "raboid" is filled with derision. How about describing the person in this manner "received his ordination from someplace called Rabbinical Assembly Seminary? Probably so named because in his time, the RA was seen as the desirous organization to be connected with.

SAM: Thanks for your perspective. As I noted, I'll be doing this funeral to be there for the mourners. Yet I think that we ought to be wary of people who assume the title when they haven't earned it or don't deserve it.

There have been several such "rabbis" who do real harm and are a real embarrassment to those of us who work diligently for *Klal Yisrael*. In my area, there are several who have made it to the news. One who defrauded elderly people; another who opened up the equivalent of "Intermarriages R Us." Another guy, who was a *shul* executive director in the Pacific Northwest, crossed state lines and started calling himself a rabbi.The only thing that I can say about his Hebrew is that it SOUNDS like a Semitic language! My wife was at a funeral that he conducted last week and said that he was both inept and inappropriate.

From what I understand, a very qualified and properly ordained rabbi was just replaced by a rabboid who was ordained by the first rabboid from the Pacific Northwest. The ability to sing Debbie Friedman's "*Mi Sheberakh*" does not a rabbi make. Even if we don't allow them into the R.A. or the local board of rabbis, they damage the reputation of our profession. They reflect poorly on you and me, whether we like it or not. It just so happens that this fellow with whom I will officiate actually had a decent reputation and helped grow a fine unaffiliated Congregation. One colleague who knows him tells me that he's a really good guy. I'll leave it at that.

Then again, there are some rabbis with fine credentials who do some unspeakable things, from all denominations with all sorts of abominations.

By the way, who said anything about this guy being a *hazzan*? Do you know something I don't know?

Finally, I am not a fan of faux rabbis. But I'm a big fan of truth in advertising. However, this isn't a time for egos, so I'll just go with the flow.

DON: Well, said, Sam! Go with the flow.

SAM: Not to change the subject, but here's a good one. My nephew is a rabbinical student at a school in the New Jersey area, and is known as a traditionalist in the school. He was asked by a rabbi in the area to participate in a *Bet Din* for conversion, and he agreed. The rabbi has *smikhah* from the *rabbanut* in Israel. Now, he is being told that the rabbi requires that the *Bet Din*, which is composed of three males, be present in the *mikvah* when the *giyoret* does her *tevilah* and *kabbalat mitzvot*. I have never heard of such a thing. If the rabbi does not change his requirements, my nephew will refuse to participate.

What I would like to know is whether you know of such a requirement. Why would this be required now? Is it common in Israel?

SUSAN: In every conversion I have ever been involved with where the *Bet Din* is all male, there is a female *shomeret* in the *mikvah* room, and the men stand just outside with the door ajar. They listen for the splash. If they are questioning her then – and I know what the sources say – they should stand just outside the room with the door ajar where they can hear one another. They are NEVER in the room with the candidate when she is undressed. That is really immodest and inappropriate.

DON: We have always assumed that our witnessing was valid if we stood outside the door and a trusted *mikvah* attendant was inside. We know the candidate went in and we heard a splash and she comes out with wet hair. This is all pretty convincing. There is a level of trust, that the immersions were properly done. But an experienced *mikvah* matron can be trusted. Why violate standards of *tzniyut* [traditional standards of modesty]?

I have heard that some places cover the entire surface of the *mikveh* water with ping pong balls – seriously. This would allow immersion and protect modesty. Although ingenious, I would hope it wouldn't be necessary.

Personally, I think I would decline to sit on the court that would expect me to be inside. I would not be comfortable with that. The candidate needs to be comfortable, and so do we.

You ask: "Know of such a requirement?" Of course, Judaism never trusted the testimony of women, and therefore "other women place the *giyoret* in water up to her neck, and two '*talmidei hakhamim*' stand outside. Supposedly they can see only her head above the water, and not the rest of her naked body. . . ." This is from Talmud Bavli, Yevamot 47b. I spoke with two Orthodox rabbis in Israel, and they allow the *giyoret* to wear a very loose robe when entering the *mikveh*, so she does not feel embarrassed.

BOB: At all the *mikvehs* I'm aware of, we always have female *mikvah* attendants for female converts.

I have two candidates going to *mikvah* this week and they described the visit they had with our conversion institute. The modesty that is taken by the woman *mikvah* attendants is something that is unbelievably refreshing.

The only way it would be permissible to us for the men to be inside is when they cover the entire water area with a cover so that modesty is observed. I have actually seen this, and there is a hole where the women's head is or when she wears a loose fitting bathrobe where no nudity can be revealed.

Your nephew should do two things:

1. Refuse to participate out of the rules of modesty

2. Share the information with the Dean of the rabbinical school

The Talmud, in *Yevamot* 47b, seems pretty clear about the accommodation to a woman's dignity that's called for in such a situation. My reading of "*omdim lah mibachutz*" ["stand outside"] is: stand outside the *mikvah* room, not stand outside the water. Thus, it seems to me, the ancient rabbis depended on "*mikvah* ladies" just as we do in contemporary times.

When I was at JTS, a professor, whom I won't name, since it seems almost like *lashon ha-ra*, opined: Women appear undressed before male doctors and it's not a big deal, so what's the big deal regarding three male rabbis? As I recall, he didn't see the necessity for loose robes, pingpong balls, or doors left slightly ajar. Although he might have known far more Talmud and Codes than any of us, we considered his opinion to be *narishkeit*, if not lunacy.

When my aunt was in social work school, some years ago, she did some ethnographic interviews, and a woman reported that, when she had converted, the rabbi had insisted on being in the *mikvah* room with her, to give her his "special blessing." Hmm, special blessing indeed.

Shame on any male rabbis who insist on being in the *mikvah* room with a female convert, and kudos to your nephew for refusing to participate.

A traditional colleague of mine, in a different community, told me that when he served on Orthodox-rabbanut *batei din* for conversion before migrating to the *Masorti* world, he says that in the Orthodox world the *dayanim* do indeed stand in the *mikvah* room during the *tevilah*. However, the women are clothed. They go into the *mikveh* wearing a loose-fitting black cloak-like thing.

See *Iggrot Moshe* and other *shu"t* [*Sh'aylot u-Teshuvot* – Responsa literature] who talk about how having the *Bet Din* stand outside the *mikveh* room is not enough. The *dayanim* need to actually witness the *tevillah* [dunking]. FYI, this is one of the reasons the Orthodox tend to invalidate non-Orthodox conversions – that in Conservative conversions, often the *Bet Din* wasn't in the *mikveh* room.

Although I think that current Orthodox rabbanut protocol is to accept *bediavad* [after the fact] an Orthodox conversion done in the Diaspora where the *Bet Din* was right outside the door, *lekhathilah* [a priori] they – and I – would never do it that way.

The women are fully clothed. So there is much *tzniyut* [modesty] (צניעות).

You wait outside until the woman is already in the water up to her neck, and then you go into the room. After she dunks, you leave the room before she comes out. You only need to see her head going under the water.

DON: A colleague of mine was assistant to the president of RCA. [Rabbinical Council of America, the national Orthodox organization].

He had many, many conversions, and the *Bet Din* ALWAYS was out side of the room where the *Mikveh* lady was.

Also, he told me that when he was in New York, the *Bet Din* was never in the room with the convert. I once had a question about using the "ocean," and I think it was some Orthodox *posek* [decisor] who said to wear a loose dress. Someone said one can wear a wool bathing suit.

SAM: This has been an extremely useful discussion, and I thank all of you for your thoughts and experiences – and mostly for your *halakhic* views.

SUSAN: I wonder how many of you noticed that Shimon Peres, Pope Francis and Mahmoud Abbas met at the Vatican, and prayed together for peace. It is amazing what a non-event Peres, Pope Francis and Abbas praying together at the Vatican turned out to be. Some brief, tepid reports in the media and not much more. I say *Barukh Hashem* because the less Israel is in the media the better it is for Israel.

DON: Susan, be grateful for any good thing. How long had it been since Shimon Peres last prayed?

BOB: I don't know about recently, but about a year ago he spoke at the *Masorti* convention, and I spied him saying *amen* to *birkat ha-mazon*. *Halakhically* that counts [laughter].

Anyway, let me pose this interesting question to the group. I have said on various occasions that, if I were not in the Jewish business, I probably wouldn't keep my head covered all the time.

As you can see, I have mixed feelings about uncovering my head. For decades, I have kept my head covered most of the time. On the other hand, the reasons why I said that I didn't feel strongly committed to the practice – the recognition that the practice is *halakhically* sketchy, a desire to take full part in the world around me, and a critical if positive stance towards Jewish tradition – still stand. At our *Tikkun Leyl Shavuot*, one of the presenters read from some *frum* book about why we eat dairy foods on Shavuot, starting with the nonsense about the Jewish people's not having separate dishes for meat and dairy ready at the time. Those in attendance nodded gravely, and I almost took my *kippah* off then and there. On the other hand again, I once heard Nahum Sarna tell about his teacher Cecil Roth, who, according to Sarna, used to lecture bareheaded but would put on a *kippah* whenever he would quote from some classical Jewish text. I can identify with Roth's position, but Sarna seems to have regarded the on again-off again routine as comical. On the other hand yet again, for some reason, I was thinking recently about I. L. Peretz's story "The Three Gifts," one of which was the bloody *kippah* of a Jew who was forced to run the gauntlet in the Russian army, and who was killed when he stopped to pick up the *kippah* which had fallen off his head. That story made me think of the experiences which prompted me to keep my head covered. Once, in New York City, many years ago, I happened to have a *kippah* on in the street, and a passerby aimed an anti-Semitic remark at me, something which I had hardly ever experienced before. At about the same time, I was moving to an unfamiliar part of the city. I was reassured when I saw a man in a *kippah* in the neighborhood, and I asked him a bit about the area.

I am curious to know how other people feel about the issue.

DON: Here's what a colleague and friend told me about his policy regarding wearing a *kippah*. He always wears an Israeli crocheted *kippah*, even if he is eating dairy or fish in a non-Kosher restaurant. "Do I wear it because I'm so *frum*?" he asks. "No." "Do I wear it because I am still a rabbi, albeit retired?" he asks. "No." He wears a *kippah* simply as a symbol of his identity as a Jew and a supporter of Israel. He, too, believes it may help to "flush out into the open" anti-Semites who may make disparaging remarks or gestures or both. It may also stifle some from making such remarks. He feels fairly safe wearing it, partially because he has a concealed weapons permit and always has his small .380 in his pocket loaded, with a round in the chamber, ready to fire in self-defense should the need ever arise. It's easy to be "brave," he says, when you have an ace in the hole.

It is a *minhag hasidut*, but it's still a *minhag* that's pretty universal and to many, seems to have the status of *halakhah*. Rav Eliezer Melamed presents a fascinating history of the *kippah* in the *Likkutim* of his *Pninei Halakhah* series. Maybe it comes from the Chaldean astrologers who warned Rav Nahman bar Yitzhak's mother to make sure he covers his head. Maybe it comes from the anti-Semitic Judenhut, but headcovering still caught on. Melamed also has a section that speaks directly to your question, where he quotes Rav Moshe Feinstein, affirming that if it would make you uncomfortable to wear a *kippah* at work, or feel that by wearing it you risk monetary loss, you don't have to wear it. However, he also says that this is in the case that there are many who wouldn't understand the importance of covering your head. I think if you are teaching a theology class, your students and colleagues would certainly be understanding.

SAM: For me the salient question would be, not is it required but what statement do I want to make? If I were in your position – I think once you said you were teaching a course at Xavier College – I would want to make the statement: Here we are, Jews and non-Jews, discussing theology, and I am identifying as a Jewish teacher, so I am wearing a *kippah*. But it is you not I who will be there, so decide how you want to present yourself.

From the name Xavier it sounds like the place is Catholic, so marking your status by your attire is well understood.

BOB: Thanks to everyone who has responded to my question about attitudes towards keeping one's head covered. Let me clarify that I am not worried about negative reactions, at Xavier University or elsewhere, to my wearing a *kippah*. I have worn a *kippah* for decades, in all kinds of places. The question is, as some of you have noted, what kind of statement I want to make to the world about myself. I have been thinking about that question recently.

SAM: So here's a question that you all have probably faced. Many families want to schedule their child's bar or bat mitzvah before their thirteenth birthday. It may be for family reasons, such as a grandparent is ill and may not make it to the actual birthday, or because some family members live far away and can only come after school is over for the season, or something like that.

SAM: When I was a rabbinical student, a seminary professor told us that the age of thirteen was chosen as an average, rather than check for המביא שתי שערות [checking for two hairs]. He said that since, on average, kids mature earlier today than they did two thousand years ago, we can be lenient and observe the *simhah* earlier than the thirteenth birthday if necessary.

SUSAN: I agree that the age of bat or bar mitzvah should be flexible. I have another question to ask. I wanted to check in with those who follow the triennial cycle as to what you do with *maftir*.

Until now, we have followed the *maftir* as listed for triennial except when we end a book, since we do not want to miss the opportunity for *hazak*. We now have a proposal on the table that we go forward to the traditional *maftir* each Shabbat, no matter which year of the triennial we find ourselves. The thinking has to do with the idea that, especially when there is a bar or bat mitzvah, in future years those students would be invited back to read the *maftir* . . . either in the sanctuary or the junior congregation service, and that this creates a community of *maftir* for the *parashah*. I am wondering what you currently do, and your advice on this proposal?

BOB: I'm not pretending that the rabbis don't change *halakhah*. Having co-authored one of the *teshuvot* on same-sex marriage that was too radical for the majority of our Law Committee to tolerate, I'm pretty sure my liberal credentials are solid. But I do believe that the burden of argument falls on the one who wants to change. In this case, I don't see it.

SAM: OK. But if the ancient rabbis could choose to make changes, so can WE. The last time I looked, WE were rabbis, too.

The past is entitled to a vote, not a veto. Someone famous who also taught at JTS once said something along those lines. I'm surprised that since we removed *korbanot* from the *Siddur*, in effect, we haven't eliminated the endless reading of its messy details from our *kri'ah*. NOT, of course, from the Torah, but from our readings. Doing so would show more consistency than our Movement could handle.

Please don't call me an *epikorus* [heretic] or any such labels. If anything, just call me a consistent rationalist.

The CONCEPT of sacrifice certainly remains a valid one; reading or chanting the endless details of a bygone cult, in my opinion, not so much.

We changed the "traditional" Yom Kippur *Minhah* Torah reading to an alternative, more reflective of the lofty ideal of *Kedoshim Tih'yu*, than the nitty-gritty of forbidden sexual liaisons.

Yes, the mating season in ancient Israel, blah, blah. The Book of Jonah extends the theme of *Teshuvah* and stresses God's willingness to accept true repentance even from the most depraved – Jonah, the A.W.O.L. Jew, not the Ninevehites – even when corrective action doesn't necessarily reflect a changed attitude.

Korbanot had a good run. They stopped two thousand years ago, yet we are still here.

Skipping, selectively quoting or misquoting and ALTERING passages of Torah, especially when it suited the rabbis to change things they didn't like so much, is a time-honored tradition, even more so in the Conservative and Reform movements than in rabbinic times. For example, *Birkot HaShahar*, '*asu v'hikrivu*, *Sim Shalom baOlam*, designating Torah readings, *Hallel Maleh*, *Al HaNissim* and *Haftarah* for *Yom Ha'Atzma'ut*, adding the *Imahot* to the *Amidah*, commitment ceremonies and a *ketubah* for same sex couples; *Aliyot*, counting women in a *minyan* and declaring them equally obligated with men.

Let's not use "Tradition," or our commitment to *halakhah* or past precedent, as an excuse to shield things we don't want to change. Believe me, even since the codification of *halakhah* in the *Shulhan Arukh* in comparatively recent times, we've still got a lot of catching up to do. Let's not pretend that the rabbis preserved all of the *halakhah* they "received" and transmitted it all without change. It just ain't so.

BOB: Sam, you make a very strong case. I'm not sure that all of us agree, but we've raised enough questions to chew on for a long time.

SUSAN: Friends, I have a funeral question.

Increasingly, I find my role at funeral to be emcee. Everyone wants to talk, for better and for worse.

Of late, though, a new issue has emerged. Now they would like to do the talking and not have me eulogize the person at all. I am usually dealing with non-member children who do not know me or affiliate. With all modesty, I give an excellent eulogy. More than that, the process of telling someone's life story to me as a family is almost always very healing for the family and hearing it told back from a third party also, I believe, carries great weight.

What to do? When this happened a few weeks ago, I let them call the shots, I gave a very abridged eulogy – they said I could talk about her Jewish involvement – and I felt something was missing. Now it has come up again. Do I insist? Defer? Recommend strongly but then defer?

Thanks for your counsel.

SAM: It is your role, as rabbi, it seems to me, to place the deceased in the context of Jewish tradition. Each of us has a place in the long continuum of Jewish history, and when a rabbi talks about the deceased's name, or connects the person with the Torah portion, or some other teaching in our tradition, we put the deceased in that context. To me, a eulogy is more than just a remembrance. It's more than just telling stories. That, the family can do. We do something more, something different.

By the way, we were not taught this in Rabbinical School. I learned this in CPE [Clinical Pastoral Education], from my non-Jewish colleagues! Hope this is helpful.

DON: I wonder if some of this need for so many people to talk at the funeral comes from having shorter or non-existant time for sitting *shivahs*. When the time for sitting *shivah* is shortened, there is no time in which people feel they will be able to share their stories or memories, and so the funeral becomes the only opportunity, rather than just the beginning. The focus becomes more on who and how many get to speak, than on the caring for the body side. There is also less sense that the "traditional" rituals, which are in our hands, offer any meaning or comfort, simply for being traditional, let alone for anything specific we might teach about particular elements.

Interesting, I was doing a support group for people over eighty at the JCC, and yesterday one of the members opened a discussion about whether they should be planning the content of their own funerals or memorial services – laying out in advance who should speak or sing, what music is played, which restaurant it should be at. To some extent it was more about memorial services, since more people are choosing cremation, and not having funerals, or both family, friends and the deceased live at such distances that immediate burial is done, without many people being present at that time.

SUSAN: Don, I think you are right about the absence of *shivah* being a factor. Hadn't thought of that. Around here as well, ten minutes of *shivah* or private period of mourning, whatever that means, is common.

BOB: I agree that sharing memories of the deceased, telling stories about him or her, etc., important though they may be, do not accomplish what a well-crafted eulogy, which connects the deceased with Jewish history, tradition and values can. I have grumbled to myself about eulogies which were like newspaper obituaries. I heard one rabbi say, in his most expressive voice, "He was active in his professional association." However, I don't see how one can force himself in here. One could say, "You know that you, friends and relatives can tell more stories about x than I can, but I think that there is some value in connecting his or her life to Jewish tradition," but, in the end, if they don't buy it, they don't buy it.

SAM: Well, despite what I just said, just to offer an alternative perspective on this discussion, I do believe that the biography-focused eulogy is comforting and consoling. Spending time with the family and allowing them to reminisce about their loved one, a day or two before the funeral and not an hour before the funeral, is healing. Taking notes, even on a laptop or tablet during that session, is just fine if the family feels as if you are listening. And then, to reorganize their thoughts into a cohesive eulogy which also connects the deceased with Torah, will result in a eulogy that works.

I would dare say that the insistence by family to have family members get up and speak is due in no small measure to decades of our colleagues giving eulogies which may have been full of Torah, but absent are the critical references to the person that the gathered were there to mourn. It was viewed as canned and impersonal, and failed as an instrument of solace.

Just want to give an alternate view of how eulogies may be crafted.

BOB: I agree that having some aspect of the eulogy which is biography-focused is extremely comforting. When family members compliment us by saying "You spoke as if you knew her," we realize that they appreciated how we listened to them and expressed some of their sentiments.

When hearing a colleague offer a eulogy, I may not always know if that colleague knew the individual, but I generally can determine when a colleague did NOT know the individual. When a eulogy is filled with Torah quotes and few personal reflections, it is a eulogy which is generally impersonal.

Last week I had to eulogize a woman who pretty much wasted her life. My brief remarks included words of comfort, but they also included an honest reflection about how this person lived her life. The family was effusive in their praise, mainly because I provided comfort but candor also.

Our professor in Seminary, in homiletics class, often said DON'T BE CLEVER, BE HONEST. There is no great magic to a meaningful eulogy. It is mainly about honesty and about our ability to listen. We can add words of Torah in a global perspective, but we should never minimize the value of sharing biographical information.

Also, increasingly, I hear, "Rabbi, we would like you to handle the prayers – the ritual stuff – and family members and close friends will speak about the personal stuff." Well, unfortunately, "stuff" often gets stuffed and stuffy.

If the idea is to bring honor to the deceased and comfort to the mourners, so be it. I have always listened intently as the family reminisced, and I took notes, later reordering, condensing, summarizing, recapitulating, and most often adding something from the weekly *parashah* or an upcoming Jewish holiday.

What once was meaningful to Jewish families seems less so these days, a measure of how far the next two generations have strayed. *Kavod HaMet* [honoring the deceased] may be present, but certainly not *Kavod HaRav* [honoring the rabbi]. We are merely functionaries reciting the incantations that the family knows should be said, but don't themselves know how or care to say.

Smile, touch their shoulders gently and nod knowingly. Yes, of course, whatever you wish. I always introduce family eulogizers with the words:

"*Devarim hayotz'im min halev, nikhnasim el halev.* [Words that come from the heart, enter the heart].Who better to reflect on his or her life and family relations than _____."

Back off respectfully and let them share what they have to share. Cut or tear *Kri'ah*, do Psalms and/or a reading, and if you had any relationship with the person or family, say so, but defer to them if they so desire. Chant the *El Maleh* and lead *Kaddish.* Go home with them. Make *Hamotzi* and explain *Seu'dat Ha'avelim* and, if they are sitting *shivah*, three is the new seven, visit, and if they wish, have a BRIEF *Minhah* or *Ma'ariv* service, preferably not both.

Then I would follow up with them just before *Shloshim. Barukh Dayan HaEmet.* Blessed is one who can discern the Truth!

SAM: Having listened to all of you, my distingtuished colleagues, I want to add a few further thoughts. I strive to set a consoling and compassionate mood as the funeral begins.

I permit others, like family members and perhaps a close friend to speak, and try to ascertain whether one or both will offer biographical background. I insist that they write their comments down. This is not the time to be spontaneously inappropriate, due to the emotions of the moment, and keep their comments to not more than five minutes. When a child speaks I don't mention a time limit, and I encourage them to share biographical information that others won't know.

I am the final speaker at every funeral, and offer insights from Jewish tradition that connect the deceased's life with our tradition, and conclude with more consolation. I also make certain that I don't repeat myself.

My mentors taught me that at funerals people listen more carefully and with more intensity than in synagogue for services. After all, life is on the line. We are symbolic exemplars of everything Jewish, and each person and their family deserve a eulogy composed by a professional. I would urge you to insist that you speak. Officiating means sharing your wisdom with the mourners.

BOB: Similar to what Sam said, I also want to add a few more thoughts, having listened to all of you. My role at funerals over the last decade or so has changed from eulogizer to "closer," adding my final two words – sometimes literally two words: "Please rise" – to the many speeches that have preceded. I will not repeat what has already been said. Sometimes many times over, and have adjusted somewhat comfortably to my new role.

Having heard many family speeches over these years, and several in the past week, I can say that some are truly inspiring and a true act of *kibud av v'em* [honoring father and mother], etc. Sometimes, of course they don't meet that standard, and eulogy overkill can make one begin to envy the departed. On occasion, I have had to physically restrain my well-worn copy of *Moreh Derekh* [the rabbi's manual] from walking out of the chapel on its own.

In response to this change in funeral practice I found the following column in the Canadian Jewish News, written by our colleague Rabbi Philip Scheim, some years back, which some may find helpful:

Family Speeches at Funerals

Rabbi Philip Scheim

The greatest change that I have witnessed in my rabbinic career has been the role of the rabbi at funerals. In the earlier years of my career I would deliver the eulogy at a funeral. On very rare occasions in those years, a family member or friend would be invited to speak as well.

Anybody who attends funerals today knows that the reality now is quite different. Rare today is the funeral without family speeches, with the rabbi's role largely confined to ritual. In many instances, this change is welcome, because there are times when family speeches are beautifully delivered, deeply moving, and articulate a vision of the departed family member that brings great honor to all involved.

Having heard at least a thousand family speeches over the last several years, I offer some unsolicited suggestions regarding family speeches.

First, I respectfully suggest that the number of speakers be limited. The most meaningful services I have attended have usually involved one or two speakers, to a maximum of three. There are alternative venues available for others to offer their memories, including the tribute pages on the funeral homes' websites. Tech-savvy family members could set up memorial pages that would host written recollections, video and audio clips. Not everybody has to speak at the funeral in order for his or her words to contribute meaningfully to the honour bestowed upon the departed.

I would also remind mourners that they are under no obligation to speak, and should not be pressured to deliver a eulogy, especially when they are not accustomed to public speaking. On several occasions, family members have shared their discomfort with me, feeling that by not speaking, they are disrespecting their loved one. I suggest to them that being a mourner is hard enough, without adding the burden of public speaking, when that is outside of one's comfort zone.

For those outside of the immediate family who are speaking, I offer one caution. Be sure that your subject matter is the deceased. Too often, a well-intentioned speaker spends as much time on him or herself as he or she does on the departed. "He and I used to . . ." or "she and I often . . ." should be kept to a minimum, since the room is filled with many others who have similar experiences with the departed, and the speaker's personal experiences are not the subject of the hour. Those preparing eulogies should avoid the word "I" as much as possible, focusing, as fully as possible, on the life being remembered.

Finally, in the absence of family speakers, one should not be wary of the rabbi fulfilling his/her traditional role as eulogizer. Even in cases where the rabbi did not know the departed, s/he is trained to ask the right questions, to listen to family members and to build an appropriate tribute based on the recollections s/he gathers. I know that some of my

best eulogies have been for people I never met, whose fam-
ily members' accounts of their lives deeply moved me, and
provided me with all that I needed to deliver an appropriate
eulogy.

SAM: I have a *halakhic* question. Three times in the past two
days, questions of *hatafat dam* [drawing a drop of blood from
the penis, as a "token circumcision"] have come to my attention.

The family of an upcoming bar mitzvah boy recently joined
the *shul*. The mother is not Jewish, the kid was circumcised in
the hospital on the first or second day after his birth. They agreed
to *mikveh* but not to "lancing."

In another case a boy from my *shul* moved away to the big
city, married a non-Jewish woman, who eventually had a baby
boy who was circumcised in the hospital. Suddenly, six months
later, they want to have a naming. They are willing to do *mikveh*,
but not *hatafat dam*. Here's their question: Will the lack of blood
letting be an impediment to his being raised as a Jew? They also
wondered if the blood could be drawn from the foot or any other
area other than the penis.

These are both families who are seeking ways to be Jewish.
Do we have any *halakhic* position about this? Families who are
part of the *shul* and have boys all have *bris milah*. These two
families that I'm talking about are outliers. I've explained Jewish law to them, and have had warm conversations with them.
I explained that it's really not painful, and said that the twelve-
year-old can do it on himself, I just don't know what else to do,
except to tell them that it's required, and risk their walking away.
Any thoughts?

BOB: I am no expert on *bris milah* but would suggest the following questions could be relevant to a study of this question:

1. What are the details of circumcision that are not disquali-
fying *be-di'avad* [after the fact], though prescribed *le-khat'hilah*
[a priori]?

2. What is the traditional stand on the validity *be-di'avad*
of a hospital circumcision in the case of a boy born to a Jewish
mother?

3. What is our best guess as to the intention, in the cases mentioned, whether the reason why the father chose to have his son circumcised, albeit in a hospital and not by a *mohel*, was that he regarded the boy as Jewish and regarded circumcision as something that a Jewish boy should have?

SUSAN: *Katonti* – In all humility, I am hardly an expert on this topic, but am drawing from practical experience, and thus sharing the results of research done and advice received.

There are two operative points here: *milah* not done for the sake of *bris* or *giyyur* [conversion], and *milah* done prior to the eighth day. In general, both situations, according to *halakhah*, require *hatafah*. I'm unaware of any exceptions, other than those which would exempt *milah* altogether and are not operative here.

I have to wonder what kind of mental image the parents of both boys have regarding *hatafat dam brit*. Or, alternatively, what they may have witnessed or heard. I once participated in a *Beit Din* for *hatafah* and *mikveh* on an adult, and was horrified to see the rabbi, doing *hatafah*, pull out a sewing needle.

Our local *mohel* – as I expect is the general rule – uses a spring-loaded lancet of the kind used by diabetics. He assures those about to undergo *hatafah* that each time he gets a new one, he tests it on himself first, so that he can say with confidence that there will be very little or no pain. Now THAT'S dedication to your work!

I've used the over-the-counter disposable lancets to do *hatafah* on infants and toddlers, without noticeable discomfort. When there is understandable resistance, I've shared those experiences as well as what the local *mohel* has said.

As for risking a family walking away, if we are committed to our ideology and our understanding of *halakhah*, we need not compromise or seek ways to circumvent it, in order to prevent it. And in my humble opinion, if the family left, it would simply confirm that they are more comfortable in another movement.

DON: As I understand from traditional *halakhic* sources, none of which I have at my fingertips at the moment, *giyyur* without *hatafat dam brit* – if a male is already circumcised – does not invalidate his acceptance. In other words, the tradition dictates: *lo m'akev, v'lo m'vatel* ["it doesn't prevent and it doesn't invalidate"] after having *t'vilah* (immersion) and appearance before a *Beit Din b'di'eved.* I just re-read that somewhere a few days ago.

SAM: Friends, let me turn to another question. A recent widower, who happens to be a convert to Judaism, is preparing his late wife's tombstone. He wants to include her name and dates, of course, and *also* wants to include his name and birthdate, leaving only the space open for his date of death.

I've never encountered this and don't think it is common. Is it permissible?

DON: I don't think it is forbidden. I can tell you that I see it all the time. It gives them peace of mind to know that everything is prepared. My in-laws did it. My wife didn't like it, but they did it anyway. Often it is because they just don't trust their children to take care of things, or they simply don't want to burden them with anything.

BOB: I have seen it, although I felt at the time it was rather morbid and altogether strange. I realized later in discussion with the person who did it that it was to ease the expense on survivors later on, as the cost PER LETTER of the engraving was already high and steadily climbing. This way, all that the survivors would have to pay for was the engraving of the final date of demise. Another instance of prudence – and of *has al mamono shel Yisrael* ["being parsimonious with Jewish funds"].

SUSAN: I have seen this and while it might be "spooky" or "uncomfortable" there is no *halachic* prohibition.

SAM: I want to share with our group a recent experience. It's not a question that needs discussion. Just an experience which I think will be helpful in regard to conducting funerals. Since we've just been discussing tombstones, this matter came to my mind.

The other day, I officiated at the funeral of a woman I'll call "Sarah," who was the mother of a congregant, whom I'll call "Shlomo." Preparing for the funeral was for me a bit complicated, for Shlomo is one of four children born to Sarah during her first marriage. Sarah was only forty-three years old when her husband, Shlomo's, father, died suddenly at the age of forty-two, leaving his mother with four kids under fifteen. This was a long time ago. A few years later, Sarah remarried. Her second husband, who died about seven years ago, was a widower with two children. So the house and the family suddenly and dramatically expanded. The relations between step-siblings were not great. They weren't terrible, but they weren't great. Over the years there were ups and downs, and these have persisted. Case in point: when the time came to prepare the obituary, one of Shlomo's step-brothers wished to be included, but one refused. In the obituary and at the funeral, there was no mention of him. He didn't attend the funeral.

I have long had a very good, warm, respectful, relationship with Shlomo. He is kind and caring, and gives a lot to the *shul* and to people in need. It surprised me that, although I knew that his father had died many years ago, I hadn't known the details. When I learned them, during my meetings with the family, I was struck by the similarity of our stories. My mother died at the age of forty-three, leaving my father a widower with three children under nine. One difference is that when my father remarried, and a new step-mother came into our household, she had no children and no additional children came along. So we didn't need to get along with step-siblings. But my sisters and I did acquire step-grandparents, and an aunt, an uncle and cousins on my new step-mother's side. It wasn't terrible, but, on the other hand, "it wasn't great."

This is neither here nor there, although perhaps it is. I provide these details to give a sense as to my own mental state walking into the funeral. I was, if not anxious, very focused on "getting it right." More than wanting to say the right thing, I didn't want to say the wrong thing. I remember the feeling I had as I was ascending to the podium to speak at the funeral: introduce the right people in the right sequence. Don't say something like, "*all* of her children have gathered here," but on the other hand, don't, of course, say something like, "*some* of her children have gathered here."

Fortunately, the funeral went well. I didn't make any mistakes. The four biological children spoke, and spoke well. In my own remarks, I focused on Sarah's caring – which was real – aware nonetheless that the absent step-brother might have had a different impression of her.

All that is an introduction to what I learned yesterday. Shlomo came to *shul* with his wife to say *Kaddish*. Afterwards, at *kiddush*, my wife spoke with him. Shlomo told her something he hadn't told me: that when he and his family walked into the chapel for the funeral service, he was afraid he was going to faint. Shlomo is not histrionic, so this was surprising for me to hear, as was what he said next. He said that when he heard my voice, as I began the funeral, he knew he was going to get through it.

Now, there's nothing special about my voice. And the words I was saying at the beginning of the service are words that I say at the beginning of many funerals: "Psalm 90. *Adonai maon atah hayitah l'dor va-dor, b'terem harim yuladu, vatikholel eretz v'tevel, me'olam ad olam atah El.* O Lord, you are our refuge. From generation to generation, . . . you are everlasting. . . ." I was reading those words, though, I must admit, by now I've got them memorized.

As my wife related Shlomo's reaction, I realized a profound truth: I had spent hours worrying about what I was going to say and what I was going to refrain from saying in my eulogy, but what brought comfort to this mourner was my presence and my voice, and the words I recited at the beginning of the funeral. Somehow, that provided assurance that things were going to go OK, and that we were going to get through this together.

This reminded me of a term I first learned from a wise rabbinic counselor, with whom I studied in rabbinical school, and who has remained a mentor ever since. In a class I took with him, he referred us to the work of the late Rabbi Edwin Friedman, who talks about the importance of being a "non-anxious presence." Ever since, I have recognized the importance of being a non-anxious presence, particularly with individuals or families under stress. What I learned from this experience is that sometimes, even when you are in fact anxious, and you're focused on your own responsibilities, and you're not concentrating on being a non-anxious presence, you can still be one anyway.

Perhaps Shlomo was sensing something else: that when I was reciting those words from Psalm 90, I was speaking to myself as well, and drawing as much comfort from them as I was hoping she and the others present would.

So, in sum, I just wanted to share this experience, for whatever it's worth, for your consideration.

BOB: Thanks, Sam! Very interesting and useful.

SAM: I have a *halakhic* question. I am curious if people could let me know about some of their practices of areas that you would let a talented child lead during Shabbat morning *tefillot*. There is a youth in my congregation who attends regularly and is looking to participate in more areas. He is only ten years old, so it will be a while till his bar mitzvah. He has been leading *Ashrei* since he was four. I would appreciate the advice.

DON: When my son was about age six he began to lead the congregation on Shabbat morning from *Ein Kelohaynu*.

BOB: I believe, with the exception of the *arba parshiot*, they can even receive *aliyot*. Ashkenazi practice is to allow a *katan* to have *maftir* and *haftarah*, but not another *aliyah*.

SUSAN: Sounds to me that there is a wide range of practice on this issue. If there's nothing else to be said on it, let me raise another interesting and challenging matter.

On Sunday mornings, usually the first part of the New York Times I look at is the Sunday Styles. I generally scan for Jewish weddings and rabbinic colleagues officiating. I bet I'm not the only one with this habit. I've noticed more and more over the last few years that with greater frequency there are wedding announcements in which no ordained clergy participate. I can understand this where there is an interfaith marriage. However, increasingly I notice this trend even when both parties are Jewish. This weekend alone was a busy weekend for Jewish Justices on the Supreme Court: Ruth Bader Ginsberg and Elena Kagan each officiated at weddings in which both bride and groom appear to be Jewish. On one level, I'm happy to see Jewish couples getting married, and even seeking out prominent Jewish jurists to officiate to validate their apparent ethnic pride. On the other hand, why aren't they choosing rabbis? What, if anything, should we be doing as rabbis to address this issue?

SAM: They are not choosing rabbis, because they have no congregational affiliation, and they believe Judaism is irrational, outdated, etc. There is nothing you can do with such people. My mother was like that. Unfortunately, it is not likely that these are Jews that can be depended upon in any way. Justice Breyer is another ethnic Jew on the Supreme Court, but he married the daughter of a British Viscount. His daughter is an Anglican priest who serves a church near Cambridge, England. She is undoubtedly socially acceptable in England as the daughter of an American Supreme Court Justice and a member of the British nobility. Here's what I suggest:

Be more welcoming and less insistent on having things only our traditional way. Fuss not about the Lieberman clause or prenup.

And here's some more advice from my years of experience:

Don't be too insistent that the meal be kosher in order for us to officiate.
Let them personalize the ceremony with participation by family and friends.
Don't dissuade them from having "Here Comes the Bride" played during her entrance.
Explain and translate more for the likely majority of non-Jewish or non-Jewishly educated guests.
Let Uncle Joe Cohen give them the "Priestly Blessing" under the *huppah*.
Leave the concertizing *hazzan* at home.
And offer them a free first year membership with High Holiday

tickets included in your synagogue. Welcome them to the congregation as newlyweds during the High Holiday services, and
involve them on innocuous committees where they are less likely
to encounter strife and get "turned off."
No Supreme Court Justice can compete with all that we can offer
them. What, you say, prestige? Poppycock!

BOB: There are a lot of reasons why people choose a particular officiant. Few couples care what's in the Hebrew part of the
Ketubah, and most will defer on the details of the liturgy to get
an officiant that they feel will give them a personal, meaningful
ceremony.

Given that I'm willing to compromise on a non-kosher meal
following, I find that the single biggest reason why I end up being unable to officiate at a wedding where I might have otherwise
been the rabbi of choice is Shabbat. The problem is that couples
want to get married on Saturday evening, and for half the year,
that is a "non-starter" until much later than any sane bride or
groom would want.

SUSAN: We all lose many Saturday night weddings. I don't
even bother to count anymore. Legitimate Reform Rabbis will
do them one hour or even earlier before Shabbat is over. I love
it when the bride says: but I want to be married while the sun
is setting!! I once asked the Reform rabbi innocently what date
he put on the *Ketubah*. Well, he said, we certainly can't put the
date of Shabbat, so we put the Sunday date and they do justify
it by pointing out that by the time the wedding is over they are
certainly well into twilight. OK.

But most of my weddings are either because they are getting
married in my *shul*, or because I converted them, so in those
cases they wait for after Shabbat no matter what. Plus many
of them are Latinos and Israelis so starting at 9:30 or 9:45 pm
doesn't even phase them. I have just this summer four Saturday
night weddings starting at 9:45 pm. I had one in June. I rushed
like a crazy person after a *Mincha-Ma'ariv* bar mitzvah. I got
there and found everyone still shmoozing at the cocktails and in
no rush to start. In fact we didn't start for another twenty-five

minutes! This flustered rabbi was exhausted. The party I heard went on to 3:00 am! It was an Israeli family and a Turkish family. I should have known better than to rush! I've been doing this so long and I still just don't get it.

While I have the floor, I want to raise a different *halakhic* question. Someone just asked me about a prohibition on visiting other graves after a funeral. I had never heard of this. If you're in from out of town for a funeral, doesn't it make sense to visit graves of other loved ones? I do remember a recent post about doing an unveiling after a funeral, and the person who posted the question wrote of walking around the block between the ceremonies, so there obviously is something to this question. Can someone please enlighten me?

SAM: Simply a personal observation. Whenever I perform a burial service in the cemetery where my in-laws are buried, I visit their graves and recite an *El Maleh Rahamim* before I leave. I feel it is an act of *kavod* I owe them. I would classify any such prohibition if visiting other graves, which I understand IS a custom, as a "*minhag shtut*" [nonsense custom] that we should categorically reject.

DON: I disagree. The ethics behind the *minhag* is that the mitzvah of attending a *levayah* and a *kevuurah* is one of the greatest of *gemilut hasadim* because the deceased cannot repay us and we have no ulterior motive. To use the funeral as an opportunity to visit my own relatives is an ulterior motive and detracts from the selflessness of the mitzvah. It is easy to simply drive, or walk, out of the cemetery and then back in, which is what I do and what I counsel. It is a legal fiction that reinforces focus on the importance of attending a funeral. No mere *shtut*.

There is a *minhag*, a custom, to not visit any other grave when you have gone to the cemetery specifically for a burial. The idea here is to not use a sad event like a burial as a convenience to fulfill one's obligations to visit others. Trips to the cemetery, therefore, need to be dedicated. When we go for burial, it is for burial alone. When we go for a visit, and this would include an unveiling – an unveiling, however popular, has very little foundation in Jewish tradition – we can visit as many loved ones who have passed on as necessary.

Having stated the *minhag*, let me tell you of my *kulot* [lax rulings] on the matter. The Jewish community no longer lives within a radius of fifty miles from the cemetery. When someone from out of town is in for a funeral and wishes to visit the graves of loved ones, I think it is wrong to prevent them from so doing on the basis of this *minhag* alone. If the visitor is a mourner and at the cemetery for burial, I would definitely discourage any additional visits to other graves. If the people who attend the visit are not mourners, but who live within a reasonable radius of the cemetery, I would also discourage the visit. But when someone is not a mourner, even if he or she is at the cemetery for a burial, and this person lives a distance that would prevent routine visits to the cemetery, I would be hard-pressed to deny them such a visit.

I hope this helps and I hope that you will be invited to many more *b'nai-mitzvah* and weddings, than funerals.

SAM: OK. *Eilu va-Eilu.* As the Talmud says, "Both this opinion and the opposite opinion are the words of the living God." I understand your point. I think we sometimes go out of our way to physically demonstrate a spiritual idea, when there is a simpler solution. To me, it would be more cogent to say – to myself, perhaps – I am here for *Ploni's* sake, but I acknowledge that there are other family members buried here, too, and, while I am here primarily to honor *Ploni*, I also will pay respects to the others. Extending that, I have been asked by congregants attending the funeral of a friend to say an *El Maleh Rahamim* for their own relatives who are buried there AFTER the rites for *Ploni*. Since many are elderly and don't travel much, I readily accede to their wishes, so they may honor their deceased as well. I see no conflict or any diminution of respect to the one who is being buried. I see no conflict of interest or lack of respect. There is no claim to exclusivity of attention for the most recent deceased once the current funeral and burial service for him or her has been completed.

There have been times when after a funeral, I have said prayers

at the graves of other congregants who are buried at the cemetery and who no longer have relatives living in the community.

One can argue as to whether it is *minhag shtut* or *kevod ha-
most-recent-met*, but as to a hierarchy of values, I put *kevod
kulam*, honoring all of them, on a par, without preference or priority, once the present service is concluded.

DON: Well, a reason to rely on Ashkenazi rather than Sephardi
custom might be if one is Ashkenazi. But reflecting more on why
I am reacting so conservatively here, I hear my colleagues speak
of when the elderly at a funeral are in from out of town and want
to see their relations. That is common sense to respect that. But
my experience, having served in the densely Jewish New York-
New Jersey area for some years in my career, is that most often
it is people attending a funeral and want to then see their other
relations there at the cemetery, when they in fact *do* live maybe
an hour away and could visit their family graves on *yahrzeits* or
in Elul, but don't. By my teaching the *minhag* of not doing so, it
is really for *kavod* of those deceased, to teach them the mitzvah
of visiting graves once a year, rather than only when already in
the cemetery. It is just as much then to teach that, as to give
kavod to the most recent *met* being buried.

SUSAN: This approach sounds most reasonable. We already
have too many "legal fictions" for my taste, in my humble opinion.

Anyway, here's another "death-related" question. Do any
of your congregations have the practice of putting up *yahrzeit*
plaques, or, in our case, adding names to the electronic display,
for non-Jewish relatives of congregants? What about for non-
Jews who are NOT relatives of congregants?

The question was broached here. We have our perspective,
but it's helpful to know what's happening in other parts of the
community.

SAM: I'm all for it. We have some *yahrzeit* plaques for non-Jewish relatives. If folks want to honor their loved one's memories by
contributing to the *shul*, I think it's great. We have a large plaque
honoring the memory of a beloved non-Jewish custodian. My

synagogue also has a *yahrzeit* plaque for JFK. His family did not pay for it. . . .

BOB: In my last congregation we had plaques with the names of non-Jewish spouses, something that I initiated. In the *shul* where I used to *daven* on weekdays, on the large *yahrzeit* board in the room where they *daven* there are the names of two non-Jews. These two plaques memorialize righteous gentiles who saved Jews during the *Shoah*. They also include English – the only plaques that do – and obviously they are not related to anyone from the *shul*. I also recall seeing a plaque in a *shul* in Philadelphia, commemorating the victims of 9/11.

I have a recollection that when I was in my first pulpit, there was some discussion about adding a plaque honoring Martin Luther King, Jr., on our memorial board! I'm not sure who else we had there.

But if we are both Americans, and Jews, I personally have no objection! Dual loyalties are not in any way a problem for me!

Of course, the previous does not in any way apply to the Brooklyn Dodgers. That loyalty did NOT transfer to the Los Angeles Dodgers.

SAM: Today's Washington Post had a picture of a funeral of one of the IDF soldiers. There was a large mound of flowers.

Any comments? Seems to be at variance with the general Jewish practice. Mind you, while I have never recommended that people send a floral tribute, it seems inoffensive and is clearly well intended. If it brings comfort, how can we reasonably object?

DON: My friends in Israel tell me that in Israel, it is customary to lay wreaths and place flowers on graves. Laying wreaths is also part of the official protocol at state and IDF funerals.

SAM: And I have no problem with that.

The usual justification is *"hukkat goyim"* ["You shall not follow the ways of the nations" – Deuteronomy 18:9]. Ok. So is wearing a tie to a funeral or using a black hearse. There can be no end to this and, in the final analysis, it all seems pretty arbitrary.

One might argue that the money can go to a charity. Yes, but sending flowers doesn't preclude *tzedakah*. As I say, I've never encouraged it, but I would never discourage it either.

SUSAN: Fact is, we had the custom first. In Talmudic times, they used to put fragrant flowers, leaves, and herbs on the graves – likely to counter the putrefying effect of the hot Mediterranean sun. Giving *tzedakah* in memory of the deceased was a later development. We stopped using flowers, wreaths, branches, and herbs at funerals when the non-Jews started using them extensively, and expensively. In Israel, flowers ARE used at funerals, and increasingly, also here in the U.S.

Families have requested permission to place roses on the coffin or into the grave after the coffin is lowered, and some Israel earth is sprinkled. I have not objected at all. I do think huge displays of costly flowers would have upset our sages who sought dignity, equality and simplicity – *takhrikhim*, a plain pine casket, and no flowers – or even overly flowery eulogies. Jewish burial practices counter the tendency for the well-to-do to try to out-do one another even in death.

Given what is going on these days with *b'nai-mitzvah* bashes and lavish destination weddings, I can see their point!

Flowers are beautiful, fragrant, and highly perishable – as quoted in Isaiah 40:6 and Psalms 103:15, "We are like flowers or grass that flourish for a day and wither and are gone." Therefore, they serve as an appropriate symbol of life's beauty and transience at a funeral. We should encourage a modest use of florals at funerals. Together with sprinkling soil from Eretz Yisrael, and washing hands when leaving the cemetery, they can be another symbolic element testifying to the brevity of beauty and the fragility and mortality of all that lives.

BOB: Here's an interesting question inquiring minds want to know. I am officiating at a wedding and the bride wants to be identified as the daughter of both her birth parents and her step father, who basically raised her. I am really asking about the inclusion of the word "and." Would I add the *vav* to the second and third name or only the third name? So would it be *Plonit bat Ploni v'plonit v'ploni* or simply *plonit bat ploni, plonit v'ploni*?

DON: No bride can possibly have three parents. If the bride wants to honor her adoptive parent, she has to find some other way. Naming a person as *"bat"* of three different people, whether written with one *vav* or two *vavs*, will only make the Jewish document an object of ridicule.

SAM: I would find another way. If a *ketubah* shows a woman has two fathers, some rabbi might conclude that she is a *mamzeret*, and thus invalidate the marriage, and declare any offspring from her as *mamzerim*. Especially a danger if she or anyone born to her may have wedding dealings with the Israeli state rabbinate.

And let me raise another issue. For those fortunate enough to own things like the Bar Ilan or other computer searchable sources, would you be kind enough to look up citations that I can use to bolster the argument against using G-d [G-dash-d]? Or arguments to the contrary, for that matter, so as to be prepared to encounter them?

SUSAN: See: "The Names of God" in J. David Bleich, *Contemporary Halakhik Problems*, 1977, and sources cited there. You will note that throughout the article, Bleich, consistent with his view, writes "God" and not "G-d" or *Hash-m*."

I would also note that it strikes me as logically required that if we accept that the word "God" (a mere human convention) is a name of God that must be written "G-d," then now that "G-d" is a commonly recognizable cognomen of God, it is due equal respect. Therefore, now one should write "G–." Of course, gradually "G–" will become a name commonly used, recognizable name of God. We will then have to write "–." Ultimately we will have no logical choice but to write "." But that creates a very special problem. If, in order to avoid writing God's name, we will have no logical choice but to leave a blank space, then the blank space will become a name of God. Every blank piece of paper will then have to be disposed of in a *genizah*, since a blank page would infinitely reproduce the name of God.

I happen to have a document with me that will shed some light on this issue. It's one of the volumes of the CJLS Summary Index Conservative ["Committee of Jewish Law and Standards"].

> The 1993 CJLS Summary Index lists the following:
> NAME OF GOD
> 1. The Tetragrammaton, or other *sheimot* listed in *Shulhan Arukh, Yoreh Deah* 276:9 and in the Rambam, *Y'sodei ha-Torah* 6:2 and 3, should not be printed on synagogue stationary or other items likely to be thrown out, such as a calendar. (*Teshuvah* by Morris Shapiro, Proceeding of the CJLS, 1980–85, pp. 261–2, 082388)
> 2. The use of "God" is encouraged, while "G-d" is discouraged. (*Teshuvah* by Kassel Abelson, 1993, 051993 B)

BOB: I have to admit that I suffer from this form of pietism. Left over from my childhood. I actually use it in my teaching of twelve grade students.

My favorite absurdity was finding a bencher where the Hebrew had all the names of the Creator but in English had L-rd and my all time favourite A-mighty. It was as if English had become *S'fat HaKodesh* ["the holy tongue"]. What next?

DON: The sacred name is the Tetragrammaton [YHVH, with Hebrew letters], which should not be written on things to be discarded. But it seems to me that we elevate the word "God" to the same level as YHVH when we write G-d, and that we should not do because it defeats the whole purpose of keeping YHVH singular and most holy.

SAM: Don, I think you have hit the nail on the head! There is no end to superfluous super-pious *shtut* [nonsense]. Since we are created בצלם אלהים, perhaps we should write "-Dam" instead of Adam. Closer to the truth.

SUSAN: I've avoided entering this particular thread, since I've participated in such discussions in the past. I happen to be in the camp that feels (a) that "G-d," "Gd," "G*d," etc., are unnecessary *halakhically*, (b) that it is "unctuous neo-*frumkeit*," and (c) that to attribute such sanctity to non-Hebrew names constitutes *avodah zarah* [idolatry]. Oops, I just entered into the debate.

I'm wondering if anyone can provide a classical *halakhic* source that dismisses this practice as the purview of *amoratzim* [ignoramouses] and others.

I think it's also commonly assumed, in Conservative circles that transliterations, as well as translations, do not have to be altered in their spellings. Thus, for example, no reason to substitute *A-donai* for *Adonai* or *E-lohim* for *Elohim*.

But do we have broad consensus on Hebrew spelling, namely the ones we copy-and-paste for handouts? Should we add hyphens or change "*heh*" to "*kuf*" in all appearances of "*Elohim*," other than "*elohim aherim*"? I'm used to substituting "*he-h*"-apostrophe for the *shem ha-m'forash* [Tetragrammaton, YHVH] in Hebrew. But what about the two *yuds*, which used to be so prevalent in *siddurim*?

DON: And speaking of "no end to superfluous *shtut*," that reminds me of a joke.

A *frum* boy and girl whose parents have arranged a match are going to meet for the first time. Each has been instructed by his or her father that the other is a good and pious person, and that he or she should impress her or him with his or her own piety. With chaperones close at hand, the couple is ushered into the room. "I'm Aviga-kel," she says demurely. "It's nice to meet you," he replies. "My name is Kelikaku . . ."

BOB: Our *shul*, an egalitarian synagogue, has the reputation of being Orthodox in Conservative clothing. Maybe it's the full Torah reading. But it hit me this past Shabbat, with a sanctuary packed with guests of a bar mitzvah family that we are handing out a brochure that says G-d eight times. I put a stop to that immediately. It cannot be helping our public image. A neighboring colleague, who is a former Christian, told me that as a general rule – there are of course exceptions – Christian guests at Jewish services tend to interpret "G-d" as an indication of deeper religiosity. Since Jews and Christians alike will probably encounter both spellings over time, I suggest you add a short paragraph in your brochure that notes the variation in spelling. Maybe something along these lines: [Note: Jewish opinion differs on whether to refer to the Lord as "God" or "G-d." We at [organization name] prefer "God" [or "G-d"], but both terms honor our Creator.] Another general rule about Christians in attendance at Jewish events: they are immensely curious about what we do and why we do it. The more explanation you can offer without burdening the Jews in the audience, the better.

SUSAN: I forget who told me, but some wise person once told me that "God isn't God's name; God is God's *job*."

With all this brouhaha, about God to G-d, I suggest we keep in mind the words of Gregory Bateson, which I have found incredibly useful!

1. The meaning of one's communication is in the outcome you get irrespective of your intentions!

2. The meaning of any communication is determined by the recipient of the communication!

Please note this applies to English Speakers!

Also, please note that God, or G-d, is also known as "Yahweh," "Jehovah," "Adonai," Hashem etc., etc., etc. We are, I suppose, one of the world's most obsessive people! We love minutiae! It's our strength and our weakness!!

Nuf said; At least for now, after all I am Jewish! Whatever that means!

SAM: I think Susan is right, "nuf said" on this question. Here's another one: A congregant's six-year-old grandchild tragically died in a swimming accident. The father of the child is Jewish, the mother is Methodist. The Methodist minister is performing the service at a non-Jewish funeral home in our town. I have been asked to do the internment service.

My policy had been to do *Kri'ah* with the family and then lead the *shivah minyan*. My *shul* executive board supports me. I will do a service in this case if it is non-sectarian. I have been told that the Methodist is staunch in his Methodist ways. So it is going to be very religious.

I am getting some resistance in other circles. Any advice?

DON: Since the father is Jewish, and the mother is non-Jewish, unless the child was converted, the child is not Jewish. I'd say it's best to let the minister do the service, and you just add a eulogy or words of encouragement for your congregants. The child isn't Jewish and therefore shouldn't have a Jewish funeral.

BOB: *Kevurah* [burial service] is a separate service at a separate location, if I am not mistaken, assuming it is not a graveside service, which, from your description, it seems not to be, and therefore can be treated as a separate issue.

Even if the cemetery is non-sectarian, in my experience I have asked the funeral director to place a bag of Israeli earth under the head, or pillow, of the deceased inside the casket. At least it provides some "consecrated ground" with which he can be buried. We do this a lot with veterans who are buried in VA cemeteries.

I would conduct a proper Jewish *kevurah* at the gravesite. If the Methodist wants to add, "Dust to dust, ashes to ashes," that's OK by me, as we have essentially the same formula. Conclude with *Kaddish*, and offer *shivah* services at the home.

This should in no way compromise our traditions. The funeral service at the chapel is less significant than the *kevurah*, which is *kavod ha'met* [honoring the deceased], and which will be in accordance with Jewish practice.

SAM: Thank you for your responses to the question. It is most difficult for the family who somehow wasn't watching as their child walked into the lake and drowned. Clearly the child is not Jewish, and the goal was to be of assistance to the Jewish grandfather.

The end result is that our community will be there for the grandfather, without participating in the service.

Anyway, let's call it a day, and resume next week. Everyone have a great week!

Week 15

࿓

SAM: Hi everyone! Nice to be together again. I'll start with an interesting question.

Our Hebrew School is now a Shabbat school.

Does anyone have any written guidelines, rules, etc., that I can use to create a policy manual for our educators, who are a bit nervous about the whole "Shabbat" aspect of the school, and the impact it will have on their teaching strategies?

BOB: I have always permitted the use of chalk even on Shabbat, when teachers felt it was needed. Why? Because I consider that writing with chalk is not permanent *k'tivah* [writing].

As far as students taking notes, no. Teachers were asked to prepare and have the office preprint "handouts" – song sheets, summaries or notes of material covered, to take or send home.

Crafts were always a problem, but not in the lower grades. Kids under age thirteen are not yet responsible for ritual infractions, but the value of this decision has to be weighed against community feeling and educational value of teaching about Shabbat as a "different" day.

Snacks are provided for all students to ensure *kashrut*, and that nobody would be without, because of any parental qualms about "carrying," not that I was ever made aware of any such concerns.

Israeli teachers became more conscious of Shabbat, and, while a few grumbled, most rose to the challenge of Shabbat instruction graciously. How else to put it? Do it, or 'bye. An important component we tried to introduce with some limited success was family education, involving parents, students, and even siblings learning together, including puppet shows, stories, songs and prayer melodies, for about twenty-five minutes before the end of the session. Then everyone was invited – OK, expected – to join the main congregation for the closing prayers – *Eyn Ke-holhaynu, Aleinu, Adon Olam* – and following that, the whole congregation had *kiddush* together.

Not all parents participated, but those who did spoke glowingly of this to others and influenced more to try it. I know it's a bit unconventional, but it seemed to work well.

DON: Knowing that this was coming up, I did some research. According to all *poskim*, chalk is considered *ktav ha-mit-kayem* [writing that is permanent], unlike someone who writes with fruit juice. See for example, Tosafot on Shabbat 115b s.v. *aval*, and *hidushei harashba* there s.v. *ha d'amrinan*. According to the *halakhah*, *ktav she'eno mit-kayem* [writing that does not last] is something that is not going to last very long if left on it's own, such as fruit juice on a table top. It will get erased even without human intervention within a short amount of time. But if someone writes with erasable ink, pencil, or chalk on a chalkboard, since that writing is going to stay put forever until someone erases it, it is considered *mit-kayem* and is forbidden. See also *Yesodei Yeshurun* on the 39 *melakhot*, page 59.

SAM: Who didn't know that you would disagree, Don! I guess we each have our own opinions – and that's the way it should be.

BOB: Here's a question from a colleague in another city. I'd like to give him my personal advice, but would also like to run this by you folks here before I do. Here's what he emailed me:

My president, a wonderful man, has asked the rabbis of our congregation to call every adult member and wish him or her a happy birthday. This is no small undertaking: It will mean each of us will be responsible for hundreds of calls a year. He believes this is a wonderful way to "touch" our members and to speak with them one-on-one every year.

I'm concerned that this is an onerous obligation to accept on top of all our other responsibilities, but I do not want to share my concern with him until I have at least consulted with any colleagues who have attempted such an endeavor in their own communities.

Any words of encouragement or discouragement to share will be most welcome!

SAM: This is a creative, and successful idea. I think it's impossible, unless the president wants him to stop visiting hospitals, and teaching all classes, and probably a few other things.

Instead of telling him what *hutzpah* he has – which he does – I'd counter the offer with doing the whole congregation every five years. Even that is no small chore. If he does, I think he should tell those he calls that they can expect a birthday call every five years, in alphabetical order, so others don't hear and complain that "the rabbi calls his friends," or "the wealthy," etc.

Presidents have a way of creating work for the rabbi with no concept of what is involved. I'd be positive, and tell him what a wonderful idea it is, and how grateful you are that he cared enough to suggest it. However, this would take X hours each week, and since I already am working seventy to eighty hours a week, I'd be forced to eliminate. . . .

Hope this is helpful.

DON: I call all congregants once a year, but not on their birthdays. That would almost double the number of calls, assuming couples and families, and I may not be available to call on the week of their birthday, let alone on the birthday itself. We have times when we might be very busy, or on vacation, etc.

My experience is that 70–80% of the time I get voicemail, but very often I get notes of appreciation.

It's a nice touch, but I'm not sure if it's really manageable in a synagogue as large as your friend's.

Maybe a general letter sent out for everyone's birthday could be done on mailmerge and sent out weekly. Just a thought.

SUSAN: I would employ the "Yitro Strategy." I'd tell him to suggest, gently, that this is a WONDERFUL idea, but that Board members, Officers, Sisterhood and the Men's Club should be the ones to divide up and share this task among themselves, funneling any information garnered during these "touch" calls that might indicate rabbinic follow up to the rabbi.

Perhaps this might not sit well with the powers-that-be, but it has "biblical" precedent, community approbation and Divine approval. If it was good enough for Moses. . . .

If it backfires, tell him to pack his books first. [Laughter].

SAM: The idea of calling congregants regularly, on their birthdays or otherwise, is a very good one, and the truth is that a call from the rabbi means more than a call from an "ordinary" person. However, I don't see how the idea, as presented, is doable. As already expressed, lay leaders are often very good at thinking of new things for the rabbi to do, without having any idea of the real flow of rabbinic work. What I do is to send e-birthday-cards to most members of the congregation, with paper cards to people over eighty, or people with decade birthdays.

He can proceed with all due haste if he is anxious to open a Pandora's box. After birthday calls, there will be "suggestions" for anniversary and other simcha calls.

Perhaps, in the same way the synagogue has satchels of prayer books to lend to families who have *shivah minyanim* at home, the congregation should buy laptop computers with wireless hot-spots to lend out to people who are hospitalized so that the rabbi can make video hospital calls to them on Skype or Google Plus. This would be more personal than just a phone call and actually less intrusive than randomly dropping in on a hospital patient at an "inconvenient" time. Surely no board that permits video-taping of Shabbat bar or bat mitzvahs can oppose this.

Alternatively, do the math and share it with the President. Assuming you have a congregation of two hundred and fifty families, and each family unit consists of three people on average. Is the rabbi also going to make birthday calls to the children, say, under age eighteen? If yes, increase the number to, say, four, and adjust the math. That's seven hundred and fifty calls a year. Removing weekends, Jewish and civil holidays, vacations, etc. from the calling schedule, this leaves roughly two hundred days a year to make seven hundred and fifty birthday calls, which is roughly 3.5 calls per call day. Assuming that each call takes an average of five minutes, between dialing and briefly talking to the birthday party, or leaving a message, that's nearly twenty minutes per call day that you will be spending making these calls. And that's if you don't need to call back those who you missed but for whom you left a voice mail. These are fairly ideal hypothetical conditions, and the time involvement would expand in direct relation to the size of your congregation.

Perhaps in a smaller congregation the rabbi can find the time to work this into a schedule, although in one small congregation I served, I always found things that needed doing. In a larger congregation it may be possible to integrate this into the rabbi's work schedule, but only at the expense of something else. Ask the President from which rabbinic activities the board would be prepared to excuse the rabbi's involvement, in exchange for making these calls. My experience was, that after the board thrashed, sliced and diced this issue over a couple of board meetings, the idea was given an honorable burial and life continued as before.

And keep in mind the *klal gadol* [great rule]: No board member is EVER going to say to us, "Rabbi, you're working too hard, so ease up. . . ." This is something that we have to deal with FOR ourselves, and BY ourselves.

DON: Though it was my idea, I have almost come to regret it – sending a hand written birthday and anniversary card to every member. In the beginning, I loved it because I got myself a bunch of colorful pens and I could spend a little time "coloring." People really liked it, except the people who were unhappily married and received a "*mazal tov*" card. It is now overwhelming, even if I only do a week's amount at one time. My assistant is trying to convince me that she could do the basics, and I could add on something personal and that might make it easier, but I still think that if we're going to send these little cards, it doesn't look good to have someone else do the writing for me. A phone call will take so much longer than a card. All in all, I would tell the president that while it is a super idea, others have found that it's completely impractical and takes time away from teaching, *bikkur holim*, etc.

BOB: Thanks to all for your ideas. I'll pass them on to my colleague.

SAM: Here's a question for us to chew on. It's one that will present itself to colleagues more and more these days. I received the following letter, and am not sure of the options available to us from our *halakhic* scholars – and do not feel competent to answer this on my own, without outside guidance.

> Greetings,
> My wife and I are both Jewish and we are expecting a baby boy in January. We are using a non-Jewish surrogate and a Jewish egg donor.
> Is the child born Jewish or does he need to be converted? If conversion is necessary, must the conversion occur before the *bris*? If yes, where does the conversion take place, in the home or at the synagogue? If yes, does the *bris* still need to be done on the eighth day of life or can it be done on a different day?
> Thanks for any guidance.

SUSAN: Good questions. This is a learning moment.

It is a sort of "proof" that Judaism is not racist. A baby who is one hundred percent genetically Jewish but born to a non-Jewish surrogate needs *giyyur*.

A baby who comes from genetic material from two non-Jews, but is born to a Jewish surrogate mother does not require *giyyur*.

The *bris* would be part of the conversion. *Bris milah* must precede *tevilah* and should be *l'shem giyyur* [for the sake of conversion]. Yes, there are opinions that if *b'diavad* [after the fact] it did not precede *tevilah*, it's ok. Since the baby is not Jewish until the *tevilah*, there is no need to have the *bris* on the eighth day. If the eigth day is Shabbat you may not have the *bris* on Shabbat. It can be held before, on, or after the eigth day.

Many *poskim* prefer a non-eigth day *bris*, but the Rabbinical Assembly Law Committee is fine with it being on the eighth day in such a circumstance.

The conversion, since this is a *katan* [minor] is *al da'at Beit Din* [by authority of the Jewish court].

SAM: Thanks so much, Susan. Exactly what I needed to know!

BOB: Here's an issue that will be interesting to all of us. A friend of mine, who does not favor instrumental music at Shabbat services, recently suggested to me that all Conservative synagogues are destined to use musical instruments at Shabbat services. He views it from the perspective of a domino theory: since Sinai Temple in L.A. and Bnai Jeshurun, admittedly no longer a USCJ member, in N.Y., have had such great success at reaching out to the "unchurched" younger generation with Shabbat services that utilize musical instruments, and since quite a few of our congregations have followed their lead, eventually any Conservative congregation that does not want to be branded Orthodox or obscurantist will have no choice but to conform.

I pointed out that many congregations will permit musical instruments for *Kabbalat Shabbat*, but then put them away before *Barkhu*. He pointed out, quite correctly, that nobody seems to be chastising folks for taking their instruments home, in the absence of an *Eiruv*, on Friday night. I had to acknowledge that in many communities our movement has become gun-shy about any mention of *Hotza'ah Me'rshut Li'rshut* ["transporting something from one area to another"], even though this is one of the thirty-nine prohibited Shabbat labors, and I have heard nothing resembling a *halakhic* justification for this.

Luckily, for me, our conversation was interrupted. I want to capitalize on this interruption to think out some of the issues. Since I still nurse the hope that this group is a safe place to "think out loud," I would like to invite you, my revered colleagues, to help me with my thought process. I realize that I am a student, and a devotee, of our traditional liturgy, and that many Jews in the pews lack the historical and literary knowledge, as well as the Hebrew fluency, to be able to follow our liturgy in its more traditional forms. In some communities, it appears that rabbis have given up on getting through to any significant number of congregants – to say nothing of not-yet-congregants – via the use of traditional liturgical forms. Music is used as a substitute, sometimes music to listen to passively, and sometimes music with which to sing along – a more active involvement of worshipers, to be sure.

Yet the *halakhic* dimension remains unaddressed – a troubling trend. I recall a footnote from Rabbi Morris Adler, reprinted in Rabbi Mordecai Waxman's 1958 volume, *Tradition and Change,* page 370, in which the reader is directed to a *Tosafot* in *Beitzah* 30a. The issue in the *Gemara* is the use of musical instruments, which by the age of the Tosafists had become so complex that most people would be clueless about how to fix an instrument on Shabbat.

However, I would counter that most instrumentalists today DO have a working knowledge of their instruments and how to fix them, and it would be awkward NOT to fix an instrument that malfunctions on Shabbat, if the congregation is waiting to hear the music. One can well picture the situation: "please bear with us while we resolve some technical difficulties." It is much harder to imagine hearing the statement: "The instrumental portion of our service will be omitted due to the need to fix/adjust/repair one of our instruments, something that we do not do on the Sabbath."

I am intentionally not addressing the question of electricity that is required by some musical instruments, since there is a well-founded school of thought that permits the use of electricity on Shabbat. See, for example, Rabbi Arthur Neulander's material, which is reprinted in Waxman's book on pp. 401–407. Besides, there are some musical instruments that do not require any electric at all.

My understanding of the status of Shabbat instrumental music within our movement is that some congregations utilize it freely – and feel little or no need to justify it *halakhically*, while some prohibit it altogether. Those congregations that seek to chart a middle course resort to one of the following sets of restrictions:

a. Music within religious services forms a special *halakhic* category. I would welcome a cogent source or rationale for this, beyond "Judaism as a Civilization."

b. Limit the use of instruments to before *Barkhu* on Friday night, and look the other way regarding where the instruments spend the Shabbat, as well as any possible *muktzeh* issues.

Anyone who has read more than a dozen congregational placement questionnaires in the last couple of years has probably noticed that whatever the *halakhic* thinking may be, among rabbis, regarding the use of musical instruments on Friday night, the subtleties have not been communicated to our laypeople, or else our laypeople have simply failed to understand them, which strains credibility because, in my experience, many laypeople are highly intelligent.

Eager to hear your perspectives.

SUSAN: I'll take a stab. I suspect your friend may be mostly correct that in the long run we'll see this more and more. I assume that not everyone will accept it though. I remember that when I was a child, people expected to see instruments. Alas, he is correct that I've been labeled Orthodox for worrying about carrying and *eruv* and stuff like this.

I'm generally not in favor of instruments, not for *halakhic* reasons but for aesthetic ones. I have used that Tosafot over the years. I've also mostly been successful at having the instruments kept at the *shul* either on the *bimah* or locked in my office or a classroom or taken to the car before Shabbat officially starts. I hope they use the garage to avoid carrying, but at this point it isn't my worry. One of my most recalcitrant guitar players was a JTS student who was back visiting, and if memory serves me, either played just once or at most twice. One of my more liberal members turned out to be easy, because he just left it for Sunday school. Another was a Reform congregant who'd become quite fascinated by the liturgy and *davening*, and was getting more and more away from it, and now doesn't play at all, these days using the excuse that one can't lead services and play – usually organ or piano.

My counter query is why *Barkhu*? Don't we accept Shabbat at *Mizmor Shir L'Yom Ha-Shabbat*?

One of my congregations was a Conservative-Reform merger long before I came and music on Friday night was expressly allowed, at least as far as organ and piano. Guitar became a huge issue. I pointed out the Tosafot using guitar as the prime example of the kind of instrument they were not allowing due to the issue of anyone fixing. Sorry to disagree, but organ, piano, and most electric instruments are not so easy to fix, and often require tools, the electric guitar again being an exception at least so far as strings go. I realized that the Reform members were never going to be satisfied without a win on this one. I decided to go for preserving the minimum and letting go of the protective fence. Since *halakhah* had already glazed their eyes, I presented the scenario to them about enjoying the service and hearing a twang. Then stopping the service and waiting for the string to be fixed and the tuning. And then said that I didn't know about them, but it would destroy the mood to go through all of this. They agreed and the policy became no fixed instruments. The player either must continue playing without fixing the instrument, or have a back-up already prepared, or we continued the service without the instrument. It passed unanimously.

Odd thing was, once it passed, it wasn't used much, not in the least because the people who played – all congregants – discovered that it cut into their praying, so they didn't want to do it often. What does this say about the rabbi and *hazzan* who *daven*?

Also of interest, a scholar-in-residence asked to use instruments or tape for part of a lecture on Jewish music, and readily understood that we could very well say no, and the person was still prepared to do the presentation without either. I finally said I might be able to live with it. In point of fact I wasn't going to be there that Shabbat, but I was not going to be the one to say that we made an exception and to try to explain it to the bar mitzvah family who then would want music at the party in the *shul* on Shabbat. When I put it this way, even the Reform committee members agreed that they did not want to explain the distinctions to the family and no exception was made. It was interesting to know that even the most Reform members of the committee by this time understood the issues, and we didn't discuss the basic issues at all, just the issues regarding the exception or modification – not allowing for a party was accepted by all and not discussed, only whether we wanted a one time exception or one for educational purposes.

As to *muktzeh* [forbidden to touch because of Shabbat], once you allow the instrument for the service, doesn't *muktzeh* no longer apply for the service itself? As to getting the instrument off the *bimah*, it is in the way and we can move *muktzeh* things if they are in the way, and I would argue by extension we also need to get them out of the way of people who would otherwise handle them, hence my office. Small *shul*, so it was close. The *teshuvah* itself already allows for the service as opposed to instruments for other things, not in the least because it was allowed in the Temple, on the assumption that the Levites knew what they were doing. For those who didn't mind putting down the guitar and leaving it on the *bimah*, it always seemed to be in the way at some point over Shabbat no matter where we put it.

Of course we rely on Tosafot and not Rambam, for whom clapping is not allowed and even voice may only be allowed for praying.

What other *halakhic* issues am I missing? I'm ignoring the views of one of my teachers, Philip Sigal, *z"l*, with whom I entered into many philosophical debates but tried to stay clear of actual *halakhic* ones, and he was both my first Talmud and *halakhah* teacher, both in high school.

And of course there is the issue of *nusah*, but this is for another time.

SAM: The "sensitive" use of musical instruments on Shabbatot and Yom Tov to "enhance enjoyment of and participation in the worship service" by congregants can be compared and contrasted with the use of a choir, especially one including non-Jews.

I'm not going into that now, but of the two, if given a choice, I would opt for and give a blessing to number one over number two.

Our services are inspiring to those who are attuned to *Tefillah b'Ivrit*, but boring and sterile to non-*daveners*. To make them more participatory and "entertaining" – OK – let's just say "engaging" to cover both – singing, clapping, dancing, and listening to prayer texts accompanied with musical instruments can be a stimulating factor. Hasidim were on the right track here where *hislahavus* and la-la-la-ing trumped chanting and reciting actual words of *tefillah*. One only had to recall Shlomo Carlebach's *z"l* solution to the abysmal lack of knowledge among members of his "audience," and how he successfully dealt with that issue to realize the power of spirit over substance, and the possibility of melding the two, as he did, by including a brief interpretation or stories in the midst of a rousing round of stomping, clapping and la-la-la-ing. He got everyone participating, and eventually associating the words and their meaning in the minds and hearts of his audiences.

Of course, this can be done without instrumental accompaniment on Shabbatot et al, but given the contemporary climate, the instruments are expected and can play a part in "professionalizing" as well as the opposite, "personalizing" the prayer experience.

Halakhic problems?

Come on. Get real. How many caterers and congregation officials do their "businesses" on Shabbat, within the *Shul*?

How do most people get to *shul*?

For how many is *Adon Olam* the same as *Havdalah*?

Of course, we know that more and more are concerned with the *Shamor* than the *Zakhor* aspects of Shabbat observance, but we are fighting a losing battle in which we, *Hevreh*, are the biggest losers, whether we lose our pulpits or we lose our congregants. A spirited, engaging and fun Shabbat is far better than none, and without as much as a *minyan*, our services are greatly diminished rather than enhanced. Sometimes we just need to "let go" a little, whether based on historical and *halakhic* precedents or not, and make Judaism "rock" for our congregants, while they still are.

We can always *daven* at home by ourselves, but they can't – and won't.

BOB: I think the *halakhic* issues do come, at best, secondary to our congregants. The primary concern, after "Rabbi, are you OK with this?" is what will keep the masses coming, and what might bring more of their friends and fellow congregants.

In my own personal case, playing guitar is something I enjoy and do well enough as an amateur and, after discussing the issue with Ritual/Worship Committees in three congregations, all three agreed to Friday night instrumental music, but not Shabbat morning. It was a compromise in all three congregations, respectful of a real or imagined Shabbat morning constituency with a different *halakhic* sense than the Friday night participants.

Meanwhile, alas, the CJLS [Comittee on Jewish Law and Standards of the Conservative movement] decided not to vote in favor of the *teshuvah* that had been presented to them some years ago, which I personally think was a mistake. I don't know exactly how that *teshuvah* read, but in 2005 Elliot Dorff sent me a copy of the *teshuvah* that he and Ellie Spitz were working on with the proviso that I express the opinions written within as not the opinion of the CJLS. When I taught Rabbi Joel Roth's article about redefining *Sh'vut* [abstention from work] prohibitions, sections from David Golinkin's volumes on CJLS opinions and excerpts from the Dorff-Spitz *teshuvah* in the winter-spring of 2005, before the committees and eventually the congregational board and full membership voted on whether we'd have musical instruments on Friday nights and Yom Tov evenings other than Yom Kippur.

Let me turn to another issue now. This past week, I had the pleasure of sitting on the *Bet Din* for the conversion of a lovely young lady. In her essay, she wrote that she totally supported Israel even though her conversion would not be recognized there. I thought that her premise is incorrect. I didn't say anything at the time, but I plan to speak to the sponsoring rabbi. Conservative and Reform conversions performed outside of Israel ARE recognized by the State of Israel. They are not recognized by the office of the Chief Rabbis, but that shouldn't be an issue in most cases. If this person has children, and her children want to get married by the Rabbanut, there could be a problem, but such a scenario is far in the future and uncertain. Who knows what the situation will be in twenty-plus years? Am I right?

DON: Yes, our conversions, and, I believe, those of Conservative rabbis – not sure about Reform – done in America and elsewhere are recognized in Israel by the Ministry of Interior. Such a person is eligible for citizenship under the Law of Return and will be registered as a Jew by the Ministry. The Rabbintate, however, will not recognize the conversion and will not conduct a marriage for such a person or her children.

BOB: *Hevreh*, I would like to open a new thread, which will probably evoke a strong reaction from all of us, the question of intermarriage – in the Conservative Movement. I invite Sam and Don to participate with their thoughts, should they wish, even though they are not part of the Conservative Movement. So here goes. . . .

I concluded my Rosh Hashanah sermon about Parenting with examples of behavior parents could model, and of how to convey that Jewish values are important to them. I wanted to conclude by saying that they can tell their children that they want them to marry someone who is Jewish. But I realized though that if I did that, then this would be the only line of a very rich sermon that people would remember and would be the one thing they would discuss.

So after saying, "When choosing a college, you can insist that it have a Jewish population. And, unless they are paying for their education, you have the right to insist that they go to Hillel, and take at least one course in Jewish studies," I then added the following paragraph:

> *"And finally, you can let them know it is important to you that they marry someone who will be committed to living a life that will ensure Jewish continuity, with whom they will be able to share the beauty of our traditions so that Judaism and the Jewish people will live on in them and through them."*

I sensed that when I started the line about marriage, there were those who were holding their breath.

After all, we all have people sitting in our *shuls* who may be married to someone who is not Jewish. We do not want them to feel uncomfortable or excluded. By the same token, however, I firmly believe we rabbis should take a stand and not shy away from speaking on this important matter and expressing the importance of marrying someone who is Jewish. So I found a way to say it without explicitly saying – marry a Jew.

By stating it the way I did, I was able to take a stand and say it without offending anyone. Everyone knew what I meant. There are Jews who do not care about living a Jewish life or Jewish continuity. By putting it this way, I was able to say something even more important than just marry a Jew. It had the additional impact that all who were there appreciated that I was obviously being sensitive to everyone.

I offer here in our public forum this phraseology and suggest you may feel free to use it as well.

SAM: For a number of years I have talked about "creating a Jewish home" rather than "marrying someone Jewish," as a way to speak about the ultimate goal of "marrying someone Jewish." Using this language makes it easier to talk about how marrying someone Jewish actually makes creating a Jewish home easier – supported by the research data AND the non-Jewish parents in my *shul* . . . they are the first ones to say this. The millennials I speak with view the dictum of marrying someone Jewish as a racist comment . . . whereas speaking about a Jewish home deals with values. I know many endogamous Jewish couples who do not have a Jewish home. By speaking of "creating a Jewish home" we actually articulate a more important goal. Keep up the important work.

SUSAN: I want to jump in to this conversation if only to make what I believe is an important distinction between intermarriage and patrilineal descent. The recognition of patrilineal descent – or "equilineality," as the British Reform movement has ingeniously begun calling it – is a movement-wide issue that demands one single response from the leadership and institutions of Conservative/Masorti Judaism. A situation in which some Conservative rabbis and synagogues began recognizing patrilineal descent, while others did not, would lead our movement into complete chaos. USY and Camp Ramah would struggle to provide clear standards of admission. We would even face the prospect of a child growing up in a Conservative synagogue and seeking to become a rabbi, only to be told at JTS or Ziegler that she is not actually Jewish. Clearly, for the sake of our movement, we must have one definitive answer on this question.

The situation for officiating at intermarriages is completely different. When the barrier comes down, and Conservative rabbis are permitted to officiate, life will continue largely as it is. Some rabbis will choose to officiate at these marriages. I imagine most will not. The children from these unions will not be less or more Jewish as a result of the rabbi's presence at the wedding. There will be no personal status issues as these couples move from one synagogue to another. We will need some sort of shared approach about the need or, more likely, the lack thereof for *gittin*, but otherwise there is nothing inherent in this issue that demands one unified standard. In fact, a demand for uniformity is likelier to tear our movement apart.

As is, RA rabbis have a wide variety of practices, both personal and professional. I don't allow non-*hekhshered* cheese in my synagogue kitchen, but I inherently trust the *kashrut* of a rabbi who does permit it. My community was an Orthodox synagogue for much longer than it has been Conservative, and the cheese issue has a deeper meaning than it might in other places, so I have tried to do what I believe is best for my particular community. I don't see much of an argument against taking the same approach to intermarriage. If there are Conservative rabbis who believe that the best thing for their community is for them to officiate at intermarriages, who are we to say otherwise?

The one thing this argument is not, is *halakhic*. Given the texts of our tradition, I could make an argument for intermarriage a lot more easily than any argument in favor of driving a car on Shabbat. And yet, the integrity of our *halakhic* system has survived the driving *teshuvah*. The slippery slope hasn't been so slippery after all. Conservative Judaism has not devolved into a free-for-all, or a second Reform movement. If anything, I would say that the boundaries of Conservative practice are more clearly defined than ever.

I am familiar with the argument that one movement standard

makes it easier for rabbis to say no to their congregants, since they can point to the ban rather than have the hard conversation about their personal rabbinic convictions. Similarly, some say that if the decision were up to individual rabbis, the communal pressure to violate our consciences on this issue would be too much to bear. To that I can only say that we're all adults and it isn't the RA's job to shield us from our congregants.

I realize that this is a deep-seated emotional issue for many of us, and it pains some of our colleagues to hear that we would even contemplate a change in this area. To me that is one of the hardest parts of this issue. It disturbs me to think that I have caused other rabbis emotional distress. At the same time, and without trying to offer too much pseudo-psychoanalysis, I see the ban on intermarriage as a symbolic placeholder among too many of us. We have turned it into a talisman, as though it were a firewall against assimilation and rejection. But no one who approaches a rabbi and asks us to officiate at their wedding is rejecting Judaism.

For most of us, our personal bans on performing intermarriages will suffice. We will all do what we believe is best for our communities and for the Jewish people as a whole. To paraphrase an argument from the gay marriage debate, if you don't want to perform an intermarriage then don't perform one. Regardless, our personal convictions should not act as a veto when our colleagues disagree.

SAM: Perhaps you are not aware of the matter, but in the Reform movement, performing intermarriages has become a litmus test in placement at many – not all – congregations, with the question being asked point blank during the interview, and rabbis who won't are excluded.

It is theoretically true that "we're all adults here," but congregants often don't act like adults when the rabbi says "no," because all sorts of internal dynamics get triggered, especially when the parents of a child with a non-Jewish fiancé feel ambivalence about the marriage and project their ambivalence, guilt, even shame, onto the rabbi and blame HIM, or HER, for not being "accepting" by doing the wedding.

So I must respectfully disagree: it is often precisely the movement's job to shield us from our congregants, in all sort of matters. In this case especially, that shield forms by making it a matter of communal standards rather than personal choice. That's why I feel so relieved that the Reform movement has come out for patrilineal, which makes my job a lot easier. Perhaps indeed the issue of intermarriage is a psychological talisman reflecting larger concerns.

In that case, we'd be exceedingly well-advised to proceed very, very carefully. Religious movements have undergone schism for less.

BOB: While I understand your concern here, I think Susan is correct in what she has to say. I understand that there will be problems for colleagues who don't want to officiate at intermarriages once we begin to do that, but the job of the RA will be to come up with creative ways to try and protect them when this becomes a reality, not to try to prevent what I believe, for better or worse, is inevitable. Preventing this, in my humble opinion, will only harm us in the end. How is it that we are given, as *mara d'atra,* the freedom to make all choices, but this? We can do away with *Musaf,* compromise on *kashrut,* not have services on the second day of *Yom tov* – heck we can even eat *tref* on Yom Kippur and still be in the RA – but not make the most basic decision on whether officiating at an intermarriage is best for our own communities or not. As you may recall, historically in the 1950s the setting up of a joint Bet Din with the Orthodox rabbinate on *gittin* [divorce] fell apart over the issue of our autonomy as rabbis.

I do not see how this differs from either the question of egalitarian participation of women or same sex marriage. Surely there were many colleagues who were not egalitarian at the time we began ordaining women, just as there are many colleagues today who will not officiate at a same sex marriage. Yet we somehow managed to walk that line, because in the end our communities simply demanded that of us. We can do so again.

SUSAN: You speak as if this is inevitable and cite precedents for rabbinic reshaping of Jewish practice. While this is the practice in reality, the theory is that we function within the parameters of *halakhah* as defined by our movement. If the movement leadership says no to intermarriage ceremonies, then anyone who officiates has broken ranks. Of course colleagues do this all the time anyway. For example, many colleagues violate the guidelines on driving on Shabbat without a second thought. Your assumption that the change is inevitable makes me uneasy.

DON: I believe postulating a putative freedom as *mara d'atra* to eat *treif* on Yom Kippur is a *treif* red herring. We have no need for a community standard not to eat bacon Big Macs while reciting *Al Het*, because any rabbi who did so is proclaiming publicly that they are not in line with the prevailing standards, practices and values of the Conservative community. I would love to overhear the conversation between RA leadership and that Yom Kippur-bacon-eating-rabbi during *Hol Hamoed Sukkot* after his or her congregants call the RA to complain.

You say two things which to me strike a contrast. The first, proclaiming our power as *mara d'atra* to make the decision to perform intermarriages, and the second, admitting that we often embrace such changes because it's what our congregations demand.

If we are individual *marei d'atra*, you are also a collective organization, composed of members who have the right to impose a community standard as a professional body. As I said before, it is precisely because this is a huge, emotional, powerful, symbolic red line issue that I urge you not to rush into decisions we can't undo, but which may undo you as a movement.

These are not simple matters of local control, but go to the heart of your self-conception as a larger Conservative community.

BOB: Friends, from the far left of center, as far as I'm concerned, I don't agree with Don regarding the inevitability of the opportunity to officiate at intermarriages if that is our choice.

I have a great desire to officiate and participate in intermarriages when my close friends and family are under the *huppah*, and I thank God that the RA-CJLS prevents me from seriously considering the possibility, without losing my intertwined life with the Conservative Movement.

I am perfectly OK with my *mara d'atra*-hood being limited by the RA. I love feeling protected regarding this issue in particular, and others, in general.

In any case, I thank all of you for your thoughts. I'd like to return to this again some other time, because it will come up again and again in our ministry, for sure.

SAM: Since we're talking about intermarriage, let me raise a related issue, that of an *aufruf*. I know that the issue of interfaith couples requesting an *aufruf* comes up from time-to-time.

I was just asked by a family from my congregation about doing something to mark their daughter's upcoming marriage to a non-Jew. I have spoken with the mother of the bride extensively through the dating period and into the engagement. The family is well-aware of the limitations in regard to this request. Still, I know that some colleagues have found ways to meet such requests without bringing the non-Jewish partner to the *bimah* for an *aliyah*. As I recall, some have done something privately. I do not recall the details. If you have found ways of doing this which have been meaningful, and you are able to share the specifics, please do.

SUSAN: We offered an *aliyah* to a young man from our congregation who was engaged to be married to a woman who was not Jewish. Since in our *shul* we allow non-Jewish people to accompany Jews who come up onto the *bimah* for an *aliyah*, even though they themselves aren't called up, and are not understood to be receiving an *aliyah* to the Torah, we invited the non-Jewish spouse to join him. She, however, preferred to remain in her seat in the congregation with her future in-laws. We called up the young man, he had his *aliyah*, I offered him and his fiancée my blessing, in English, for a good marriage, and wished them well, building a home informed by Jewish values and one in which *shalom* and *shalvah* [harmony], etc., will long reign. I don't recall whether we sang a song. We may have, but it wasn't *siman tov u'mazal tov*.

In any event, a few months ago, I officiated at the dunking of their son in the *mikveh*, at whose *bris milah*, *l'shem gerut* [for the purpose of conversion] I was present. Incidentally, the wife is considering converting to Judaism, which wouldnt be a big deal since her own father is Jewish.

BOB: I came up with my idea for an *aufruf* for an interfaith couple which the parents of the groom and I called "the Un-*Aufruf*." Their son wanted an *aliyah* like all the other previous grooms in the family received prior to marrying, and all agreed that he would be called by himself, not as a *hatan*, and that we would avoid the land mine words "*mazal tov*" at all costs. We did wish him and his fiancée our congratulations and gave them a *mezuzah*, because even an intermarried Jew is commanded to put up *mezuzot*. When I met with the couple privately a year earlier I stressed that his obligations as a Jew do not diminish simply because his wife is not embracing those commandments, and that they would always be welcome as a family in the *shul* even if only he had the privileges and obligations of membership, and not his wife.

This might not work for everyone but I was not conflicted by this resolution, despite my claims to being a traditionalist, albeit egalitarian, in the movement.

On another occasion, we did the following, with the blessing of the board, to call the Jewish partner to the Torah for an *aliyah* by himself. Then after the service when we went into the Social Hall for *kiddush* I invited the couple to join me, spoke to them, and then we presented them with the same gift we give to every couple who comes for an *aufruf* and then we drank a L'Chaim. The family felt recognized and my traditionalists were satisfied that it wasn't on the *bimah*, and they were not forced to sing *Siman Tov/Mazal Tov* for something they do not condone. It worked for us.

SAM: Some good ideas. I thank you.

DON: OK, friends, I have a different issue to raise. I'm looking for good signs to use to let people know about synagogue decorum: no phones on Shabbat, no photography, head covering, etc.

I once saw a "Ten Commandments of Synagogue Decorum," but can't find it. I'm looking for something lighter and humorous that gets the point across that our *b'nai-mitzvah* families can use in their programs. I am most concerned about events with large numbers of people who have never been to our *shul* before.

SAM: Here's one that we use. I think it's cute, and very effective.

1 – Turn off you cell phone. God will not call you on Shabbat.

2 – On Shabbat the best pictures are taken with the eyes, so no smart-phone photos.

3 – Please talk to God, not to your neighbor.

4 – Wrong address . . . this is a holy place. The Disco is two blocks away.

5 – Bar Mitzvah doesn't mean you are in a bar.

I hope this can be of some help.

DON: I love it! Great! Thanks so much!!

SAM: Hey, you guys are terrific, and creative! Thanks! While I'm on a roll, here's another question for you *halakhists*. An elderly congregant just passed away. Both he and his wife, who is still alive, are Jewish. I just found out that he has already purchased a plot at a non-Jewish cemetery. His body is currently in their mortuary. I do not think there is any chance of convincing the family to sell the plot and purchase another in one of our local Jewish cemeteries.

Are there *halakhic* implications I should know about?

SUSAN: I respect the policy pronounced by the Conservative movement, but have told my three congregations, over the years, that I would not be bound by this particular policy. I have buried Jewish people in military cemeteries and interdenominational cemeteries and in non-denominational cemeteries.

I embrace the practice that every Jew deserves a proper burial, and once I officiated in New Orleans at a military funeral early in my rabbinic career, I felt empowered to officiate at other Jewish funerals as well. By the way, at that time I didn't ask anyone's permission or for a CJLS opinion, and, of course, back then Al Gore had yet to invent the information highway, and none of our colleagues had yet discovered/invented rabbinic listservs. I just thought it was the right thing to do.

SAM: I reiterate that my suggested solution to apply to National Cemeteries as well as mausoleum entombments, and non-Jewish cemeteries, is to have the mortuary people place a packet of Jerusalem earth inside the *aron kodesh* with the deceased, preferably under the head or pillow. We thereby create a small area of "sacred soil" or "consecrated ground" to compensate for the fact that the plot or crypt isn't. I highly recommend this practice. Every funeral director whom I have requested to do this has thanked me, and not only complied, but suggested it to others who would officiate at such locales.

I didn't ask the Reform law committee either. My "Rabbi" title gives me and you the authority to make our own decisions, and be creative and lenient where we feel it would be appropriate. If you ask, the answer is *"treif."*

BOB: The *halakhic* implications are that he shouldn't be buried there. That said, of course you have to officiate. In my opinion it would cause the family great emotional distress for you to not officiate, and causing a mourner more pain than they already feel at the death is also forbiden.

If military cemeteries aren't sacred soil, I'm not sure what is. See Abraham Lincoln's take on the meaning of "holy," in his Gettysburg Address.

SUSAN: I now have a matter that is particularly relevant for women, but also for men.

Throughout the years Conservative rabbis have had many discussions about the CJLS and its decisions. However, it seems to me, perhaps incorrectly, that we do not often hear gratitude expressed for decisions made by the CJLS. With this in mind, I would like to share a statement of gratitude that was written by a family friend, Deborah Harburger. She shared this statement with her congregation before *Kol Nidre* this year, reflecting on a tragedy in her family and their gratitude for Stephanie Dickstein's 1996 *teshuvah* "Jewish Ritual Practice Following a Stillbirth." Deborah has kindly granted me permission to share this with you. This is her letter:

In March of 1996, my brother was preparing to graduate from high school and was looking ahead to what his future would bring at college and beyond. At the same time, the Committee on Jewish Law and Standards of the Rabbinical Assembly was voting on a paper to provide guidance for the Conservative movement on Jewish ritual practice following a stillbirth.

Eighteen years later, in 2014, my brother is married to his perfect match, and they live in Montgomery County with their beautiful, intelligent, and very funny three-year old daughter, Eleanor. In 2014, we also found ourselves turning to this very paper from the Committee on Jewish Law and Standards.

Exactly one month ago today, my sister-in-law was thirty-seven weeks into a healthy pregnancy, when she did not feel the baby moving. She was not in pain or discomfort, but she knew something was wrong. She went into the hospital and was told there was no heartbeat. Her baby was stillborn. Around midnight she underwent a difficult, four-hour c-section that included the need for blood transfusions. Later, in the early hours of the morning, she held her son. He was a perfect five-and-a-half pounds with a full head of dark hair, ten perfect fingers and ten perfect toes. There was no apparent cause of death then or now, even after an autopsy.

One week later, my sister-in-law was home from the hospital and our immediate family gathered at the cemetery for the burial. We were led in a graveside service where we simultaneously gave the baby a name and said goodbye. He was named Menachem, meaning "one who gives comfort."

As we head into Yom Kippur and I reflect back on the end of 5774 and the start of 5775, I am grateful for the many ways that we have been given comfort over this past month.

I am grateful for the extended family, friends, and colleagues who have offered help and support, information and guidance, and food to my brother, sister-in-law, and niece, to my husband, my two children and me, and to my parents. I am grateful to the hospital for the care they provided to my sister-in-law, and for the skill with which the nursing team treated all of us and supported us as we held Menachem in those first hours after his delivery. I am grateful for the support of the Jewish institutions in Montgomery County – the funeral home and the Community Cemetery in Clarksburg. I am grateful for my niece's antics and smiles and her ability to make us laugh even when we are filled with gut-wrenching sorrow, and for the ability to cuddle, play, and read with her and my children during this time.

And, I'm grateful to the Rabbinical Assembly for establishing protocols and rituals for this tragic circumstance. I have no doubt that some of you in this room have either personally experienced a stillbirth or know someone who has experienced it, as I have learned it is more common than I realized. There are an estimated 26,000 stillbirths in the United States each year, a figure that has remained essentially stable over the past decade. If the loss occurred more than fifteen or twenty years ago, it is likely that the parents never saw or held the baby, nor would they have had the opportunity to give him or her a name nor conduct a burial service.

It is 2014, and I am grateful that Judaism has the capacity to evolve and grow. Under the Conservative Movement's guidance, now we mourn the loss of life in a stillborn, and we have rituals to support us as we bury our loved ones and begin our grieving.

In those first hours after my brother and sister-in-law received the news, they had many decisions to make. The rituals and protocols offered by the Conservative movement eased the burden of the decision-making during that time, and I am grateful for that. Importantly, they also validated our collective feelings of loss, sadness, and sorrow. Our Jewish community has provided us with the space we need to mourn; not only for my brother, sister-in-law, and niece, but for my parents to mourn their grandson and for my children to grieve for their cousin.

Over the past month, I have also been comforted by an image that has come to me repeatedly – one of my two grandmothers, of blessed memory, taking turns holding and caring for Menachem. This image continues to bring a smile to my face and bring me comfort.

In memory of my nephew, Menachem, I offer you my hope and prayer for a new year full of peace, health, happiness, and comfort. G'mar hatimah tovah.

Deborah Harburger
Reflections prior to the start of Kol Nidre
Chizuk Amuno Congregation, Baltimore, MD
2014

DON: Thanks for sharing that moving talk, Susan. I know that I speak for all of us when I thank you for bringing it to our attention.

Susan, with your sincere sharing of a personal matter, I want to share with you another matter that is very personal, in a different way. It's also about women, but also about men. Here is a column I wrote in my synagogue bulletin.

There's a terrible, shameful scandal in the Jewish world. Recently a prominent rabbi was arrested on charges that he had installed a hidden camera in the mikveh in his synagogue. How violated those women who used the mikveh must feel! And then it came out that he had misused his position as teacher and supervisor of conversions to Judaism to bully and otherwise take advantage of prospective converts. How betrayed those women who looked to him for guidance must feel!

As a rabbi, a colleague, I am ashamed that this has taken place. And I need to make sure that people who come to use our mikveh feel safe.

Typically, when a person comes to convert to Judaism, they study with me or with another teacher, and when we feel that they are ready, they meet with a three-person Bet Din – a "court" of rabbis or knowledgeable Jews, who engage the prospective Jew-by-choice in discussion, and ask questions, such as: What made the prospective convert choose this path? Who are some of the figures about whom she has studied who are models for her? What does she feel are the most important challenges for the Jewish people today? What will his Jewish life look like in five or ten years?

And then, assuming all goes well in the conversation, the candidate goes downstairs to the mikveh, disrobes, and immerses in the mikveh. There is always another person – a friend, or a parent, or the mikveh attendant, who is actually in the mikveh room with the candidate, to witness the immersion, and to ensure his or her safety and modesty.

And then, if it's a woman who is converting, the three rabbis stand outside in the waiting room, with the door to the mikveh just slightly cracked open so only the sound can come through, and the candidate is visible to no one but the mikveh attendant, and I ask the convert to repeat berakhot after me, the blessing for the mikveh, and shehekheyanu.

It was suggested to me once, that perhaps it is uncomfortable for a woman, naked in the mikveh, to hear the voice of a male rabbi floating through the door. I asked a few women who had gone through the process, they said, "No, it's fine," and I never thought about it again.

Until now.

The mikveh is such private, sacred space, that I am resolved to do everything I can to make women feel the least vulnerable as possible. And so, I, as the male rabbi of this congregation, resolve:

I will try to include at least one woman rabbi or layperson on every woman's conversion Bet Din in the future. For female conversion candidates, I will try to have a woman explain the immersion process.

I will have a woman's voice be the one that floats in through the cracked-open door of the mikveh, or actually be the female mikveh attendant to prompt the candidate to recite the berakhot. Of course, every person, and every situ-

ation is different. We need to be sensitive to every person's individual needs and comfort.

I would love for our congregation to have a woman rabbi on our staff. A woman teaching Torah, being a Torah personality in our community, would bring such a wonderful perspective to our congregation, and to our city. Until we are able to make that happen, I will endeavor to include knowledgeable female members of our congregation as part of our conversion and mikveh practices. The mikveh can be sacred space, a place allowing for a communion with what is holy. The first step is to make it safe in all ways.

SUSAN: Thanks, Don! If you will permit me, I'd like to quote this column in my synagogue bulletin too.

DON: Sure, with pleasure!

SAM: I'd like to share an experiene I had recently. It doesn't require your advice or opinions, or help. Just passing on my experience, which I think will be valuable to all of us.

I was in church last Sunday. I just wanted to see how our neighbors *daven*. About midway into the service – one hour total, for those who count these things – the pastor asked visitors to stand up, then took a "seventh inning stretch," where he asked everyone to stand up and greet the visitors and the people around them. Then, on my way out after services, many many people came over to greet me, saying,"We're delighted that you are here."

I loved it! And although we have greeters who greet folks on their way in to *shul*, and then at the end of services I greet visitors by name, I'd like to move the welcoming hubbub to the middle of the service. Do any of our colleagues have experience doing this in their Shabbat morning services? What is the language you use to instruct people that "now is the time to stand up and say Shabbat Shalom to the folks around you." When do you do that? And although I model being welcoming, and talk about *hakhnasat orhim* ["welcoming guests"] all the time, why can't I get my folks to make a point of "rushing" the visitors to say *"barukh haba?"*

Any other tips? Think about it and let's discuss it, perhaps at our next meeting. No reactions necessary right now.

All of your comments are helpful and fascinating.

Anyway, folks, let's break for today and meet again next week. Enjoy your week!!

Week 16

𐡸

BOB: Hi everybody. Great to be back together again. I'm so grateful to have this group to bounce ideas off.

Let me start today off with this question. I was asked if one would treat a brochure from Jews for Jesus which has God's Hebrew name written out any differently than any other such document for disposal or burial?

DON: It seems to me that a *sheymot* paper [with God's name in Hebrew] is a *sheymot* paper, and regardless of the source, the YKVH needs to be treated most respectfully and buried.

SUSAN: Take a look at *Shabbat* 116a. Rabbi Tarfon says that he would burn the books of heretics, even when they contain God's name. Rambam, at *Hilkhot Yesode Hatorah* 6:8, holds that this applies to a *Sefer Torah* written by a Jewish *apikoros* [heretic], but that books written by *akum* [idolators] which contain Divine Names should be buried. Anything involving the burning of books is a fraught matter. The original reference may have been to the Gospels, and, by many people's standards, I would be considered an *apikoros*. In general, we should judge people *l'khaf z'khut* [giving them the benefit of the doubt], but I would make an exception for Jews for Jesus. One can't go wrong by burying their literature, but I wouldn't be upset if it were destroyed in some other way.

SAM: Not speaking *halakhically*, I would actually take the other tack and would put them straight into the recycling bin. Just my sentiment. It seems to me that I recall one of my seminary professors making some compelling arguments that, in general, recycling of most *sheymot* should be recycled for the sake of *bal tash-hit*, for the sake of environmentalism. While I might make an argument that burial should still be done for *Sifrei Torah, seforim, siddurim, klafim,* etc., I would concur with random pages, copies, printouts, etc. that they should be recycled.

As for Jews for Jesus materials that spell out the *Shem*, they should be recycled for the sake of *bal tash-hit*, namely for environmentalism, and not be buried, because if recycling *sheymot* does have any hint of *hillul Hashem* ["desecration of God's name"], it would be infinitesimal compared the *hillul Hashem* of Jews for Jesus using the *Shem* to promote *kefirah b'Am Yisrael* ["evangilizing Jews to convert out of Judaism"].

SUSAN: Just playing devil's advocate, here's the other side of the argument. One might differ with our esteemed colleague regarding burial of Torahs. If Torah is a "living" entity, then let it continue to live through recycling, in addition to everything else with God's name. In today's world, every opportunity we have to emphasize the importance of preserving this earth we should take. This includes letting the congregations know that recycling is so important, we even include *Sifrei Torah*.

BOB: Never let it be said that this group is without diversity of opinion. Wow! Very stimulating discussion. Thanks to all.

SUSAN: Now let me proceed to another difficult issue.

This relates to a couple with whom I had difficult experiences in the past. The father in particular has a "my way or the high way" attitude, regardless of what I say as the rabbi. Recently he and his wife have celebrated their adoptive son's bar mitzvah a couple of *Shabbatot* ago. The boy underwent *giyyur* with a different rabbi, a male Conservative colleague, since they were not comfortable with me as a female, even though I let them know in no uncertain terms that I wouldn't be present inside the *mikvah*. This was a few years ago. At that moment the boy decided he wanted a different name than his parents gave him at his *bris*.

He did not like Yitzhak, I was told. He liked Yirmiyahu, since his English name is Jeremy. I was informed of this by the child's mother.

The parents did not speak about his name for the bar mitzvah, and neither did I ask them, but I called the boy "*Yirmiyahu ben Avraham veSarah*" for his *aliyah*. Now the father is complaining to other congregants that I should have used "*Yirmiyahu ben Yonatan v'Esther*," and so far has not spoken to me.

My basic question is this. I know of the *teshuvah* of the CJLS about this, and since the congregation is aware of his adoptive status, is this even a possibility? What would that say to the other Jews by choice, who are now very prominent members of the *shul*?

DON: There are conflicting opinions in this matter. However, we do have a tradition going back to *Serah bat Asher* that a child may be referred to by the name of an adoptive parent. If the child knows that he is adopted and the congregation knows as well, then the use of the adoptive father's name is not intended to be deceptive, but rather to acknowledge the connection to the parent who raised him. Under such circumstances, I would not object to use of the name of the adoptive parent for calling the child for an *aliyah*.

In fact, I know of at least one case in which an Israeli rabbinical court *dayan* advised an adopted child to use the adoptive parents' names when registering for a marriage license and on the *ketubah*, so that the rabbanut would not question the validity of the child's American – RCA – conversion.

I also know of a *haredi* family with two adopted daughters. At their weddings when the *ketubah* was read, the name used for the father was the adoptive father.

I also would identify a *ger* or *giyoret* who had a Jewish father by the father's name.

SUSAN: Thanks so much, Don! This is very helpful. I feel much clearer about this whole matter.

DON: My pleasure.

BOB: OK, so I have another issue to discuss. I'm sure this is not the first time this has come up. But it came up again last week, so let me get our thoughts.

A congregant requested an *aufruf* for his son who is to be married to a non-Jew. I'd like to simply call him to the Torah for an *aliyah* without any mention of any wedding. Any suggestions? Remember, we need to be warm and welcoming!

DON: This is a serious request which many of us are already dealing with. I would recommend that the son who is getting married be in touch and not the mother. Often the couple isn't as interested as the parents. Also, determine from the couple whether the partner of another faith is even interested in participating. Then go back to the congregants and ask what they had in mind. For some people an *aufruf* is another celebration in a line of celebrations. For others it is a very important part.

You could offer an *aliyah* for the groom, but his parents may be expecting one as well. And will you not give them a blessing? I talk with the couple and determine what they are comfortable with in the options I am comfortable with. If the partner of another faith does not want to participate, I offer an *aliyah* and do a special *Mi Sheberakh* for the Jewish partner "'who will be married soon," and ask for "compassion and good things as the new couple builds a home together with love and mutual respect and wisdom to find ways to continue to connect to Judaism."

This is basically the same prayer I do if both partners want to participate. But in this case, I would give an *aliyah*, and then ask the other partner to join us after and say the *Mi Sheberakh*. The third option is to not give an *aliyah*, but to bring the couple up at the end of services before *Adon Olam* and announce their plans and say the prayer.

I think it depends on the comfort level of the couple. I know at least one colleague who blesses them in his study and not on the *bimah*. I have also had many situations where the parents wanted an *aufruf* but the couple did not.

BOB: This is a fascinating and important thread: it really raises for me deep questions about who we are, and who we're not.

I was just shmoozing with a colleague about a reform congregation with whom he and his conservative congregation share space. The contrasts between the services would truly challenge me. In the Reform one, the bar mitzvah family takes pictures before the *davening*. Some of the Torah readers are not *halakhically* Jewish, etc. I'm reminded of what someone once told me about the Hillel at University of Michigan. It was designed so that no one *minyan*-congregation would feel totally at home. As soon as one finishes, another takes its place.

Is this really the wave of the future? I'm not so sure.

I would think that people want and need to feel that the *shul* is their spiritual home. Can it be a home if practices occur there that are so foreign to our values? I wouldn't personally be offended by a *mehitzah*, but I would be offended if a service was conducted that excluded women from active participation. I suppose that some Reform colleagues would be offended if a service was conducted in their *shuls* that didn't recognize Patrilineal Jews as full members of the Tribe.

Now, this is not an issue for some Orthodox *shuls*. Don, please give us your reaction when you feel like it.

I once was invited to perform a wedding at a Young Israel *shul* in a neighboring community. I was shocked. I called the rabbi there and confirmed that it was ok with him that I was officiating at the wedding. "Sure," he said. "We consider it a straight rental." Clearly, in my mind, the differences are such that no one would imagine that what I was doing had anything to do with what they do in their *shul*.

I don't think that this would have been the case in the days of the famous Orthodox Rabbi Moshe Feinstein. But clearly, we are so distant from some Orthodox rabbis nowadays, that they are more comfortable than they used to be. Don, again your comments when you feel so moved.

Would we be comfortable with a Jews for Jesus group holding a wedding in our sanctuaries? OR a regular *shabbat* morning service?

Wow.

DON: I'll mull over your questions, and get back to you at a later time.

BOB: No problem.

So here's another question: A couple would like to name a child after a non Jewish relative – and choose a Hebrew name based on that person's English name.

DON: Naming after a non-Jew? When I was a child, a young man who was a guest in *shul* was offered an *aliyah*. When he went up to the *shulhan*, the *gabbai* asked his name: "Christian." The *gabbai* took a moment to regain his composure and asked: "You're Jewish?" The young man replied that he was. "And what is your Jewish name?" The young man replied. "Christian *ben* Moshe." Then he added: "My parents are from Denmark, and I was named for King Christian.

And of course, Alexander isn't a "Jewish" name, but *Hazal* thought naming someone for a non-Jew who had been benev-olent toward Israel was appropriate – even good enough for an Alexander Janneus – whom *Hazal* did not like – and Alexandra Salome – whom *Hazal* did like. And then there are those other Hasmonean enemies of Hellenism with names like Hyrcanus, Aristobulus and Antigonus, and High Priests named Jason and Meneleus.

SUSAN: Names? The oddest such example I have personally heard about is from my father. In July 1944, one of his campers at Camp Yeshivah, a young eleven-year-old Hungarian/Galician immigrant child, who barely spoke English. His name? Franklin Delano Rothenberg! Needless to say, everybody called him FDR.

[Laughter].

DON: People can name their baby whatever they want. The naming ceremony only gives the child a Hebrew name.

BOB: Let me change the subject now. A student of mine and I have been having an ongoing discussion of the concept of God's

blessings and of us blessing God. With the myriad of literature we've reviewed, my student asked how we as rabbis define
"blessing," intellectually and emotionally.

SAM: I was in Pittsburgh last week, to co-officiate at the wedding of a young lady I named many years ago on the same *bimah*
where the *huppah* will take place. WOW! Talk about a blessing!

I recall an amazing issue of *Sh'ma* magazine, where Ed Green-
stein and Marcia Falk gave two deeply spiritual and very different interpretations of what it means to say *Barukh atah* . . . ,
and what it means to receive a blessing, either from God or from
another person – *Mi Sheberakh*, for example. Find that issue of
Sh'ma and you'll find some very deep thoughts about your topic.

Personally, a *berakhah* is an opportunity for me to say "thank
you" for what I have, to express gratitude daily for the basics
and the amazing things in my life, to remind myself how small
yet significant I am in the great scheme of things God has set in
motion.

DON: Bob, a great question and no easy answer. *Barukh* is a
complicated word. In the Bible people bless God, God blesses
people, people bless people, there's a lot going on there. In addition to the nice points other colleagues have written about, I
would note that the Hebrew root of *barukh* is also that of *ber-
ekh*, the knee. When we say the first *Barukh* of the *Amidah* we
bow a little. A *berakhah* is an expression of acknowledgement of
our limits, if you will. There is a power, a spirit, a timelessness
beyond us in the world, to which we express gratitude, wonder
and, probably not so PC, submission when we say a *berakhah*,
when we bend that knee. *Barukh* is where we and our abilities
and comprehension end, and the rest begins.

BOB: *Yasher koah*, Don. Best explanation I've heard. The late
Professor Max Kadushin taught us exactly that, but few picked
up on it. I always translate *Barukh* in a *berakhah* as "We acknowledge that. . . ."

SUSAN: On this topic, I recommend our colleague and teacher

Brad Artson's article in *Conservative Judaism* from 1994. He discusses the various ways that '*barukh atah*' is translated – "praised" vs "blessed," and presents his own preferred translation, "You are bountiful" – based on Yoseph Albo's connection between ברוך and בריכה.

Professor Moshe Greenberg *z"l* taught us that all blessings found in the Bible emanate from God. Thus while we may think of blessing each other – in Israel people will often offer *berakhot* for others on special occasions – according to our teacher, blessings are what we ask God for. Thus in *birkat kohanim*, perhaps the paradigm biblical blessing, we ask for God to bless and guard us. So too, by the way, in English. When we are called upon to give an invocation, what that actually means is that we are being called upon to "invoke God's blessing" on the event.

BOB: Great material you've all supplied. Thanks so much. I know I can rely on this honorable, scholarly, compassionate group of Torah scholars.

That being the case, I'd like to bring up another topic that I'm sure you all have some thoughts about.

SUSAN: This meeting seems to focus on the more liberal trends in Jewish law. Don, I hope you don't feel left out.

DON: Not at all. Though I may not agree with some of your *halakhic* decisions, you are giving me much food for study and thought. Who knows, maybe our *shul* will adopt some of these decisions. Not tomorrow, or even next year, but we'll see. . . .

SUSAN: Ok, here goes another one. During High Holidays, we live-streamed our services to the great appreciation of home-bound members. We have now had requests from some *b'nai-mitzvah* families to live-stream on those *Shabbatot*, so that home-bound or hospitalized family members can see the child celebrate this milestone.

Drawing from a *teshuvah* by the CJLS on electronic devices on Shabbat, it would seem that there is foundation to do this, provided that the camera is programmed prior to Shabbat, to commence and end live-streaming.

I'm looking for actual experiences from those who have live-streamed, who actually are live-streaming, or have decided not to live-stream Shabbat services. What *halakhic* issues were addressed? Were there unforeseen complications or benefits?

BOB: We live-stream every Friday night and Shabbat morning, as well as on the High Holidays. We follow the same procedure for all of them. We also live-stream all funeral services that take place in the synagogue.

We started live-streaming this past High Holiday period, and we live-stream every funeral that takes place in the building. The response has been overwhelmingly positive. Homebound elders are very appreciative and report *davening* along and feeling like they are sitting in the front row. At a nearby senior living center, they set up the TV and everybody sings along.

We are also able to sell DVD's to *b'nai-mitzvah*. This is a triple-win: the price is better than a videographer, I don't have to argue with the videographer about not touching the camera, and the money we take in basically covers the cost of live-streaming the rest of the year. Cameras are on timers and completely unobtrusive. I doubt anyone notices or remembers that they are there.

SAM: We received only positive responses from our congregants who were homebound, and a few who were in our chapel as an overflow crowd. The only questions came from *b'nai-mitzvah* families who needed *halakhic* explanations to justify why this wasn't "videotaping" that they wanted for their *b'nai-mitzvah*, which, of course, I provided.

We are looking to have someone donate new hardware to begin live-streaming for every Shabbat. The homebound, the nursing home residents and the snowbirds are all looking forward to live-streaming.

SUSAN: Thanks to all of you.

BOB: I have another issue for us to discuss. We are in the process of revamping our Constitution and the question arose regarding membership of non-Jews, and taking on the role of becoming a member of the Board and/or becoming an officer.

Our constitution committee is in agreement that the non-Jewish spouse can be a member of the congregation including the rights of being a member, but should not be granted the following rights: Voting at congregational votes, becoming a voting member of the board of trustees, and becoming an officer.

SAM: Here's my take. I believe that every synagogue board of directors should be required to have at least ten percent non-Jews. Here's my reasoning. I have noticed over the years that when non-Jews are present Jews behave much differently. They are less likely to be insulting and fight with their fellow Jews. They tend to disagree more agreeably. I believe that our boards will behave much better if we have a number of non-Jews present and – boy am I going to get schmeised for this – a few women. That will control the middle-aged gentleman who tend to get very argumentative and vicious with their language, but behave better around young women. Now before you hang me out to dry, please remember this was all tongue in cheek to make a very real point about how our board members sometimes act so nastily that the good board members don't want to be there. And that is a problem that is widespread. The nasty ones push away the good ones, and instead of the cream of the crop in leadership we end up with . . . well you know what we end up with. My *shul* ended that years ago by literally refusing to nominate those kind of people, and now we have a very effective and wonderful mixture of: young, older; male, female, etc.

DON: Sam's comment brought back a memory. When I was in my first pulpit, a local Presbyterian minister and I became good friends. He was curious about our High Holiday observance and asked if he could spend Yom Kippur in my *shul*. As he stayed, no one left before the break! I teased him after that I wished he'd come every year.

Truth to tell, I oppose having non-Jews as voting members.

Should a non-Jew vote to engage a rabbinical candidate, or vote to retain the existing rabbi, who espouses certain *halakhic* or overall religious points of view when the non Jew does not profess the overall faith structure of those views? Of course a Jew may not fulfill that either, but at least they are born or converted into a faith community which professes them.

Next, if one of our values is still endogamy, what does it say when a member of the board of directors who establishes policy, is not the Jewish partner of a mixed marriage, but the non-Jewish partner? Would most, say Presbyterian or Lutheran clergy encourage a Jew to occupy a place on their church Board of Governors? What about the spot on the board of directors of the Jew, whose past and future destiny is as a member of our people and faith, is taken by the non-Jew who, no matter how supportive that person is of his family's Jewishness, is not?

I say let's take counsel from non-Jews within the synagogue – absolutely. Voting members of the board – absolutely not. Unnecessary and illogical at best. At worst, worse.

I am all for being as inclusive as possible and extending all benefits of membership to non Jewish spouses – except for being a voting member of the synagogue or any committee.

To be a full member of a synagogue, it makes perfect sense that one profess Judaism. Voting membership carries with it the power to shape the policy of a synagogue. Only Jews should be doing that.

Analogy: I am an amateur radio operator. Our national organization, the ARRL, allows anybody with an interest in ham radio to be an associate member. In order to be a full member, however, having the right to vote and hold office, one needs an FCC Amateur Radio license. That is hardly "discriminatory," nor "unwelcoming."

As far as how congregations function in the "real world" I think an apt comparison is foreigners in the US. They have certain rights, but not all rights. Thus if they are not citizens they cannot vote or serve in Congress. They do however have many other rights, even things like Social Security, driver's license, etc.

SUSAN: Non-Jews who pay dues to the congregation ought to

have certain rights, one of which is voting as a member. What do congregations generally vote on? Budgets and clergy. I have no problem with them having a say in how their money is spent or even in who will be the spiritual leader of the community their children are being brought up in. I also think they should be welcome in certain committees that are appropriate such as Social Action. At the same time they are not "citizens," so they don't have the rights to govern by being an officer or on a board of directors.

SAM: A long time ago a Reform colleague of mine mentioned that they needed a bookkeeper and the by-laws required that the bookkeeper be on the board. They were considering just dropping the requirement altogether. My comment was that it would be the single worst decision of his career. They should change it for the bookkeeper, or if they want, for limited jobs, committees, and votes. I even predicted they would sit on the Ritual Committee. They went ahead and eliminated almost all requirements for all staff for being Jewish. Within a couple of years they had non-Jews serving on the Ritual Committee and they were demanding changes to the service and from the rabbi. He called me up and told me I was right. Why they did what they did, and in some cases why the Jews helped or initiated changes, is a question I won't address.

DON: The Catholic Church won't let me take communion. That isn't antisemitic. That is religious integrity. No reason why a non-Jewish spouse can't be on a mailing list, acknowledged as a member of the community, extended pastoral care, receive member discounts, etc. But it makes little sense to me to have a non-Jew as a voting member.

SUSAN: In my experience in the various congregations that I have known, I have often found non-Jewish parents as invested in their children's Jewish education as their Jewish partners are – and often even more so! I have had many conversations with non-Jewish parents about how to best work with their children and how, in their opinion, the teachers in the religious school might teach more effectively. I have learned much from them. Since they have made a commitment to raising and educating their children as Jews, would you see such parents as appropriate members of the education committee?

DON: Forgive me if I sound like I'm contradicting myself. But truthfully, I'm listening carefully to both sides of the argument. Basically, I find it mind-boggling that a non-Jew could be a full member of a synagogue. I think that a synagogue is, by definition, for Jews. Many years ago, the constitution of my synagogue recognized the possibility that a non-Jew could be a member. When the constitution was reviewed at some point years later, I said that our national organization rules stipulate that only Jews can be members, and the revised constitution included that stipulation. Having said that, let me give some reasons why membership by non-Jews might make sense:

The standard of the national organization may be irrelevant. If we think that it is all right for non-Jews to be synagogue members, then we should try to get them to change its standard. This is America, and we can say whatever we want.

Next, the analogy of citizenship and voting is suggestive but not decisive. We already include non-Jewish relatives of Jewish members in our communities in various ways, such as participation in programs and access to pastoral attention. Since that is so, why not define formal membership in the same broad way? I think, in this connection, of the surveys of the American Jewish population. They find that there are so many Jews "by birth and religion," so many Jews by birth or formal conversion, and so many people living in households with at least one Jew. All of those groups are significant in one way or another. Christian churches have different policies about communion. "Closed communion" churches, like the Catholic Church, Eastern Orthodox churches, and some Lutheran churches, restrict communion to members of that church. Most modern Protestant churches are "open communion," and anyone may receive communion there. There is usually an expectation that the communicant be a baptized Christian, but, often, nobody checks.

BOB: I've listened carefully to all of your comments, and thinking it over, here's what I come up with.

Those are correct who say that a synagogue is, by definition, for Jews. And in the 1980s, the USCJ made that clear in their standards. Since that time, however, much has changed in our world and we, the Jewish People, have changed as well. Consider the following:

Unlike the 1980s, we are now faced with a question more fundamental than who can join a synagogue. Today we ask: Who is a Jew? And, as we learn from the Pew Study and elsewhere, being Jewish means different things to different people. Not all who claim to be Jewish see their identity in the context of *halakhah*: "I am culturally Jewish but I do not consider myself religiously Jewish. I do not identify with the Jewish religion or with any religion. Rather, I identify with the Jewish People." Should these "Jews" be eligible for membership?

Today, given the rates of intermarriage, we have many non-Jews who are part of a Jewish family. That is, a Jew and a non-Jew marry and have children which they agree will be raised Jewish. As a family, they observe Shabbat and holidays. The children attend Religious School or Day School. The non-Jewish spouse is not only an active participant in it all, but pays for kosher meat, tuition and synagogue dues. The non-Jewish partner is, de facto, part of the community. Do we accept his or her full involvement and support, and yet stop them at the door?

Beyond sociology, we can also observe that joining a synagogue has no *halakhic* implications. If there are no *halakhic* barriers, one can claim that our refusal to invite the non-Jewish spouse in a Jewish family to join as a member, is chauvinistic at best.

I can understand how some synagogues might oppose membership to a non-Jew by claiming that it is inappropriate for a non-Jew to have a say on certain communal issues, such as determining the policies of the religious school, standards of behavior or the future of a member of the professional staff or clergy, or serving in leadership roles. That objection can easily be addressed. In one synagogue's constitution that I've heard about they have dealt with these issues. Leadership roles are reserved for Jews. Congregational votes are, for the most part, perfunctory.

I could go on. Suffice to say, in my experience, from what I hear from colleagues, allowing non-Jews to join us as part of a Jewish family has been a "win-win." The families feel embraced. The community is enriched. Such a congregation has gained members from this cohort. Based on these kind of experiences, this can be a good move for us.

In sum, thanks to everyone. Loads of great ideas and thoughts.

SUSAN: OK, folks, time for another very controversal topic. I want to relate a personal experience that suggests some validity to our current institutions and to our standards, and to our place and potential in the Jewish world today.

A few weeks ago I did something that in the past I never thought I would do. Having been one of the twelve CJLS "no" votes about a decade ago, on the *teshuvah* on "Homosexuality, Human Dignity and *Halakhah*," I would not have envisioned myself, this week, or ever, officiating at a commitment ceremony. How this came to be, and how the event unfolded may be reflective of great strengths of the Conservative movement, that we tend too often to overlook or deny.

About a year ago, two young professionals, Harold and Marvin, approached me with a request to officiate at their commitment ceremony. It was not something that I had ever been asked to do previously, so I had not given the possibility much thought, even though my previous negative vote would have suggested my declining the request. That was before I met with the two young men, both of whom impressed me deeply with their human qualities, their senses of humor and personal warmth, and their depth of Jewish learning and commitment. Both coming from Conservative backgrounds, they wanted a kosher *simhah*, a ceremony held in a synagogue, contrary to today's overwhelming trend of hotel and wedding-hall venues, and a commitment ceremony such as those they had already found on the RA website. Meeting the two men, hearing their request, I knew I wanted to say yes. With the support of my lay leadership, I agreed to the ceremony, recognizing that my theoretical opposition to such an event a decade earlier had melted, once confronted by two real-live human beings who loved each other, and similarly cherished every aspect of their Jewish identity. I told them that it would not be a marriage service, would not include the classic *Sheva Berakhot*, and would not use a standard *ketubah*, all of which accorded with their wishes as well. They wanted to work as closely as possible within the confines of a *halakhic* environment, in other words, to be ground-breaking while holding sacred the *halakhic* framework of the movement and tradition in which they had been raised.

Then came the ceremony. Three hundred people, representing a cross-section of the community, the vast majority "straight," the vast majority Jewish, including a significant number of young modern-Orthodox Jews who danced with the *freileikhkeit* and enthusiasm seen most often at *frum* weddings. I would not have imagined, a decade ago, when I voted against the CJLS *teshuvah*, that I would have felt this ceremony to have been one of the true spiritual highlights of my rabbinic career. These two young men walking down the sanctuary aisle, in their *talitot*, when approaching the *bimah*, taking off their *talitot*, attaching them together to poles to form their *huppah*, may have been one of the most powerful scenes I have ever witnessed. Several of my *minyan* regulars, who had just concluded *Ma'ariv* before the ceremony began, came in to witness the event, and were overcome with emotion – including a few who are far-to-the-"right" on most *halakhic* issues. They sensed, as did I, that they were witness to a holy moment.

This experience helped me frame a response to the pessimism we confront regarding Conservative Judaism and its institutions. As I said at the outset, I am not blind to the issues and the challenges we face. But Harold and Marvin reminded me of what we have been able to achieve, and what we continue to achieve, day in and day out. We can respond to the issue of these times with skill, with respect for, and knowledge of, the teaching of past generations, and yes, with standards that communities will respect, in appreciating that when we say "no," it will not be because we haven't exhausted every possible route to saying "yes."

I am grateful to my teachers, who three to four decades ago, gave me the tools to tackle today's difficult issues. I am grateful to my colleagues in the RA, whose brilliant creativity have given me the strength and the wherewithal to transform gradually my thinking and my opinions, when such transformation is in the interests of our people.

In Twainian terminology, reports of the death of Conservative Judaism are greatly exaggerated, to say the least. We are challenged, we are pressured, we are struggling, to be sure, in many areas, but I can bring at least three hundred witnesses to attest, that at the same time, we are very much alive.

BOB: First of all, *kol hakavod* to Susan. You are one of the most insightful and deliberate thinkers in our rabbinic circle. Having been the first vegetarian you ever met, I can also attest that you have travelled a long road in your life and your rabbinate with dignity and with *kavod*. This past week, while interviewing candidates for an assistant rabbinic position, one of the pieces of information which we shared with the candidates was a *dvar Torah* of a congregant who was celebrating her *aufruf*, seventeen years after their commitment ceremony that I pushed myself to do. I told them then, that there would come a day that they indeed would be married and listening to this congregant speak about the "not yet" nature of their commitment ceremony then and their parallel commitment to the congregation and to the community of which they were a central part, was both touching and at times painful. But the following day, at their wedding, it was a celebration of true love and *yiddishkeit* and your words about witnessing a holy moment was indeed a similar experience that I had watching this wedding unfold in my *shul*. We are living in a remarkable moment in Jewish life, and I agree that our world is far from dead. We are capable of transmitting a deep connection to the tradition and to its built-in ability to change that is evident in many areas. *Yasher koah*, Susan, and thank you for sharing.

OK, friends, I have another very difficult situation, and would love your wise counsel. Here is the situation. My cousin lives in Romania. His girlfriend of many years will be converting, but not before they participate in a civil marriage ceremony.

Just this afternoon he sent an email, which I'll read in a minute. My question: Do I attend or not? Part of me wants to find out who the officiant is. I would prefer a justice of peace to a rabbi.

Perhaps it's foolish of me to discuss this so publicly, realizing that I may be jeopardizing my membership in the RA by making this public – knowing that the RA has a strict ruling not permitting members to attend a wedding which is an intermarriage.

Here's what my cousin wrote:

"Since the situation in Romania is so bad and most of our friends are in business in these areas, we decided to postpone our party wedding until sometime next year, and after my fiancé's conversion process. Too many friends just would not be able to make it due to the situation unfolding in our part of the world.

"So we have arranged a date and location which I'll inform you about soon. The officiant is booked and I will announce the details in the next week. We will start sometime around 2:30–3 p.m. So if you are not out of town, mark you calendars!"

SAM: Bob, I would attend. Family trumps *halakhah*, regardless of who officiates. I would absolutely attend. Family matters more, and the damage that can be done is irreparable!

DON: It is an intermarriage regardless of her conversion process. I would go to the party after her conversion. That way you attend the celebration of the wedding, which then becomes a Jewish celebration. He already made excuses for those not attending.

When you are a rabbi, there are some things you should think about – maybe before becoming a rabbi.

The Talmud has a strange recommendation: the rabbi shouldn't "bring his eyes to the market," meaning, there are places a rabbi shouldn't be seen.

If *mar'eet ayin* [what appears to the eye] has some importance, then when we become rabbis, appearances are increased with a lot of things lay people can do, but we can't. Better "don't go there." And the first ones who should know it, understand it and support it are the family!

If they don't care, then we shouldn't "buy" their love at the price of giving away our rabbinical status.

An intermarriage ceremony is not a *pikuach nefesh* [a matter of life and death] event for us to attend under the excuse that family comes first. If family comes first, then they will understand you can't attend because also for them, family is first and you are a rabbi.

Now if the will to attend is overwhelming, your rationalization is a great way to do something we shouldn't do, and make it look right. A rabbi shouldn't officiate and celebrate an intermarriage. It's not a joyous moment for the Jewish people as it puts Jewish continuity in jeopardy.

BOB: Sounds like I have two contradictory opinions. Just where I was when I started. So I guess the decision falls back on me. I'll let you know, eventually, what I decide.

SUSAN: Sounds like we're ready for a new topic, though perhaps somewhat related. We are currently interviewing for a new Director of our Early Childhood Program. A candidate has applied for the position who, we found out, quite by accident, is married to a non-Jew. Some members of the committee are still interested in this candidate despite that fact, while others are definitely opposed to this candidate because of it.

I know this is a changing world, and I'd appreciate any thoughts on this issue. Have any of you had such a circumstance in your congregation? Do you have any thoughts that might help me guide the committee and the congregation to the right decision? Thanks in advance for your thoughts.

SAM: I wouldn't hesitate. The question really is, what is the level of this person's Jewish commitment? In the past, many would see this candidate's decision to intermarry as an indication of that. I do not, simply because I know too many people who have made strongly Jewish choices who also happen to be intermarried.

BOB: I agree with Sam, but would add two things. Hire the very best person for the job, and Jewish knowledge and commitment is a key measurement in terms of qualifications. Second, if there are two equal candidates and one is not intermarried, she should get the nod.

SAM: Our *shul* has employed teachers who were married to non-Jews for the past ten years. When we began our youth group eight years ago, we once again engaged a man who grew up in our community and congregation, and was married to a non-Jewish individual, to lead our youth program. He grew our program to having at one point over seventy-five kids who have now become leaders in their Hillels and in the Jewish community.

Five years ago we had the difficult decision of deciding whether the best candidate to be our full-time religious school director and program planner could be someone who was married to a non-Jew. As a congregation, we had difficulty with it and asked for counsel from our national movement. Our president posted our question on the presidents' Listserv, and within one hour the regional director was on the phone to me asking why we would post it, since we were bringing a lightning rod to our congregation that had ramifications. After interviewing many candidates, our best choice remained the candidate who was married to a non-Jew. Despite my reservations and hesitations, I agreed to his employment with the codicil that he could not actively discuss being intermarried. It took a while for him to understand that concept and occasionally I had to remind him that his experiences at home were to remain at home. He is up for his third renewal this year and no one questions his life at home, because what we are most interested in is what he is achieving in our building and in our building alone. Under his leadership our religious school has changed from one that used the traditional model of frontal learning to a really engaging educational experience for our kids. It is wonderful to watch the kids walk in with smiles on their faces, even on Sunday mornings and where we are making some impact on how kids relate to their feeling Jewish.

BOB: Thank you. I appreciate what you've shared, and what everyone has shared on this thread. I would only add my experience, which was in the past to guard against intermarried's influences in our Religious School and Youth Group. It took me about ten years to figure out that, at least for myself and now I know other colleagues who agree, the best candidate can be the one who is intermarried and has the professionalism to keep that out of the children's lives, as appropriately as they can do that.

DON: Sam's experience conforms to much of what we are seeing around us. The notion that intermarriage is a sin is foreign to our members, whether they are Reform, Conservative or Orthodox – and, I would assume, many of us. We obviously need a new "theology" of intermarriage to catch up with the reality that is all around us. Folks who are intermarried and are, nonetheless, living committed, engaged Jewish lives, raising Jewish children and teaching Jewish children, remind us that the old paradigm just doesn't describe the reality. Instead, such folks are often the real heroes of our communities, even though I refrain from using that term.

I can't believe I'm saying this, as an Orthodox rabbi, but, folks, the facts are the facts, and we need to make some adjustments in our thinking. I'm not sure that I'm ready to take these ideas to my board yet, but I am grateful to all of you for forcing me to rethink some of my old prejudices.

SUSAN: Thanks to all of you for your penetrating and courageous thoughts. Much appreciated.

DON: I have a question which I think you non-Orthodox folks will be sympathetic to. Not that I am not, but it's not something my *rebbes* in yeshivah taught me.

A congregant just emailed me that a beloved pet died and he was wondering if there was anything in Jewish tradition to do or say for this animal, aside from burying it, obviously. Any ideas?

BOB: When our cat died, we wrote an "obituary," and sent it to those friends who would appreciate the depth of our pain. There are poems out there that one could say. I think it would be easy to google that and find readings.

The tradition says very little, but our human need can be great. Sharing memories may be the most therapeutic thing. When we sent out our "obit" we got supportive messages from friends. THAT was helpful to all of us. I have it on my smart-phone, so I can read it to you.

Here's what we wrote:

We're writing to tell you that, unfortunately, we had to put Angel down today. Those of you in regular contact with us know that she's been in renal failure since mid-November. Over the weekend she was totally lethargic. In spite of our best efforts to medicate and hydrate her – and you KNOW that was a challenge! – she was clearly declining and in great discomfort.

Over the past many years we've come to love and appreciate being owned by Angel. From the day we let her in from the cold, she's picked out the sunniest and warmest spots, insisted on her share of meat and fish, and slept almost wherever she chose. In her younger days she'd hunt and bring us gifts (yuck!) but more recently she was content to just wander around. For all of us, she was our first four-legged pet, and she taught us innumerable lessons.

We will miss her terribly. Thank you for your support.

Susan: Bob's comment speaks beautifully for itself. I would only wish to add that grief for deceased pets should be taken seriously. A pet can become a part of the family; when the pet dies, there can be a great feeling of loss.

Let me cite my own experience as an example. We never had pets in the house when our children were little. That was due to a lot of factors, including the fact that the house was crowded with four kids. When our daughter got married, her husband wanted to have a dog. Their two children were born with the dog in the house, so she was like an older sibling. When the dog died two years ago, everyone in the family – including my husband and I – realized that she had given many gifts to us. On our next visit, we sat together for a "memorial service." There was no ritual, but we each had an opportunity to process our sense of loss and how we could build on what the dog had given to each of us. It took more than an hour, but afterward, everyone said they were happy to have done it. Their younger daughter then went to her room and painted a picture of the dog, with the words, "We Miss You" across the top. It now hangs proudly near where the dog's food and water bowls used to be.

My point is simply that the request to Don should be taken seriously. And by being present for the family in their time of grief, he can add to his rabbinic presence and authority.

Good luck, Don. I think this is a good opportunity for you.

DON: Thanks, guys! These are tender thoughts I never would have come up with. Thanks for the support!

So, maybe it's time to break, and meet again next week. What say ye?

ALL: Good idea! Have a great week!

Week 17

SAM: Hi everybody. Hope you all had a good week! Let me start with a question that I probably know the answer to. But let's see what you think.

A non-Jewish woman was part of my community for a good amount of time. She was not in the process of converting, but wasn't exactly not in the process of converting either. Hard to explain, but suffice it to say that she was connected with *shuls* for a good number of years, learned a lot of Torah, and was a regular on Shabbat.

She passed away under unusual and very sad circumstances, and without family to arrange for burial. It is likely that someone will ask me to perform a funeral for this woman. There is no other clergy who is more appropriate to perform a funeral service for her.

What advice can you offer about a situation like this? Also, it is possible that this woman will be cremated. Of course, she is not Jewish and therefore there is no prohibition against that.

Anything I should consider if she is cremated?

DON: Seems to me that it would be a *hesed* to do her funeral. If she did not identify as a Christian you would not be depriving her of what to a Christian would be the right and privilege of Christian burial.

SUSAN: I can see no reason why you couldn't do her funeral. Nothing I can think of *halakhically* would prevent it, unless her family were adamant about including Christian prayers or something. Seems like it would be *tzedek* and *chesed* to do so.

SAM: Thanks, friends. I was leaning in that direction, but it helps to have some *hizzuk* [support] from like-minded people.

BOB: Now I have another short question. A congregant is making some stained-glass windows and has asked me if a couple of his initial drawings are appropriate, given our traditional ban regarding images of people in the *shul*. One of his drawings has basic renderings of angels, no faces included, and another has a very rough figure of Jonah inside a big fish.

I told him it's probably fine, but I'd double-check. Happy to get a few opinions.

SUSAN: Bob, there is a long history of human images in synagogues. Mosaics of ancient synagogues – for example the synagogue at Bet Alpha – have them. Even worse they contain images which the Mishnah does forbid. I remember Prof. Lee Levine once took us on a tour of some of the mosaics of ancient synagogues in Tiberias and the surrounding region, and pointed to the beautiful mosaic in front of the preacher's lectern which had most of the forbidden images of the Mishnah included in it. He remarked that it is known that Rabbi Yehudah HaNasi preached in that *shul*, and how do we think he felt looking at how the people felt about his *halakhah*. Of course, we knew exactly how he felt. For the most obvious and amazing depictions of human images in a synagogue look up Dura Europos on google. We should all pray that ISIS does not destroy it.

SAM: The late Rabbi Solomon Freehof wrote about it several times. Notwithstanding all the comments about it today and about Yaakov Agam, the issue isn't simple as Susan mentioned. Figures of humans were specifically and additionally prohibited. *Tur* and *Shulhan Arukh Yoreh Deah* 141 prohibit only three-dimensional objects, not paintings and embroideries, etc. In the Middle Ages some Franco-German authorities objected to birds

and flowers. Rabbi Eliakim ordered the removal of such deco-
rations from the synagogue in Cologne in the eleventh century,
because they distracted the worshiper.

Interestingly, one of the most ancient synagogues in Babylon
had a bust of the monarch. See the Talmudic references in Tractate *Megillah* 29a and *Avodah Zarah* 43b, and also mentioned
in a letter by Sherira Gaon. The synagogue was called *Shev
Veyashiv*. The Talmud says that King Jehoiakhin founded this
synagogue, and he used soil and stones from the Talmud in the
foundation. The worry that someone might worship there only
exists in a private place, but not a public place.

Going back to the *Tur* and *Shulhan Arukh*, only complete
statues with all limbs are prohibited, but partial statues, such as
a bust, are not.

Rabbi Solomon Freefof concludes that while it is not a problem even to put in a bust of a former rabbi, nonetheless one
should keep in mind the needs of worshippers and the possibility of distraction, and that later authorities do have a problem.

In sum, since vague human forms have been an accepted
phenomenon, unless you have people who care or who are influenced by more extreme traditional opinions, or such people
who may visit your *shul* and would object in principle, though
they wouldn't *daven* there, if you take a historical perspective, I
see no problem.

BOB: I kind of thought so, but I appreciate your thoughts and
historical references.

SUSAN: I have an interesting question. A family is making a
stone for a father who outlived his children by about ten years.
The cemetery has advised that the stone should only refer to relationships of people still alive at time of the death of the person
for whom the stone is created. That is, it can read: "grandfather,
brother, uncle" but not "father." Anyone have any experience
with something like this?

DON: When I ordered my mother's *matzevah*, the representative at a reputed gravestone maker advised me that the Jewish

practice is to have a Magen David at the top of the stone. A musical note, as I requested, since she was a musician, "was not Jewish," he said. The draft which arrived for me to check showed a Magen David. When I replied that I am taking my business elsewhere, a new draft immediately arrived with the musical note.

SAM: As a general rule, the marker is there to mark the living's relationship to the deceased. For those who use it for genealogy, it certainly would indicate that the children were deceased at the time of his death.

I'm not aware of much in Jewish sources on this issue. There is a general trend to talk about the *matsevah* in terms of the living deciding what to do, and that one of the purposes of the *matsevah* is for the living. However, there also is a general trend to say that it is *l'shevah ha-met* [in tribute to the deceased]. So in the Bible, Avshalom makes one to keep his name known. So too in the Talmud, tractate *Berakhot* 58b and *Kitsur Shulhan Arukh* 199:17, which also talk about the living. In case you're wondering, I just checked these sources on my smart-phone while you were chatting.

If part of praising him is that he was a parent, then I see no reason not to include it.

In sum, I would leave it up to the family. If it brings up good memories or bad memories, or if it means something good for the family, the family will decide. The monument maker will do what the family wants if he wants to get paid.

He was blessed in his life to have been a father. That's exactly what "father" means on his stone. I'm sure he would have been insulted if it didn't reflect it.

DON: Why would the cemetery make such a suggestion?

SUSAN: Some people love to tell other people what to do. It's spiritual cocaine.

Thanks to all. I think we all agree.

BOB: Here's a really important issue. One that I know you all have to deal with at some time or another. I am looking for some practical wisdom regarding managing emotions. Please share if you have a mantra, quote, or text from our Tradition that helps you focus in times of anxiety, or that enables you to maintain a non-anxious presence.

DON: I've never been able to do that! But our late colleague Jack Bloom edited a book on *Jewish Relational Care A – Z*. It does cover much of what you ask for.

SUSAN: I used to meditate before stressful meetings and chant *Elohai neshamah*, but I've since replaced that with *Ozi ve'zimrat Yah*. It works every time.

To maintain a non-anxious presence in an anxious situation, it is often best to keep it as simple as possible. Thus one of the names of God in our tradition can serve well as a mantra. It is particularly useful if you make it a habit to quietly recite the name during non-stressful times. Then it will come to you naturally and be helpful during difficult moments.

The famous line from Psalm 16, "*Shiviti . . .*" ["I place God before me at all times"] is a good mantra, especially if you understand the word *shiviti* to mean "maintaining equanimity."

"I maintain equanimity, therefore *Adonai* is with me, in front of me."

You might also find that a line from Psalm 131 is helpful as a mantra.

I always try to recite for myself these Hasidic sayings from the book, *Hasidic Wisdom*, edited by Simcha Raz.

Rabbi Mordechai of Lechovitz taught:
All worrying is forbidden,
except to worry that one is worried.

Rabbi Yechiel Mikhal of Zlotchov taught:
I learned this wisdom from my ancestors:
There are two things it is forbidden to worry about:
That which it is possible to fix,
And that which it is impossible to fix.
What is possible to fix, fix it, and why worry?
What is impossible to fix, how will worrying help?

BOB: Some great ideas. Thanks, guys!

SAM: Here's a good question for you *halakhic* masters. Does anyone have a digital screen that displays announcements, upcoming events, yartzeits, etc.? If so, does it run on Shabbat?

Any experiences you can share about leadership and other congregants wanting or not wanting it?

We're working on setting up one now, and I'm fine with it, though our ritual committee chair, who is not at all observant, chafed at it when mentioned during a meeting last night. He said "We're trying to get away from screens on Shabbat!"

SUSAN: Sam, we have one that is manufactured in Israel. It has three screens. It's actually wonderful, and very creative things can be done with it, such as adding pictures of recent events. It's simply not an issue regarding Shabbat.

We run multiple screens in our building. They show program announcements, daily listings of where things are happening in the building, etc. Since Shabbat is the day on which the synagogue is fullest, we make sure our system is ready to run properly on Shabbat. It's all automatic. Obviously, if our system goes down on Shabbat, which rarely but occasionally happens, we leave it down.

We copied ours from a colleague and friend of mine. They have one in the main lobby entranceway, and it runs 24/7 with no complaints. If it goes down on Shabbat, alas.

It has the God-Cast weekly parashah, *shul* leadership, upcoming *b'nai-mitzvah*, upcoming events and updated pictures. It's connected to our executive director's laptop and she does the updates weekly. It means slightly less paper and lots more attention from congregants and guests.

They have another video screen upstairs, between the sanctuary and the chapel, which is exclusively for *yahrtzeits*. It is very well done and updated when necessary.

Now, let me raise another interesting question. Recently, my husband asked me "Why is there no specific blessing that we recite when we do an act of *tzedakah*?" I have my own philosophical thoughts, but am curious if anyone has any leads as far as sources go on this topic. It seems like this could be a really good second-day Rosh Hashanah sermon.

DON: One nice *drash* on the "no blessing before giving *tzedakah*" is that saying a blessing takes time, time that could add to the suffering of the poor person waiting, even to the point of *sakanat nefashot* [endangering a life].

In Saadya's breakdown of the 613 *mitzvot*, according to the Ten Commandments, *tzedakah* belongs to *Lo tirtsah* [Thou shalt not murder]. In other words, reciting a blessing slows the giver down in the process of giving *tzedakah*.

In fact, Reb Bunim said that the reason is that, once the very pious would finish with all the *kavvanot* before saying the *berakhah*, the poor person would have died from hunger.

SAM: Here's another thought. I would imagine that we don't say a *berakhah* over giving *tzedakah* because we would not wish to take joy or thank God for someone else's suffering. Moreover, you don't give *tzedakah* because of yourself, or because you're doing something for God, or because you're doing something for the Jewish People: you give *tzedakah* because someone else is in need, and it is your responsibility to bring such justice as you can to their need.

And here's another reference, Don. The question of the recitation of a *berakhah* for the performance of an interpersonal mitzvah is taken up in *Worship and Ethics: A Study in Rabbinic Judaism*, by Max Kadushin, of blessed memory, pages 12 and 235–237. I just found it on my phone.

DON: Just thought of another reason. Unless the gift of charity is used to enhance the life of the one who receives it, there is no mitzvah. In like manner there is no blessing made before intercourse, because there is no certainty that a child will be conceived from that act.

BOB: For those who may not know, I once found that the USY source book on *tzedakah* written by Danny Siegel also had some decent suggestions and a source text on this subject.

SUSAN: Thanks so much, everyone. I can now report all this back to my husband.

SAM: Here's an interesting question that I'm sure we all deal with. What is the Jewish teaching about reciting personal wedding vows under *huppah*? As far as I have learned, it is not prohibited, though possibly discouraged.

I'd love any direction to sources and any of your thoughts.

SUSAN: I don't know of any traditional material on the subject, but I include the following in the orientation material which I give to couples at whose weddings I am asked to officiate:

> The familiar formula "Do you . . . take this woman . . . in sickness and in health, for richer or for poorer . . ." is from the Anglican *Book of Common Prayer*, and it is not part of the Jewish wedding ceremony. However, in addition to the formulas mentioned above ["*Harey at . . .*" etc.], the bride and the groom may make appropriate declarations. What follows are my suggestions, based on themes from Jewish sources. However, the bride and the groom may compose their own declarations. They should have the rabbi confirm their appropriateness.
>
> a. The groom may say:
> I will be your life's companion. I will love and respect you. I will care for you, come what may, and I will provide for your needs in the manner of a Jewish husband.
>
> b. The bride may say:
> I will be your loyal partner. I will cherish and honor you. I will care for you, come what may, and I will attend to your needs in the manner of a Jewish wife.

DON: I don't see where there would be an objection, unless the vow contradicts the assumptions of the Jewish wedding. I had one case where they told me what they wanted to say and I said that if that was the case I was not the rabbi they wanted to do their wedding. It was for me inconsistent with the message of the Jewish wedding. I don't remember exactly what they had written as it was a while back, but basically it said that they were getting married now because at this moment it reflected their relationship and feelings for each other, but that was just their commitment now, and that it shouldn't be seen as a "permanent" situation. They were very "modern," very "sophisticated" and highly educated people, as you can see. So someone else did their wedding, which was OK with me.

Otherwise all the vows I have heard have been very wonderful and moving. I ask them to tell me what they will say so I can either use it later in the service or avoid anticipating it at the beginning of the service.

BOB: Here's a suggested format which I offer to couples about to be married. It's on my phone, so I can read it to you:

MARRIAGE VOWS A = groom or bride B = bride or groom
A Affirming our people's covenant with God, may be consecrated to each other by this ring.
B Let our lives be intertwined forever.
Let our hearts be united in faith and in hope.
A Let our home be rich with wisdom and reverence.
A&B Limitless is my love for you and my devotion without end.
A I take you to be mine in love and tenderness.
B I take you to be mine in faithfulness.
A May our hearts beat as one in days of joy and trouble.
B May our life together be illumined by our people's heritage.
AorB/A&B May our home be built on Torah and loving kindness.
A&B May my love for you last forever.

I also have the following on my phone, which I offer to the young couple:

From the Hertz Siddur:
The readiness of the bridegroom and the bride to assume

those duties is sufficiently indicated by their presence for the marriage ceremony.

Still there are those who desire verbally to declare their consent, and their acceptance of the undertaking set forth in the *Ketubah*. To them the minister may put the following questions, either before or after his address: –
Minister – "You (A) and (B) are about to be wedded according to the Law of Moses and of Israel."
"Will you (A) take this woman (B) to be your wedded wife? Will you be a true and faithful husband unto her? Will you protect and support her? Will you love, honour and cherish her"?
Bridegroom – "I will."
Minister – "Will you (B) take this man (A) to be your wedded husband? Will you be a true and faithful wife unto him? Will you love, honour and cherish him?"
Bride – "I will."

SAM: These are lovely ideas. Thanks to all of you. I'm sure I can use them in the future.

BOB: Permit me to change the subject. I have an issue about bar-bat mitzvah scheduling. Our long-standing policy has been to advise and guide families as to what is appropriate – and not – for the timing, location, menu, and content of *b'nai-mitzvah* celebrations. At the end of the day, however, we recognize that we cannot control what actually happens, nor can we enforce the guidelines, short of revoking membership, which is a sort of cutting off of one's nose to spite one's face.

As a result, we have our share of Saturday night parties which begin before Shabbat ends. To add some context, some of our Jewish communal organizations have done and continue to do likewise on occasion. And where even "kosher style" doesn't apply. We have had "Boo Mitzvah" parties with a Halloween theme and similarly marginal-to-questionable content.

BOB: Anyway, here's a thornier problem. I would appreciate any insights into how different communities have approached welcoming and including patrilineal-identifying Jews – for those who are not Reform. I'm not sure I'm phrasing the question as clearly as possible. There are so many parts to it. For example, what do we do in religious schools? How do we have the conversation about what a Patrilineal Jew can do and cannot do in terms of ritual participation? How can we talk about "conversion" for a patrilineal person who had a complete religious education, youth group involvement, etc., including issues like *hatafat dam brit*?

Thank you in advance for any and all insights you are able to share on this topic.

SUSAN: Some time ago when I was an assistant rabbi in Denver, we had a bar mitzvah coming up of the nephew of a very distinguished, well-respected member. This child was adopted and had not undergone conversion. Around that time, the senior rabbi decided to institute the practice of immersing all *b'nai-mitzvah* prior to their ceremonies as a means of preparation for becoming bar or bat mitzvah. Since there was a *mikveh* nearby, he avoided having to confront this prominent family, and avoided other cases that might arise subsequently. It became a lovely tradition in the congregation.

SAM: I read an article recently by a Conservative rabbi that may be of assistance. It made some interesting proposals, such as:

(1) That a Patrilineal Jew who has received a basic Jewish education and bar or bat mitzvah under other auspices – Reform, Reconstructionist, or Renewal – and in the case of males has also been circumcised, be accepted as fully Jewish on the same basis and by the same criteria that converts from these movements are accepted as Jewish;

(2) That a person of Patrilineal Jewish descent without these confirmations of Jewish identity be required to undergo study and conversion the same as anyone of no Jewish descent.

I'm not sure if this was ever acted upon, or approved, but I thought when I read it that it made a lot of sense.

SUSAN: To be realistic, Am Yisrael is already splintered. It began when Reform Jewry accepted patrilineal descent. That is part of the reason why this is an issue for us Conservative Jews.

A girl whose father is Jewish, mother is not, is raised as a Jew in the Reform Movement with all the attendant education and bat mitzvah. She meets a boy whose mother is Jewish and father is not, who was raised as a Jew in the Conservative Movement with all the attendant education and bar mitzvah. They decide to marry and ask their respective rabbis to officiate. Her rabbi says, great, when is the date. His rabbi says, great, let's get her converted, just a dip in the mikvah, and we are good to go. Unless the man is really committed to Conservative Judaism, then they will probably go with her rabbi and then join the Reform *shul* and we have lost another potential family over what might seem like a technicality.

Definitely worth pondering.

BOB: I think this issue affects Conservative Jews more than we realize. Our children, as Susan points out, are marrying Patrilineal Jews, and this marriage in turn affects their families and congregations. I happened to be in the office of an esteemed colleague when a congregant walked in upset because his patrilineal son-in-law can't get a High Holiday *aliyah* at the *shul*. For him, his son-in-law had a *bris*, attended Hebrew school, and had a bar mitzvah, so he is Jewish. The son-in-law refuses to convert because he "is already Jewish." He couldn't understand any other way of thinking, and every year has a painful disagreement with the ritual committee over an honor for his son-in-law.

Last year, I was told by another Conservative colleague from a pulpit in a small Jewish community where the Conservative and Reform *shuls* coordinate a lot, the role of the Patrilineal Jew came up. For example, the Reform colleague more than once told the Conservative rabbi that he did not under any circumstances want a Conservative rabbi to tell any of his patrilineal students they weren't Jewish. They do things together like Community Shabbat where people from the congregations share prayers from the *bimah*, and it rotates through the synagogues. It was always a dance.

On a personal note, I have patrilineal cousins. They never

went to Hebrew school. One did birthright and considers himself very Jewish. I have never told him I don't think he is Jewish, and I dread the day when I might have to say something. I always hope he meets a nice Christian, or someone of another faith, so I won't have to have the conversation if he meets a nice Jew and asks me to do the wedding. In my mind I struggle to come up with wording that would be respectful and sensitive to him and his identity, yet true to our beliefs.

To be clear, I am not advocating for change in Conservative *halakhah*. However, if people have successful strategies or wording for these conversations that would be helpful.

SUSAN: OK, here's my "heresy," and it's ok since I've never been "PC," and am not about to start now.

1) What I'm about to say only applies if the child was in fact raised with a Jewish identity and no other religious education or connections.

2) If the mother is not Jewish or was converted by a Reform rabbi and there was no *mikveh*.

3) The child has always viewed himself as a Jew and was identified as one.

They come to the *shul* to participate. I explain the complications as to the "technicality" of their status in the eyes of many Jews and Jewish institutions. I suggest that a way to remove that technical difficulty in terms of status is to do *mikveh*, and or if there was no *bris* milah but only circumcision, to do *hatafat dam brit*.

Here's what I insist on: that they do *hatafat dam brit* if there was only circumcision and no *bris milah*.

But I don't insist on the *mikveh*. Why? *Mikveh* for a child is without *da'at* [conscious choice] obviously. It is simply the idea that they went and immersed. So after the fact I can be sure that the child was at some point under water in a body of water that would qualify as a *mikveh* – an ocean or a lake – and that the child was considered as a Jew at that time, since everyone who knew the family, and in the family, knew the child as a Jew. So I accept the act of immersion after the fact as their *mikveh* if they really see the redoing of the *mikveh* as "insulting" since it would suggest they haven't been Jewish all these years.

The same applies in terms of a wedding. But there the problem is almost always solved by a pre-marital *mikveh* visit, which I have been able to convince them would be great as it is valuable in and of itself and gives them a "certificate" that might mitigate future problems.

In almost all cases, because I validated their Jewishness before suggesting a technical dunking to solve issues that might arise in the future that can't be anticipated, now they do the *mikveh* anyway.

I've actually never had a case where the boy didn't have a *bris* unless they weren't actually identified in any clear fashion as a Jew and therefore need conversion anyway.

The only reason I have been against our considering patrilineal as an acceptable definition of a Jew is that I have seen what it has done to conversion in the Reform movement, and I don't want that to happen in our movement. Sam, you'll have to forgive me for that comment. Maybe you agree.

SAM: No comment, except to say that I think it's time to break until next week.

DON: Agreed!

Week 18

DON: Hi everybody! Nice to be back again, and hash through some of our back-home issues. I'd like to start today. I received an email from a dear friend and colleague this week. He is obviously confused, troubled and in a state of anxiety. He is not experienced in synagogue politics, and I'd like to help him as much as I can. So I'd like to read his email, and hear your thoughts and advice, so that I can pass it on to him. Here goes:

Colleagues,

I am looking for advice, and to hear of your experiences, on a matter that has just come up in my new synagogue. They have just voted in a new board and new co-presidents. To my knowledge, these co-presidents have not served on the synagogue board previously and don't seem to have experience with how synagogues run. They do, though, have lots of business experience, and seem intent on running the board more business-like.

They are both good people whom I like. And at the same time, I feel like there's lots of potential for problem here as well.

One of the things that concerns me is an email that was just sent to the new board, cc'ed to me and to my cantor. The email contains the following note:

"Like all future meetings, this week's board meeting final topic will be a review and discussion related to our staff. As such, our professional staff will be asked to leave the meeting once we get to this topic. This will enable us to ensure as

a board that any feedback to the staff is routed and vetted through the co-chairs."

The intent of this idea is honorable. They want to spare me and the cantor from having to listen to silly, inconsequential complaints, decide what is worth asking us to change and what is not, and so on. However, in practice, I think it has the potential of being quite problematic or harmful to my career and the cantor's. Having a formal point on the agenda at every meeting to discuss what we are doing right and what we are doing wrong without us being present is just asking for trouble. What if there's nothing that I'm doing wrong, and yet, by seeing it as a point on the agenda, board members feel they have to think and come up with something to complain about? It gives great potential for rumor spreading. "Why does the rabbi do X?" leads into a ten minute discussion with them all trying to guess why he does something, when, if the rabbi had been present at the meeting that question might have had a really simple answer that could have ended the discussion in thirty seconds. And we all know that by discussing false accusations, even when they are decided to be false, in some subconscious way, more often than not, just by being discussed, it has a bad effect on what they think about the person being discussed. This also contradicts the halakhah that a Bet Din cannot hear one side's version of the events without the other side being present. Here, they are serving both as the Bet Din and the witness or plaintiff, and you would think the employees – basically, the rabbi and the cantor – should have a right to hear what is being said about them and have the opportunity to respond.

I would also much rather that if a board member either has a complaint or hears one from a congregant, that they come to me directly and discuss it with me, rather than bringing it to the board first and letting the board decide whether or not to bring it to me. I don't need so many people hearing about those complaints, whatever they are. It's just lashon hara.

I would think that the procedure for dealing with a complaint against the rabbi or cantor should be that first, the one complaining or the board member who received the *complaint should speak privately, directly, with the rabbi. If they feel the issue hasn't been resolved, then they should speak about it with the president who should again speak about it privately with the rabbi or tell the board member that it's not an issue that needs to be discussed. If they then feel that it hasn't been resolved, they should tell the rabbi that it will need to be discussed at the next board meeting, and the rabbi should be present to be able to respond and give his position immediately to all listening to the discussion. If the board feels the issue has still not been resolved, and this is an issue of the rabbi's performance, possibly breach of contract, then they should call a special meeting of the board which the rabbi is not invited to. And then, our contracts have clauses in them about dispute resolution, involving United Syna-gogue or the Conservative movement leadership, and so on. This model that they are proposing to implement just doesn't seem right.*

Now I'd like to hear what some of my colleagues have to say. Perhaps you know of somewhere on the RA or United Syna-gogue websites where there are guidelines or suggestions for synagogue boards, for proper conduct in board meetings and/ or proper conduct in interactions with their clergy? Or other ideas.

Incidentally, my contract contains the following clause:

"The Rabbi shall be notified of all meetings of the Board of Governors of the Synagogue and, with the exception of Exec-utive Sessions of such meetings declared by the President of the Synagogue, shall have the right to attend such meetings and participate in their deliberations, without any voting rights."

Thanks for your time.

DON: So what say you folks?

SUSAN: Without commenting on the situation at board meetings, I would like to suggest something that I learned from my Protestant colleagues, which we do in our *shul*. We set up a Committee on the Rabbi, with six members: three that the Board chose and three chosen by me. We tried to have representatives of different groups within the synagogue, by geographic location, gender, age, etc. They were considered ombudspeople, there to hear concerns congregants expressed about the rabbi, and also to deal with my concerns about the congregation. That way, these types of disagreements did not reach the board level of discussion unless they were really, really serious. That never happened, *barukh HaShem*. We did this only recently. I wish we had done it earlier.

DON: I like Susan's idea. And I think the problem my friend describes stems from the unusual structure of synagogues. Normally, in nonprofit organizations, the day-to-day operations are not the board's purview. They're responsible for fund raising and overall governance. And they are not the customers of the organization.

But in *shuls*, they are, and unless they know better, they get sucked into discussions of every last detail in daily operations, including how good the sermon was last Shabbat and whether congregant X got offended by the thermostat in the sanctuary.

Well, that's the problem. What the solution is, I'm not sure. But I'll say this: we share our custodian with Chabad, and of course the rabbi there does not report to any board. The custodian wonders how we get anything done, and he's right.

SUSAN: In another congregation I'm familiar with, here's what they do. They set up a liaison committee for every professional. It consists of three people appointed by the president. All issues with professional staff are given over to this committee which meets with the professional once a year or more if a certain problem or issue arises. If it can't be dealt with by the committee it would then go to the executive board, but that almost never happens unless the real issue is that they are ready to not renew or terminate.

SAM: He's right to be concerned. I feel for him. The trust is already gone. It may be too late to salvage, or it may not be.

The challenge is that he's already there, and yet the procedures for review, which is valuable to both the supervisor and the employee, have not been established.

I would tell him to ask to meet with the president before the board meeting, and share with him his concerns. I'd prioritize. To me, the key problem with his approach is that the board is assuring that he will be unable to address concerns properly. How so? Well, if the board comes to him and says, "You were rude to someone at *Kiddush* last week," and he says, "Who was it? I'd like to apologize," they're going to have to say, "We can't tell you that."

That's the one principle I've always – gently, yet firmly – insisted upon, namely, that the board not consider any criticism unless the criticizer is willing to be identified. I think that he can try to make some headway on this principle.

It isn't inherently a terrible thing to have an executive session once in a while, and he should make clear to the president that he understands the need for that. It's potentially humiliating and even infuriating, but that has to do with the difficulty coming to grips with the situational challenge of being employeed by *ba'alei batim*. Think of it this way: *ba'alei batim* think they're doing a mitzvah. They believe in their fiduciary obligation to guard the finances of the *shul*, and this is one of the ways that they think that they can accomplish that. I would suggest that trust is a critical feature of *shul* life. Once it's gone, it's almost impossible to recover it. He could suggest to the president that he consider quarterly executive sessions of the board.

Depending on how that conversation goes, he may be in a better position to know whether the situation is salvageable. As I said above, it may be too late. The question is whether the president realizes that and cares. If he realizes it and doesn't care, it's time to look for a new job. If he doesn't yet realize it and cares, he may be able to influence him!

Wish him good luck. And he should be sure to stock up on antacid tablets this week. Prayer can be helpful, too.

BOB: It's possible that someone with an agenda is giving them advice and they don't see the potential trouble. It's also possible that it's nothing but them trying to figure out how to apply a business model to the strange world of a religious institution, which is not exactly the same as either a for-profit business or a not-for-profit business. Just as one example of our inherently strange world, we're supposed to be the bosses of our bosses, and to some extent make them uncomfortable, apply guilt, etc., as well as support, encourage, etc. If we don't adopt some business ideas, we can't raise funds and survive. If we operate only like a business we also can't survive.

My take is that if he really has a read on them, and he likes them and they like him, he can manage it. If he doesn't have the correct take on them, then he is in major trouble.

In the pulpits I've served in, I generally went the route of the liaison committee for most of my career. Sometimes they tried to meet monthly. They quickly came to the conclusion that monthly was too frequent, and we often met quarterly, and once I'd been there a while even less often, and frequently only met when issues arose. Sometimes these issues weren't necessarily about my actual performance but my being the only one to try to control a situation involving others before it went out of hand.

Hopefully with two successful and highly placed business people running the meetings he will avoid the interminable and generally non-productive meetings that other people run. If so, assuming they like him, they should be able to control the meeting from devolving into chaos when it comes to the issues surrounding him. Again, if he's wrong in his read, he has an uphill battle that will be difficult to survive. I have managed to survive some people with an agenda, including in one place a president, and another a vice-president, and sometimes I've chosen not to try to stay and fight.

One would think that the national synagogue body, which has been in operation for many decades, would have effective protocols in effect guiding synagogue boards in how to properly respect their כלי קודש and run a synagogue. Not so. The Chabad model is the proper one. The Rabbi is the CEO.

SAM: I think he has gotten the message that this is a pretty major red flag, and if possible needs to be dealt with as soon as possible. He states that "they are both good people." I have found over the years that there are many people who seem to be "good people," but when they are given a position of responsibility in the synagogue, they seem to lose their "goodness." Don't underestimate the power of lay people to screw up a synagogue and the professional staff, especially the rabbi.

I would suggest that he ask to meet with them before the next meeting, and if it's possible to have a third party there, whom he is close to – maybe a past president – just to keep the discussion on track, and make certain that it is clear to all what is decided.

It is unfortunate that our national organizations do not seem to have anything to say in exactly the area they might contribute to synagogue life. They somehow seem to be more concerned about our proper representation at their annual meeting than they are about such things as this. There are really three things that every board member should have. They should know something about Judaism, they should be active in the organization, including financially, and they should know something about how non-profits work. Unfortunately we often get people, including leaders, who lack some, or even all, of these qualities. That can be disastrous. There are fewer people less qualified to run something than people on a synagogue board, and we often succeed in spite of them. I believe a well-known and well-respected rabbi was quoted as once saying to his board, "I will make you a deal. I won't come to your board meetings and you don't come to my services." [Laughter].

He should just remember that if he perseveres, most of these difficult people will eventually give up trying to make his life difficult and he can do what he does best – being the rabbi.

DON: That's certainly a difficult situation. I'll pass on some of your ideas.

To change the topic, here's a very contemporary issue that will resonate for all of us. Our synagogue has a growing elder population. How do I find out what physical or other changes we need to make to keep our elders safe, and make it an easy place for them to come and participate? We have a loop-hearing system with headphones. We have a power-assist front door. People come in with walkers, and we stow them in the back – and sometimes trip over them. We have fixed sanctuary seats, and several portable "elevating seat boosters" that elders move into whatever seats they sit in. We have taken out six or eight seats in the sanctuary rear corner to make room for a children's play area. Someone suggested that we take out more seats to make room for wheelchairs. Our elders are living longer, and coming to *shul*. *Bimah* accesiblity is a problem, but we have installed parallel stair rails, and our *gabba'im* know to closely accompany elders up and down. The layout of our *shul* makes a ramp prohibitive. We have handicapped parking spaces, and a no-curb area from the parking lot to the sidewalk. What else have *shuls* done to retrofit for elders?

SAM: This is an agonizing issue for synagogues built in the sixties and earlier. In our recent renovation of our entire building, lowering the *bimah* was my only goal that we could not accomplish. We widened the aisles, made multiple seat spaces for wheelchairs and space for rollators. We more than doubled our special spaces for parking. All building entrances and rooms have one power assist door. We built brand new bathrooms that are designed to accommodate an oversized wheelchair.

We consulted with experts locally and nationally about the *bimah*. We were able to do a total redesign of our chapel, but no solution was found for our main sanctuary without eliminating the heating and air-conditioning system. During a Renovation Committee discussion a wisecrack actually solved our *bimah* issue. A heated debate took place over the issue of the visibility and location of the *amud* [rostrum] on the *bimah*. Finally, someone quipped "For God sakes, put the *amud* on wheels and then you all get your way and we can go home tonight." So . . . it dawned on someone, this is a solution to providing an *aliyah* to someone who can't do the stairs. We had a beautiful portable Torah reading *amud* made that has rollers and is kept below the *bimah*. It takes seconds to reposition it when we need to have an *aliyah* or do the Torah service on the floor level. It has worked for us.

DON: Thanks, Sam! If I need more advice I'll have my chairperson get in touch with you, or perhaps your committee chair.

SAM: Absolutely. It will be a pleasure.

SUSAN: I came across a very interesting fictional *mea culpa* written by a Conservative colleague. I brought it with me today so I could share it with you all and get your reactions.

BOB: Sure, go ahead!

SUSAN: OK, here it is. It's called "**The Dilemma of Conservative Rabbis – A (Fictional) Story**"

IT WAS MY FAULT . . .

When I was ordained by the Jewish Theological Seminary in the 1970s, the Conservative Movement was at the zenith of its strength and popularity. More than forty percent of American Jews identified as "Conservative." After my forty years in the field, the Conservative Movement is in sharp decline. Today, only eighteen percent of American Jews identify as "Conservative," and those that do are rapidly aging and show less commitment to Tradition and to supporting the dwindling number of synagogues affiliated with the Movement. You do the math: It's obvious that I must be the reason for the decline.

Et Hata-ai Ani Mazkir Hayom ["I make mention today of my offenses"] (Genesis 41:9):

1. I supported the decision of the Committee on Jewish Law and Standards to allow Jews living in the suburbs to drive to synagogue on Shabbat. Or at least I didn't order a chain across our parking lot on Friday nights and Saturdays. Those who were offended that almost all our *Shabbes* worshippers drove to synagogue left and joined the Orthodox *shul*.

Or maybe it was because I was too *strict* about Shabbat observance. I wouldn't allow the caterer to begin setting up on Shabbat afternoon for the Saturday night wedding, causing him to lose a number of bookings to Country Clubs and Reform Temples. . . . Two families with June *simchas* quit the synagogue.

2. I allowed women to lead the *davening*, and counted them in the *minyan*, even though the *halakhic* process in those decisions was open to question. A vocal minority of our *shul* regulars felt this was a betrayal of the Judaism of their fathers, and left us to attend the local Chabad, or to form a "break-away" traditional *minyan* housed in someone's living room.

Or maybe it was because I wouldn't allow women to serve as witnesses on *ketubot*, even though I was a believer in egalitarianism. My concern was that the "legality" of the marriage, and the potential status of children born to that couple, might be called into question by the signatures of female *edim* [witnesses]. This led to a handful of feminists joining a Reconstructionist *Havurah*.

3. I refused to officiate at interfaith weddings, angering many parents in my congregation whose children married non-Jews, including my *shul's* past-president. "If my own Temple rabbi won't do my kid's wedding, what do I need him, or the Temple, for?" He quit.

Or maybe it was because I permitted the non-Jewish father of a bar mitzvah boy to stand on the *bimah* with his Jewish wife and recite the *Sheheheyanu* blessing – in translation AND transliteration. Two men on our Ritual Committee quit.

4. I regretfully officiate at Jewish weddings in venues where "kosher-style" or even "*glatt treif*" food is served, reasoning that my threat to not officiate won't cause the parents to change the menu, but would only alienate the Jewish couple and their family from me and the synagogue, AND that in these days, two Jews marrying one another is something to celebrate, even i . . . an't stay and eat. I lost one member who was ashamed that his rabbi would "give his blessing" to a *treif* affair, and one family who was offended that their rabbi wouldn't stay and partake in the celebration with them, especially since they would arrange for a kosher meal, *double* wrapped in aluminum foil.

Or maybe it's because I wouldn't allow our Sisterhood president, who swears she has a kosher kitchen, to bake at home for her son's *aufruf* and bring the cakes into *shul* for the Kiddush. She felt insulted, and quit.

5. I declined to perform a "same-sex" Jewish wedding with *Erusin* and *Sheva berakhot* for two wonderful men, as I continue to struggle with the biblical prohibition of Leviticus 18:22. They quit.

Or maybe it's because I allowed a congratulatory note to the couple to be included in the Temple Bulletin, offending some of the older members – who quit the Temple.

6. I agreed to do a funeral for the man whose remains would be cremated. His children, my congregants, were against his decision, but he had sworn them to obey his wishes. A founding member of the synagogue, a Holocaust survivor, was so upset that he quit.

Or maybe it's because I refused to allow a member to bury his non-Jewish wife in the synagogue's cemetery. He quit.

All these people left our synagogue, and our Movement, because of decisions that I made over the years. I hereby acknowledge all my mistakes, and I take the blame. If we're in decline, it's clearly because of me.

Though to be honest, I'm not sure if I would do anything differently.

BOB: You know, Susan, if it weren't so sad, and true, it would be funny!

I am reminded of the comical Talmudic story about a man who had two wives, one who was up in years, and the other was much younger than her husband. The older wife is trying to pull out his dark hair so as to make him look older, and the younger, of course, does just the opposite, and wants to pull out all his gray hair, to make him look younger. The net result? He ends up being bald! [Bava Kama 60b].

A typical example: I suggested to the *minyanaires* one morning that שלא עשני אשה appearing in the Birnbaum Siddur is no longer acceptable for a Conservative congregant to recite. My proposal to change at least the prayer if not the prayer book, fell on deaf ears. But when I showed displeasure for having even minor sisterhood affairs in a *treif* restaurant, I was thought of as a man from the "old school."

DON: Thank you, Susan, for sharing this thoughtful piece. We do get caught in the middle and often have to make difficult decisions in accordance with our hearts and beliefs – or sometimes standards of our movement – that alienate others. As long as we can look ourselves in the mirror and believe we are acting correctly and with integrity, we can continue on, knowing that we are doing the right thing.

SUSAN: Well said, Don. I agree!

SAM: I, too, enjoyed reading the piece that Susan brought. It reflects a keen insight into the issues Conservative rabbis, and in a way, all rabbis, face. However, I think we also should reflect on a more global issue. To wit, the problems of being a movement of the center. That's why I'm a Reform rabbi.

In the middle of the twentieth century, the country moderated toward the center – politically, culturally, and socially. The Conservative movement fit nicely into that scheme, especially since its very structure allowed, or perhaps even celebrated, a diversity of opinions and practices.

At the beginning of the twenty-first century we see the country moving toward polarities – certainly politically, but also in terms of cultural and social norms. Every religious group which flourished fifty or sixty years ago, for example, Episcopal, Presbyterian and other main line churches, and liberal Catholics, are losing members because people are moving toward the extremes of fundamentalism and secularism. In my humble opinion, seeing the situation as an outsider, the Conservative movement is being buffeted by the same winds.

If we live long enough, and I pray that our younger colleagues will, we may see a return to the center, so that both Conservative and traditional Reform colleagues like myself, will be comfortable. In the meantime, let's keep emphasizing our strengths, even if the numbers are shrinking. This will reward our *ba'alei batim*, and bring satisfaction to ourselves.

My two cents. And thanks to Susan for challenging us with this fascinating, if ironic, article.

While I have the floor, here's a quick *halakhic* question for us to chew on. A question regarding the *sheliah tzibbur* [prayer leader]. Can a *sheliah tzibbur* lead when sitting – be it because of a permanent or temporary disability? I would certainly think the answer for a permanently disabled person would be "yes," as the person wouldn't be obligated to do what he is physically unable to do. For a person with a temporary disability, should the community wait for the person to heal and stand before enabling the person to be the *Shatz*? I would appreciate any enlightenment you can offer on either of these issues.

DON: When I visit the Jewish Home for the Aged, many of the folks are not able to stand with comfort, or in some cases simply cannot stand at all. My view is that permitting those for whom standing at the *bimah* is an unfair challenge, they should have the option to sit or even read portions such as the *haftarah* from their own seat. I take my cue from the Talmud, Tractate *Shabbat* 81b, where Rav Hisda offers us the lesson about respect for human dignity. His admirable view is that respect for human dignity can even supersede a Torah commandment. That ideal of *kavod ben-adam*, "respect for human dignity," is very important to me and to the congregation at the Jewish Home. For that reason, they offer those who served as cantors or prayer leaders the chance to still take an active part, even if it's from their seat rather than the *bimah*. I would recommend that position to all of us.

SAM: Great reference, Don, thanks so much! A noble ideal which we should all follow.

SAM: OK, my turn. Here's a tough one. A young woman who grew up in my congregation just had a baby daughter. Her husband is Catholic. She'd like to speak to me about the ramifications of having her daughter baptized. I suspect she wants to know whether or not the daughter will remain Jewish for naturalization purposes. In other words, will she or will she not need to be converted to Judaism should she wish to embrace her Jewish identity. I'd value a referral to something I could read to bring me up to speed on the ins and outs of this. Yes, I'm familiar with this entire area of rabbinic practice. I'm looking for a precis of the operative *halakhah* and standards in our various movements.

SUSAN: Her daughter will always be Jewish on some significant level, because she has a Jewish mother. I was once reprimanded by an Agudas Yisroel rabbi in Dallas regarding a child, with a Jewish mother, who had been christened and raised as a Catholic, and suddenly as a college student declared she was Jewish. I insisted she not teach in our Hebrew School or staff our youth group or our day camp until she learned about Judaism and went through some public affirmation, like an *aliyah* to the Torah after she learned the basics, just like a conversion student would need to do. The Agudas Yisrael rabbi had used her as a baby-sitter and said he considered her Jewish. Can you believe?!

The church will consider her Catholic and free of original sin if she is christened. In terms of "naturalization" purposes, does that mean moving to Israel? Or something else? If it's Israel, this is a great question for our Israeli colleagues to address. Her parents have a serious problem. How will this child be raised? What kind of religious symbols and messages will be part of her home life and her school life? Jewish Day School or Catholic Parochial School, or Public School and supplementary religious schooling? On and on and on.

The majority of Reform rabbis I've worked with have taken the patrilineal issue seriously in terms of either insisting on an exclusive Jewish education for the child to be considered Jewish, regardless of which parent is Jewish, or only holding that rule for children whose mothers are not Jewish.

For me the *halakhah* has been uncomfortably clear: born of a Jewish mother, you're Jewish. How this relates to baby naming, *bris*, bat mitzvah, and wedding, is up to the *mara d'atra*.

I heard a story about a *mohel* in Charleston who was called by a Reform affiliated family to schedule a *bris* and it turned out that the scheduling was based on the day the child was being christened earlier that morning. When the rabbi refused to schedule the *bris* and the family was indignant and obnoxious on the phone, he called their rabbi who told him that he had already refused to officiate with the *mohel* at the *bris* because of the christening and he apologized for not giving the *mohel* a head's up.

Of course, the problem of *halakhic* Jews being baptized as babies and children has been going on for centuries, more often than we know.

BOB: I'd like to add that David I. Kertzer's 1997 book, *The Kidnapping of Edgardo Mortara,* which is the basis for the film, makes for fascinating, surprising reading. It raises important and interesting questions about Jewish identity, about Jewish-Catholic relations before Vatican II, about the acceptance of Jews in an open society, about justice and rights and family and state. . . . and it reads like a novel, one with an improbable plot.

And since I have the floor, let me pose an interesting question. Does one observe *shivah* and *shloshim* for a former spouse from whom one was divorced? I would presume no, but want to verify.

And to amplify the question, while such mourning may not be required, is it permitted? Can one elect to observe some or all aspects of *aveilut*?

SUSAN: That's the whole idea of divorce. They aren't married any more, and the only obligations are financial. Then there are "moral" obligations if there are children, because he is the father of the children. I have seen a case in which the divorced father came every day with the son for a month for *Kaddish*, and stood with the son every day.

And, I have also seen a case in which the divorced spouse wants to say *Kaddish* with the children and the children get angry. "You divorced and abandoned our father, you have no right to say *Kaddish* with us."

DON: I would make one exception to allow mourning practices for an ex-spouse. If there was a civil divorce but no *Get*. Sadly, there are many former couples who fail to get a *Get*, and in such a case, Jewishly they would still be married, and thus there would be a *halakhic* obligation to observe all the normal mourning customs.

SUSAN: In that kind of extreme case the best approach is for the parent to ask the child if there is any way he could be helpful and let the child of the deceased say what she wants. Sometimes getting out of the way is the best strategy.

Seems to me that by sitting *shivah* for an ex-, you are helping make peace with the life-loss that you have suffered. Look at it as a way of "laying them gently down," so you can be at peace.

BOB: An interesting conversation I've started. I think that just because two people cannot live together does not mean they don't have feelings for each other. In reaction to all of your comments, it seems to me that this is a case of just because *halakhah* does not require it does not preclude or forbid it.

SAM: Like most such instances, a simple yes or no will not resolve what may be behind the question. Certainly, there are no *halakhic* obligations. If that's the question, then the answer is indeed no. But each case is individual. You have to ask why the divorced spouse wants to observe *shivah*. It may be, for example, that neither spouse remarried and they remained close friends, and the children would be comforted by the surviving parent sitting with them and saying *Kaddish*. It may be, on the other hand, that the children are offended by the surviving spouse observing mourning practices. Or, it may be that there are no children. The answer to the particulars of the situation ought to determine the answer to this question.

BOB: Very wise advice, Sam. All of you have given me good ideas. Thanks so much!

SAM: OK, here's one to chew on. Any of you have a membership category for those who only have cemetery plots? We call it a "cemetery-only" membership. I am looking for an alternative category name. People walking around saying they are "cemetery-only members" of _____ (fill in the blank) is not really good marketing for your synagogue.

DON: How about "The walking dead?" Or here are some more: An Afterlifetime Membership? Deadheads? Members in perpetuity? Real estate members? Land holders? Members in good repose? A Jewish Underground Membership?

SAM: Don, what have you been drinking? Nasty guy, you are! I know you have a great sense of humor, but really???

SUSAN: Don's tongue-in-cheek responses to Sam's original question, cute as they are, don't address a fundamental issue that many synagogue-owned cemeteries face: Should we sell burial plots to non-members and, if so, under what conditions?

I've known cemetery committee chairpeople over the years who have defended a policy of selling burial plots only to members. After all, many of them legitimately feel we have devoted many years of efforts, not to mention significant financial support, to maintain a Jewish cemetery for our members. It's wrong for people who can't be bothered to join a synagogue for many years, to expect to benefit from that synagogue's tireless efforts when they're making funeral or burial arrangements.

Some synagogues establish a price differential for member purchases and non-member purchases of burial plots. Sometimes, not coincidentally, it's the equivalent of one or two years' synagogue membership.

While I understand the position of the above-mentioned synagogue cemetery leaders, in fact the situation is not always so simple. It's not always just a case of someone who can't be bothered to join a synagogue, but who wants to benefit illegitimately from the synagogue.

Many years ago, my late father-in-law was diagnosed with a terminal illness. Though he had lived for many decades in Ft. Lauderdale where he and his wife had been longtime synagogue leaders, he looked into buying a burial plot in the cemetery where his parents had been buried, in northern New Jersey.

The synagogue responded appropriately and with *rachmonos*.

They did not say: You're not a member of our synagogue, so you may not purchase a burial plot in our cemetery.

Instead, they sold him a burial plot on the condition that he join the synagogue for two years. So he joined the synagogue, in which he had been married about fifty years earlier, even though he lived hundreds of miles away. I don't remember if his membership was called "associate" or had some other label.

A few years later, he was buried a few spaces away from his parents – an arrangement that gave him great comfort in his last years, and that has given his family great comfort in the years since.

I share this story with you to remind us all that not all unaffiliated Jews are simply people lacking in commitment, whose needs deserve more of our disdain than our outreach efforts. The issues of High Holiday tickets, weddings, and other pastoral care for non-members are analogous to, but not identical to, the issues of burial plots for non-members.

And of course it's complicated. I have a lot of sympathy for, and agreement with, the position of cemetery leaders who assert: "We break our backs working for our members, and we just can't be that concerned about people who don't want to join our synagogues but who want to mooch off of us in times of need." But it's a complicated Jewish world these days. And the non-affiliated Jews and even no-longer-affiliated Jews – alas, a growing cohort in the Jewish community – warrant our attention, our concern, and our ongoing outreach efforts.

DON: Susan, you shame me with your maturity, in the face of my sarcasm! In all seriousness, you are absolutely right. And you gave the mature, honorable response. I could not agree with you more. Thanks! And forgive my *yetzer hara* [evil inclination]. It just pops out now and then, uncontrollably.

SAM: OK, guys, are you ready for this? It's a tough one. Have any of you done a transgender naming ceremony? If so, did you do a separate special ceremony or a *Mi Sheberakh* during a regular service? Did you discuss it with your ritual committee and board first?

BOB: Some years ago, after having worked with an individual in addressing their understanding of the need to transition, we did the following. During a morning *minyan* – on the day the hormonal treatment was to begin, this person had an *aliyah* for the last time as "Julie." After the service we went into the main sanctuary where "Julie," surrounded by family and friends, and me, shared a ritual of transition which we had worked on together. It was a beautiful and perhaps one of the most moving moments of my rabbinate. Seven years later, "Jim" remains a precious member of our *shul* community, and I am not sure that most people remember his past. I remain proud and amazed by the sense of inclusion our *shul* community has demonstrated for the GLBTQ community dating back many decades.

SUSAN: I haven't done anything like this yet, but I am a staunch advocate of getting Ritual Committees and boards to have buy-in on such potentially controversial issues. When dealing with issues like this – for me it was same-sex *aufruf* and an upcoming interfaith pre-marriage Shabbat morning blessing – I always educate the Ritual Committee and board, asking if there are any questions they have or issues they want to raise. They sometimes will give me something to think about that either makes the experience better or helps to avoid conflict.

I do know of a case performed by a colleague and friend, which I can report on. Some years ago my friend did a conversion for a female to male, and she did the naming ceremony as part of the conversion ceremony, after the *Bet Din* and *mikveh*. The *Bet Din* and *mikveh* were held at her synagogue. But I didn't think it appropriate to mention it to anyone. She did, however, consult a few senior colleagues, who helped her quite a bit with details. I'm proud that we can do ceremonies like this in our day and age.

DON: Perhaps it's time to shift our focus to something a bit less weighty, though not unimportant. Like most of us, I am generally in favor of throwing candy in *shul* to mark joyous occasions. This practice helps us to underscore the fact that the synagogue is a place of warmth and of sharing, not just a bastion of austere formalism.

Unfortunately, I had a negative experience this week involving the celebratory throwing of candy. Usually, the distribution of candy prior to the throwing thereof is noisy enough that I am aware of the activity as it is taking shape, and I know when to get out of the line of fire. The positive thing that I can say about this event is that the distribution of candy, during the *aliyah* for which the *ba'al simhah* was called up, took place quietly. I was unaware this time of what was taking shape. My first indication arrived in the form of a small bag of rather solid candy that struck my right eye. Needless to say, this exposes me to a slightly different perspective on candy-throwing. My eye still feels sore, but I don't think that any notable damage has been done.

I am still in favor of the throwing of candy during services. However, I have come to realize that there is a need for a framework governing such activity. It's not so much that I am fearful for my own safety. The *gabba'im* are at risk, too, along with the celebrant, and the innocent bystander who happened to have been called up for the previous *aliyah*. Being joyous does not necessitate making the *shul's* environment *hefker* [anarchy]. Some logical rules might include: (a) a requirement to use soft candies – difficult to enforce, though – and (b) a requirement that people throw underhand, to shower the celebrant with sweetness.

I would greatly appreciate it if those among us whose *shuls* have some established written policies in this area would share them with me.

SAM: Here's what we do. We also have candy-throwing for *semahot,* and it is a wonderful moment in the service. The way that we resolve the issues that you raise is by providing the candy, which is invariably sunkist gels, the only real choice that satisfies the three cardinal rules: soft, not messy, kosher. We minimize the noise by having the gels wrapped in little organza drawstring bags that are re-used for each *simhah.* We limit them to the first four rows and have them placed under the seats, usually by kids, after the Friday night service.

It takes a little extra volunteer work before the *simhah,* and we choose to cover the expense so we can buy the sunkist gels in bulk. It's worked very well for us so far.

Hope this is helpful.

BOB: I am certain I am not alone in wishing that my *shul*, among many other congregations suffering the aging of the Conservative Movement reality, had many *semahot* to celebrate so we could have to ponder this question beyond where we are today. Our current practice has evolved out of my first few years here. You can guess the problems we had then.

Like Sam, we took ownership of the entire process. First, the candy, soft kosher fruit gels.

Second, for *b'nai-mitzvah* celebrations we have a "candy drop." After the *haftarah* one or more of the siblings or cousins stands behind the child during the final *haftarah* blessing and, after *mikadesh hashabbat*, drops a basket of about fifty candies on the child, while I lead the congregation in *Siman Tov*. In other words, we change the focus to the *haftarah*, take the *gabba'im,* etc., out of the "line of fire" and invite the children up to pick up the candy, place it back in the basket, and the candy is distributed at the *kiddush* luncheon, so there's no crinkly sounds during the later parts of the service. Then the child gives a *d'var Torah* followed by the rabbinic charge.

Third, for an *aufruf*, baby naming, anniversary and other joyful experiences, we do the candy throw and I use my *tallit* as a "Bat Cape" to protect the *bimah* participants from harm. But since there is a lower sense that this is a try-out for the Phillies' Pitching Staff, and no one wants to damage the guy celebrating his seventieth bar mitzvah anniversary – we have one scheduled this coming July, he should live and be well – or the ninety year old great-grandmother naming her great-granddaughter, we rarely have problems from the Junior Congregation, or anyone else in the *shul*.

It all changed for the better when we defined the issues in the worship committee, and created a policy that insisted we buy the candy we want to have thrown and we take the candy out of the hands of playful and age-appropriate early adolescent boys and girls, not to mention everyone else in *shul*.

Taking ownership and responsibility for those in the synagogue on a given Shabbat is the key for me.

SUSAN: So I will be the one to throw some cold water on this. I do understand that it makes *shul* "more fun" and the family celebrating likes it. It is also a royal pain in the neck and in my opinion takes as much as it gives. First, the planning must be down to the last detail: who gets to throw, which candies are used, when it is thrown, etc. Of course more often than not something goes awry in the process and the bar mitzvah's friends think it's just hysterical, if they get a hold of some candy, to try and hit him – or the rabbi or cantor – in the head. Or the family forgets to hand it out. Or, while the bar mitzvah is reading the *haftarah* everyone is paying attention to the cute children handing out candy. Second, I find many families obsess over the candy more than the *haftarah* or other "real" rituals. It can actually take away from what's truly important.

We do allow it upon request but fortunately it is only rarely requested. I know my response is a bit of a buzz kill here, but I'm guessing I'm not the only one who feels this way.

One Shabbat on the *bimah* the candy was flying, and my president, an insurance executive wincing along with me, recalled that he knew of a lawsuit because of an over-zealous candy attack.

Joy can be expressed in synagogue without the disruptive hilarity of projectile-hurling.

DON: Well, even though we don't have full agreement, at least I have some ideas and ways to mitigate the damage that sometimes occurs.

BOB: I have an interesting question. I hope you folks can help with this one. It's a tough issue.

How do we welcome a Jew who has accepted Jesus as his savior who wishes to come to our *shul*, not to proselytize or share his experience but just to "hear the word of God" in the synagogue?

Last week a new face came to *shul*. A young man with his wife. His wife was clearly not Jewish, and she also was struggling with health problems. But he wore a *tallit* and *kippah*. I asked him a little about himself before services, and he shared that it had been awhile since he had come to a synagogue, though he told

me he had lived in Cleveland for ten years, originally from Columbus. That was a little odd, to live in town so long and not
connect with one of the synagogues, but could have been for lots
of reasons. I offered him an *aliyah* and he gave me his Hebrew
name immediately. He followed the Hebrew in the service. So
I am thinking, "New Jew, intermarried, did not find a spiritual
home yet in town, maybe his wife is interested in conversion."
He pulls me aside after services and tells me he does not want to
be guilty of deception. His parents were Jews, he had a bar mitzvah, but has accepted Jesus as his savior. He would like to come
to the synagogue because this is where "God's word is shared."
He is not interested in proselytizing, but he had to let me know
what's what.

I appreciate his honesty. I assume he is sincere when he says
he is interested in coming for personal spiritual reasons, and not
to proselytize. I don't see how we can say "you are not welcome"
as long as he keeps his promise. Here is where I need some advice from those with similar experiences:

How do you introduce him to members? Do you share that he
is a Jew for Jesus? Do I tell him to keep the whole apostasy experience on the down low? People feel uncomfortable with such
individuals, like they have a disease. A person at *shul* was asking
who the new couple is, and I mentioned that he was a Jew for
Jesus. The person recoiled.

Unwittingly we offered him an *aliyah*. Do I explain to him
that he cannot participate in rituals any more? Do I point him
out to the *gabba'im* that he is not Jewish? Do I say, "Please don't
where a *tallit*," which is what I tell non-Jews or those interested
in conversion? *Kippah*, yes for all visitors, but only Jews wear a
tallit.

I plan to have a sit-down discussion with him to understand
exactly where he is coming from. He also indicated that besides
his wife's health issues, he himself has a disability that keeps
him from driving long distances, and therefore he lost his job
recently. Perhaps he is in the midst of existential crisis. Nevertheless, is it bad form to try to discourage his belief in Jesus?
Not that I can convince a person of a certain faith to dispel their
converted views, but you can plant seeds of question and doubt.

Should it be a goal of the conversation, or do we simply accept that everyone has a right to their belief, even if such an apostasy brings sadness to our community?

Any thoughts would be welcome.

SAM: We've had a couple of Messianic Judaism types come to our *shul*. MJs, in my experience, do actually tend to be different than Jews for Jesus, in that MJs are not always interested in proselytizing, but I have yet to encounter a Jew for Jesus who wasn't a missionary. They'll go to great lengths to score converts, and are not to be trusted in that regard. But I've encountered MJs who are not that way. They are *kofrim* [deniers], but not out to make more *kofrim*.

My position is that if they're up front about it, and they don't proselytize, they can be there. As long as they're *halakhically* Jewish, I count them in the *minyan*, but I don't offer them honors. I try to converse with them as I can, recommend that they come to my classes, come to me with questions, and so on. I try to look at it as an opportunity for *kiruv*, just as I do with intermarrieds. The difference, of course, is that I give a lot more lattitude to intermarrieds, since after all, a *hoteh* [sinner] is not a *kofer b'ikar* [denier]. But I see nothing wrong with gracefully and diplomatically trying to bring back an apostate, or with gracefully and diplomatically trying to steer an intermarried couple toward conversion of the non-Jewish spouse.

I did have one individual who broke his promise about proselytizing behavior, and I had to inform him in no uncertain terms that this was unacceptable and unwelcome, and any further such behavior would result in his no longer being welcome in the *shul*.

I don't see any reason why you cannot inform your *gabba'im* that this individual is not to be given *aliyot* or other honors. You might not even need to explain, just say "for *halakhic* reasons," and treat it as either a pastoral affair or "*hamevin yavin*" ["those who understand, understand"]. I would probably not make a big deal of pointing out to the guy himself that he can't have any more honors, but if it comes up, I wouldn't mince words. I'd just state simply and without rancor that *halakhah* prohibits him from taking *aliyot* and such while he professes another religion.

No reason to step softly. This guy made his choices, he knows what he's doing is not acceptable, but also no reason to be mean about it. I don't think you can prevent him from wearing a *tallit*, and I don't know that doing so is necessary. But I'd probably let him tell others about his *kefirah* [heresy] himself, unless there's a compelling reason for you to disclose it, such as someone wanting to use him as a witness on a *ketubah*, etc.

Oy. Such times we live in. . . .

SUSAN: Let me turn now to a practical question. A complex situation has arisen in my congregation. A wedding is scheduled for Sunday. The groom's grandfather is *goses* [dying], and may die on Friday before the wedding. The normal time to bury the grandfather would be Sunday. If they bury him on Sunday morning, can the father of the groom, who would be sitting *shivah*, come to the wedding? Would this justify postponing the *kevurah* [burial] until Monday? Any thoughts about this?

BOB: This happened with me twice in one year, once with a wedding and once with a bat mitzvah. Both times we postponed the funeral because of the wishes expressed by the grandparent, to the family and to me, not to ruin the grandchild's *simhah*. The bat mitzvah's grandfather died on Wednesday and we had the funeral on Sunday, rather than Friday.

Tough call, depending on your community and your own sensitivity.

DON: Years ago I had this situation. I checked the authoritative book on Jewish *halakhic* practice on mourning, *Kol Bo Shel Avelut*. Based on my reading, and with the wishes of the family, we postponed the funeral to the day after the wedding. The father was not an *avel* [mourner] so he could attend and dance at his daughter's wedding.

SAM: OK, friends, time for a question on medical ethics. How does one name a child conceived through artificial insemination? My first thought was to use the mother's Hebrew name, so that the girl would be Shoshana *bat* Rahel, but I have had second thoughts. I don't know whether the sperm donor was Jewish, and, for that matter, I don't know whether the mother knows who he was. Does it make a difference? To the best of my knowledge, he has played no role in raising the girl.

SUSAN: I would use the names of the birth mother and the husband, that is, the father, not the donor. To my mind, it would be deeply offensive to do anything other than that. Calling the donor the father is offensive to the mother's husband. I follow the approach of a *teshuvah* I read recently, namely, the approach that we shouldn't be following a halving practice we would be embarrassed about.

SAM: I agree, Susan. I think that's the best route. Thanks.

BOB: After Sam's question, here's another contemporary issue. I have, for years, made it eminently clear from the pulpit, and in articles, that the synagogue and community I serve is an open and welcoming community to all people, regardless of sexual orientation. That said, for whatever reason, I have not had significant numbers of members of the LGBTQ community become an active and involved part of our synagogue.

Obviously, I need to institute some kind of programs that will enhance that message of welcome, but I need to draw on the experiences of those of you who have made similar efforts. My gut feeling tells me that sponsoring a Friday night dinner for LGBTQ is not per se the way to go, because I sense – perhaps rightly, perhaps wrongly – that the members of that community don't necessarily want to be singled out, as much as treated like every other member. Am I way off base here? What have you done to create programming to facilitate a greater sense of belonging for the members of the LGBTQ Community?

In some ways, most of my members are about twenty years behind the time, and ten behind me, in terms of being socially progressive. So please understand that I'm not quite as much a Neanderthal guy as this question might make you think . . .

SUSAN: I think you raise an interesting question. My first question is do you have any members of the LGBTQ community in your congregation at present? If yes, I would discuss with them what their ideas would be. Secondly, this is now a long way off, but I would consider hosting a Friday night dinner celebrating Pride. This would be open to the whole community, but send a message that the concerns and feelings of the LGBTQ community matter to your *shul*. Other paths for this approach include hosting programs for your whole community that speak to concerns and interests of the Queer community. Perhaps hosting a forum for the sharing of coming out stories on National Coming Out day. These are my initial thoughts. Additionally, I would make sure that your materials speak to all forms of families such as member 1 and member 2, instead of hetero-normative blanks of Husband and Wife. Otherwise I would say keep doing what you are doing and holding the door open, and perhaps with time more will join your synagogue.

BOB: Thanks, Susan. I'll give that a whirl.

By the way, I have to leave early today. I have a funeral in a few hours, and have to get going. Before I go I want to mention something very significant.

DON: What's that?

BOB: A group of rabbis in the next town, rabbis like us, a mixture of Orthodox, Conservative, Reform, etc., wants to join our group. Why don't you all give that some thought and we can discuss it next time.

SUSAN: Sounds like an interesting idea. Meanwhile, I have some things I need to attend to also. So let's break for today, and discuss that next time. Everybody enjoy the rest of the day.

BOB: Should I enjoy my funeral?

SUSAN: Oh, Bob, you know what I mean. . . . Don't be a smart-aleck, as usual. . . .

Glossary of Hebrew Terms

AGUNAH, AGUNOT   Woman whose husband refuses to grant a divorce

ALEHA HASHALOM   Peace be upon her

ALIYAH, ALIYOT   Honor of being called to the Torah

AMCHA   Literally "your people" the average Jew

AMIDAH   Central prayer of Jewish liturgy

AMUD   Pulpit desk

AM YISRAEL   The People of Israel

ANI MA'AMIN   "I Believe" (first words of Maimonides' Creed)

ARBA PARSHIOT   Four special portions of the Torah

ARGAMAN   Purple

ARON KODESH   Holy Ark

AV, AVI   Father, my father

AVEIL, AVEILUT   Mourner, mourning

AVINU SHEHBASHAMAYIM   Our Father in Heaven

BA'ALEI BATIM   Lay leaders

BA'AL KOREH   Torah reader

BAHUR   Young person

BAL TASH-HIT   Prohibition against destroying property

BARUKH ATTAH   Blessed are You

BARUKH DAYAN HAEMET   Blessed is the Righteous Judge

BARUKH HASHEM   Blessed is God's Name

BAR'KHU   Blessed (First word of prayer)

BASAR V'HALAV   Meat and milk

BEDEKEN   Part of wedding ceremony, veil covering of bride

BENCH GOMEL   Blessing of thanksgiving

BERAKHOT   Blessings

BEIT MIDRASH   Study hall

BET DIN   Court

BET HAMIKDASH   Holy Temple in Jerusalem

BIKKUR CHOLIM   Visiting the sick

BIMAH   Pulpit

BIRKAT KOHANIM   Priestly blessing

BLOT   Page of the Talmud

BRAKHAH   A blessing

BRAKHAH L'VATALAH   A blessing recited in vain

BRIS (BRIT) MILAH   Ceremony of circumcision

BRIT AHUVIM   Literally "Covenant of the Beloved" usually referring to
    commitment ceremony for LGBT

B'TZELEM ELOHIM   In God's Image

CHALITZAH   Ceremony of removing a shoe

CHAMETZ   Unleavened bread

DALET   Four

DAVEN   Pray

DAVKA   Especially

DAYENU   It would have sufficed

D'VAR TORAH   A Torah teaching

EHAD   One

EL MALAY   Memorial prayer

ELOHAI NESHAMAH   Beginning words of prayer "My God, my soul is
    pure"

ELUL   Name of Hebrew month prior to High Holidays

EREV   Eve

ERUSIN Engagement

ERUV   A ritual enclosure of wire surrounding a Jewish community

ESHET HAYIL   Woman of Valor (Proverbs 31)

FRUM, FRUMMIE   Religiously observant

GABBAI, GABBA'IM   Synagogue official

GELILAH   Wrapping the Torah Scroll

GEMILUT HASADIM   Acts of lovingkindness

GENIZAH   Hiding archives

GET   Jewish divorce

GEZEIRA Legal decree

GIYYUR   Conversion

GIYORET   Female convert

GLATT   High-Standard of kashrut

GOYIM   Gentiles

HAKHNASAT ORHIM   Welcoming guests

HAFTARAH   Reading from the biblical prophets

HAG, HAGIM   Holiday, holidays

HAGBAH   Raising the Torah

HALAKHAH   Jewish law

HANUKKAH   Jewish holiday in December

HAREDIM   Ultra-pious

HASHEM   God

HATAFAT DAM BRIT   Drawing blood in case of uncircumcised male

HATAN   Groom

HATIMOT   Sealing (final) words of a blessing

HAZAK   Be strong

HAZAL   Our Rabbis, of blessed memory

HAZARAT HA-SHATZ   Hazzan's repetition of the Amidah

HAZZAN   Cantor

HEKHSHERED   Granted kosher status

HESED   Lovingkindness

HETER MEAH RABBANIM   Decree of 100 Rabbis

HEVREH, HAVERIM   Society, friends

HILLUL HASHEM   Desecration of God's Name

HISLAHAVUS   Enthusiasm

HIYYUV, HAYYAV   Obligation, one who is obligated

HIZZUK   Strengthening, reinforcement

HO-DA-AH   Thanksgiving

HOLEH   One who is ill

HOL HAMO'ED   Intermediate days of holiday

HUKAT HAGOYIM   Ways of the Gentiles

HUMASH Pentateuch

HUMROT   Strict interpretations

HUPPAH   Bridal canopy

IYYAR   Hebrew month

KABBALAT MITZVOT   Acceptance of the commandments

KADDISH   Doxology

KADDISH YATOM   Mourner's prayer

KADOSH   Holy

KOSHERED   Making something kosher to use

KASHRUT   Jewish dietary laws

KASHYA   Question

KAVANNA, KAVVANOT   Devotion, devotions

KAVOD HA'MET   Honor to the deceased

KAYYEMET   Existing

KEDUSHAH   Prayer of Holiness

KETUBAH   Marriage contract

KEVURAH   Burial

KINNUS   Gathering, conference

KIDDUSHIN   Marriage ceremony

KIPPAH   Yarmulka

KISHKES Belly (feelings)

KITNIYOT   Legumes

KLAL GADOL   An important rule

KOHEN   Priest

KRI'AH   Reading

KRI'AT SHEMA   Recitation of Biblical passages

KULOT   Lenient decisions

LAG B'OMER   Jewish holiday (33rd day of counting the Omer)

LASHON HA-RA   Gossip

LE-HITRA'OT   Au revoir

L'HAYYIM   To life

LO TIRTSAH   Thou shalt not murder

L'SHEM B'RIT   For the sake of the covenant (of circumcision)

LULAV   Palm branch used on holiday of Sukkot

MA'ARIV   Evening prayer service

MAFTIR   Concluding reading of Torah portion

MAGGID   Story-Teller

MALAKH HAMAVET   Angel of death

MALKHUT   Kingship (of God)

MAMZERIM   Bastards

MARA D'ATRA   Ruling authority

MAR'EET AYIN   Optics, appearance

MATZEVAH, MATZEVOT   Grave stone(s)

MEGILLAH   Scroll

MEHITZAH   Separation in a synagogue (to separate males and females)

MENSCH   An upstanding person

MESADER KIDDUSHIN   One who officiates at a wedding

MEZUMAN   Quorum of 3 to lead Grace after Meals

MEZUZAH　Scroll of Torah on doorposts

MIDRASHIM　Biblical interpretations

MIKADESH HASHABBAT　Sanctification of the Sabbath

MILHEMET MITZVAH　A divinely-approved battle

MINHAH　Afternoon prayer service

MINYAN　Quorum for prayer

MINHAG, MINHAGIM　Custom(s)

MINHAG SHTUT　A foolish custom

MIKVEH　Ritual bath

MI SHEBERAKH　A public prayer recited for an individual or group

MODIM　Prayer of thanksgiving

MOHEL, MOIYEL　Circumciser

HA-MOTSI　Prayer over bread

MUSAR　Ethics

NACHAS　Pleasure

NARISHKEIT　Foolishness (Yiddish)

NEBUCH　An unfortunate person

NETILAT YADAYIM　Ritual washing of hands

NIHUM AVEILIM　Comforting the mourner

NUR AUF SIMCHAS　An expression meaning "only at happy occasions"

NUSAH　Liturgical melody

OSEH SHALOM　Prayer for peace

OZI VE'ZIMRAT YAH　"God is my strength. . . ."

PARASHAH　Section of the Torah

PASUL　Invalid

PESACH　Jewish holiday of Passover

PESUKEY D'ZIMRA　Verses of Song

PIYUTTIM　Liturgical poems

POSKIM　Decisors

P'SAK　Legal decision

PUSHKE　Charity box

RACHMONOS　Compassion

RE'EH　Torah portion (Literally "see)

RIBONO SHEL OLAM　Master of the Universe

RISHONIM　Early Medieval Sages

SEDER, SEDARIM　Passover meal, meals

SEFER TORAH　Torah Scroll

SEFIRAH　Fifty day count from Passover to Shavuot

SEUDAH   Ritual meal

SEYAG   Fence

SHABBAT ZAKHOR   Sabbath of Remembrance

SHAHARIT   Morning prayer

SHAIMOT   Pages with God's name written on them

SHALIAH TZIBBUR   Community representative (The prayer leader)

SHALOM   Peace

SHALOM ALEIKHEM   Greeting, meaning "peace unto you"

SHALOM BAYIT   Domestic harmony

SHALOSH REGALIM   Three Pilgrimage Festivals

SHAVU'OT   Holiday of Pentecost

SHEHEKHEYANU   Prayer of thanksgiving

SHEM, SHEMOT   Name, names (usually God's Name)

SHEM U-MALKHUT   Section of a blessing meaning "God's Name and sovereignty)

SHEVA BRAKHOT   Seven wedding blessings

SHOMER YISRAEL   Guardian of Israel

SHEYGITZ   Pejorative for a Gentile

SHIVAH   Seven days of mourning

SHOAH   Holocaust

SHLOSHIM   Thirty days of mourning

SHOFAR   Ritual ram's horn

SHUL   Synagogue

SH'MA   "Hear O' Israel" (Deut. 6:4)

SHVITZ   Sauna

SIDDUR   Prayerbook

SIMCHA   A happy occasion, life milestone

SIFREI KODESH   Holy Books

SMIKHAH   Rabbinical ordination

SOFRIM   Scribes

SUKKOT   Jewish holiday of Tabernacles

TAKHRIKHIM   Shrouds

TALLIT   Prayer shawl

TALMIDEI HAKHAMIM   Scholars

TAMUZ   Hebrew month

TANAKH   Bible, Holy Scriptures

TEFILLAH B'TZIBUR   Public worship

TEFILLIN   Phylacteries

TEHIYAT HAMAYTIM   Resurrection of the dead

TEKHELET   Blue

TENA'IM   Engagement, Jewish ceremony

TEKIA GEDOLAH   Long blast of the ram's horn

TESHUVAH   Repentance

TEVILAH   Immersion in a ritual bath

TIKKUN LEYL SHAVUOT   Collection of readings recited the evening of Shavuot

TIRHA D'TZIBURA   Burden on the community

TISHAH B'AV   Fast day on the ninth day of the Hebrew month Av

TOKHEHAH   Rebuke; a scriptual passage of rebuke

TORAH MIN HASHAMAYIM   Belief that the Torah was given by Heaven (God)

TORAH MISINAI   Belief that the Torah was given at Mt. Sinai (by God)

TREIF   Non-kosher

TZADDIK   A righteous person

TZEDAKAH   Charity

TZIDDUK HADIN   Justification prayer (at a burial, acknowledging the rightness of Divine judgment)

TZITZIT   Fringes on tallit

TZNIYUT   Modesty (in clothing)

UPSHERIN   Three-year-old Jewish boy's first haircut

VIDUI   Confession prayer

YAHRTZEIT   Anniversary of one's death

YAMIM NORAIM   Days of Awe (High Holy Days)

YASHER KOACH   An expression meaning "congratulations," or "well done!"

YETZER HARA   Evil inclination

YIZKOR   Memorial prayer

YOM TOV   Holiday

About the Author

Dov Peretz Elkins is a nationally known lecturer, educator, workshop leader, author, and book critic, and is a popular speaker on the Jewish circuit. Rabbi Elkins is a recipient of the National Jewish Book Award and is the author of over fifty books. His *Chicken Soup For The Jewish Soul* was on the NY Times best-seller list. Among Rabbi Elkins' other books are *Rosh Hashanah Readings: Inspiration, Information and Contemplation, Yom Kippur Readings*, and *The Wisdom of Judaism: An Introduction to the Values of the Talmud*. His most recent books are *Jewish Stories from Heaven and Earth: Inspiring Tales to Nourish the Heart and Soul*; *Tales of the Righteous*; *Simple Actions for Jews to Help Green the Planet*; *Heart and Scroll: Inspiring Stories from the Masters*; *In the Spirit: Insights for Spiritual Renewal in the 21st Century*; and *For Those Left Behind: A Jewish Anthology of Comfort and Healing*.